$\frac{8\cancel{2}=10^-}{0}$

27553

$Fi(5)$

BEYOND

THE

HUNGRY

COUNTRY

OTHER BOOKS BY LOUISE A. STINETORF

WHITE WITCH DOCTOR

CHILDREN OF SOUTH AFRICA

CHILDREN OF NORTH AFRICA

BEYOND

THE

HUNGRY

COUNTRY

by Louise A. Stinetorf

J. B. LIPPINCOTT COMPANY

Philadelphia and New York

Library of Congress Catalog Card Number 54-6110
Printed in the United States of America
By The Haddon Craftsmen, Scranton, Pa.

To our own beloved

JO ELLEN

FOREWORD

I have told the story of my life in Africa to several people, folk to whom I have had to explain the decisions I have made, those from whom I have sought advice, others who I hoped would approve of the course I have laid out for myself. It is on their advice, insistence even, that I am attempting to compress an honest, unembellished account of missionary life between the pages of a book. All of you understand the purpose of missionary work and most of you know something of its history. But when many of you talk with me, I sometimes wonder if you realize that those of us who are professionally "Men and Women of God" are born and remain until the hour of death, simple human beings with feet of clay. The Light which leads us on burns clear and steady; but we who follow It into the faraway and sometimes dark corners of this earth are no different in our human imperfections from those of you who follow the plow, or with chalk and maps expound from textbooks, or direct the labor of the millions who manufacture the physical necessities of life. We follow our devious paths in the name of the Divine Christ and we carry all our human frailties along with us. Perhaps there have been a few Solomons among us—as in every other profession! —but generally even the most consecrated has made his mistakes. And like all other men, we have lived with the results of those mistakes. We have lived some down, and have risen above others. But the important thing is that like every other human being who walks this earth, the man himself has made them, and being ever human, will continue to make others.

How much of my own life has been mistaken in effort and direction, I cannot say. Judgment of that lies elsewhere. I only know that I, like so many others in their fields, lived my life from day to day in the village of Fusora, doing the work opened up to me, believing it was according to God's plan.

If I wanted to use grandiloquent phrases, I could call this the odyssey of a woman's soul in search of direction. More simply, it is an honest account of a missionary life—yesterday, today, and for at least a few more tomorrows—in the heart of the Dark Continent. It is an answer to the question that has been asked me a thousand times, and that I must listen to for another thousand times during the next few years.

"Why did you go to Africa? Why are you going back *now that you don't have to?*" The last phrase is almost a command: "Stay here and shape your life after *my* little pattern. It is the only thing *I* know, therefore it must be good for *you*."

"Oh, but I do have to go back to Africa," I begin and usually end right there, for by that time my questioner is already speaking gaily, with just the right amount of socially prescribed charm, to someone else, and about something else. And even if this were not so, who can endure one hundred thousand words of explanation over a teacup?

BEYOND

THE

HUNGRY

COUNTRY

CHAPTER
ONE

The bones clicked softly in the instructor's hands, as dry bones will that have been wired together loosely. His words dribbled on monotonously like a half-hearted, off-season rain. Today's lecture at the university, where I was the first woman ever enrolled in their College of Agriculture, was devoted to the docking of lambs. I knew from other lectures that in ten minutes I could have said everything the instructor was going to say, completely and with some emphasis. Then, in another five minutes, I could have demonstrated the technique on a live lamb. What more is there to say than simply: "Just so far down the tail, probe firmly with the end of your thumb until you find the place where one vertebra can be forced apart from the one below it. Then with any sterile, sharp knife, if the tool especially designed for the purpose is lacking . . ."

But how many women, and what percentage of men for that matter, are ever going to dock lambs? Even I am a freak, sitting here in this class in Animal Husbandry. I believe I am here because I finally lost my temper with the dean of the College of Agriculture. The dean is a white-haired man, only a little younger than my father would have been were he alive. When he interviewed me, he sounded and looked as though he could have talked for hours about the state of grace and well-being of my soul. As for the physical body, regardless of disease or accident, any mention of an organ ordinarily covered by a strip of cloth, left him red-necked and tongue-tied.

For two hours the dean had stammered, cleared his throat, and shifted his plump posterior in his chair. Little Timmy, my son, had long since tired and was fighting sleep as he sat on my knee. The dean was trying to make me agree with him that my presence would be an embarrassment to young men making scientific tests of The-Facts-of-Life on the larger mammals in cow barns and pigsties.

I have seen a lot of men, black and white, primitive and civilized, clothed and naked, brazen, embarrassed, or completely unaware that anyone should take offense at sight of the undraped human body. And every one of them not only knew about all there is to know of the so-called facts of life, but took it for granted that the women they met were likewise informed. I tried to reason logically with the dean. A rush of blood purpled his already crimsoned cheeks, but he swallowed hard and went on, "In my day, we expected purity in a Christian woman. We demanded virginity of mind and spirit as well as body—"

"In Africa where the Christian missionaries of your denomination work, the natives whom I serve demand children of a woman, as many children as she can bear," I interrupted rudely. "And some tribes even demand proof before marriage that a woman can bear children."

"Cattle!" he spit at me contemptuously. "Just female animals to be bred—"

We were both angry now, each out of patience with the other. Perhaps that is why I do not remember exactly what I said. I suppose it would boil down to something like this: "For heaven's sake! In the eyes of my People of the Fan, I am *cattle,* the same as a cow, but I certainly never expected to hear such a statement from you."

He started to interrupt but I brushed his futile gesture aside, drowned out his words. *I* wasn't embarrassed. I had grown up in a very naked Africa.

"Very well, I'm a cow," I thundered on. "And like any cow I've been bred and I've borne and produced young. Here's the living, breathing proof of it sitting on my knee. I don't want to enter your precious school in order to learn about the facts of life. I already know them. I've learned from experience. And as for the shy young men I might embarrass— Well! My years in a hospital and my years as a wife lead me to believe they know fully as much about mating and breeding as I do."

What with two Irish grandmothers, my tongue waggles fast once it starts. Anyway, a few minutes later I draped Timmy—now sound asleep and limp as a bag of barley—over my left shoulder, clutched the signed forms the dean pushed toward me, and marched down the hall to the registrar's office. There I was duly enrolled as the first and to date only female student—I almost said *human cow*—in this proud College of Agriculture. As a result there I sat that October afternoon hoping I could listen for the required hour and a half to the repetition of what could be adequately described and demonstrated in fifteen minutes.

"It is usually between the third and fourth caudal vertebrae, although of course there is variation in bone structure and growth, and it might well be the fourth and fifth vertebrae—" I was tired. The instructor was tired. His sentences were bumpy, like a bee striking against a windowpane in a vain struggle toward freedom. Almost everyone else in the lecture hall was either tired or sleepy.

Suddenly I wondered if my presence there was really causing anyone discomfort of any kind and I looked around me. Most of the young men were sitting on the small of their backs, their long legs thrust out into a maze of chair rungs. Some of them propped up weary heads on clenched knuckles. The heavy eyes of others followed their chins chestward. As usual there was a poker game in progress to the left of me, a desultory game played for matches. The shy boy to the right was reading a story from a magazine entitled: "Love Unleashed, or Passion in the Park."

"So far as I know, science has not as yet discovered a use for the severed portion of the caudal appendage—unless the sheepman has a hungry cat." A feeble attempt at humor on the part of the instructor. I forced my eyes back to him and my lips into a grin.

"Of course these could be processed for fertilizer, but the quantity in any locality is too small, and the cost of collecting them out of proportion to the value of the derivative product. Aside from flies which seem to find discarded tails left lying around, an ideal incubation ground for their pupae, nothing else has found a use for a severed sheep's tail."

I could have contradicted him flatly, and then have proved my point with a dozen North African delicacies all concocted on a basis of sheep's-tail fat. I did not, however. It would have embarrassed him—and he probably would not have enjoyed the sticky sweet and slimy grease of *boorma* and *bucclawye*.

I glanced back at the boy beside me. He was licking his lips and almost drooling over his salacious story. Suddenly it was all I could do to keep from laughing. Would it have been possible for me, or any other woman, to embarrass this carefully cloth-draped product of a civilization dependent in so many ways on inhibitions? I tried to imagine what old Tuou, Chief Mu'muou's mother-wife, would have said to such drivel. Tuou had no illusions about men, their vagaries, their rights real and fancied, and the demands they made of the female human *cattle* they bought. Perhaps that is why she made such an excellent instructress in Fusora's "bush school."

An African bush school! How different instruction there from this class! Between half-closed eyelids I looked through a window into a maze of white and mottled-gray limbs and dying golden leaves on a big sycamore. It was as bright, as golden out there as an African plain at this time of year.

"As I have said, I know of no use whatsoever for the severed tails . . ."

I slid my thumb under my thigh and clenched the seat of my chair with taut fingers. I felt I must, else I would surely rise and shock the class awake, break up the poker game, tear the young lecher beside me away from his pseudo-brothel. And what would the young instructor do if I arose and shouted, "You fool! Don't you know that half the sheep in the world are raised primarily for their tails? That they are bred to produce enormous tails? That if I were to dock such an animal—"

". . . the severed tails can be disposed of in several ways: They can be drenched with kerosene and burned, but that is a slow proc-

14 ·

ess, and smelly . . ." He wrinkled up his nose like a kindergarten teacher who must act out every emotion for her pupils.

For a few seconds he looked like Jimmy, my husband, the day he had sprung to his feet babbling something about zebra tails—or the lack of them. It was because of Jimmy that I was here in this man's school trying to digest enough man's knowledge so I could return to my Africa and do a woman's work. That was what Jimmy had tried to do, a woman's work, and, indirectly, it had killed him.

"Your husband was a visionary, too big and fine for his job," one white man had said to me.

Old Maa Koo, black, wrinkled, wise and unafraid, but nevertheless respectful of this ephemeral thing we call life, was a better judge. "We do not determine the shape our children shall wear," she told me once. "Life was molded for us before we were conceived. One man in a generation may improve the pattern ever so little. None can recast it into a different mold. When a man tries to do a woman's work, however big and strong his body or agile his mind, he is still too little, too stupid for life." There were no banalities about the excellencies of Jimmy's character. He had failed. That was what mattered in Black Africa.

Of course, Maa Koo did not use my words. She spoke little English. I translate for her, guessing at innuendo and spiritual context as a good translator must. To do that, one must be fluently bi-lingual. Those of us who grew up in mission compounds always are.

But Jimmy, my husband, was not bi-lingual, either of tongue or spirit. He was a good, Christian man, and I loved him, but I know now as Maa Koo always knew, that he was—naïve. Good—but not wise enough to realize that a house cannot be rebuilt on other lines without destroying the original design, or a civilization shaped on other concepts than those to which the mass of human beings so affected are native.

As for me— If I say things which sound crude to you, please forgive me. It is because "I speak with two tongues," as my people beyond the Hungry Country would put it; and they might add that

"I think with a divided mind and love with a doubled heart." That is because in many ways I am as much African as any little *pickinin* whose skin is the color of heart ebony, and whose sole piece of clothing is a string of blue beads wound around her body just below her preposterous pot belly.

I was born prematurely. My parents were on trek, and my mother, with only father to assist her, gave birth to me in the scant shade of a trailside bush just like any native woman. Maa Koo, who became my black nurse, was less than a generation from savagery at the time, less than a decade from the "bush." She undertook my rearing seriously, and because of her, I never had any silly idea that my mother found me in a mango tree, or cabbage patch, or that a big bird had brought me.

But please don't think that Maa Koo was an immoral woman. Far from it! Nor was she immodest. It is simply that the inhibitions of that civilization in which she grew up do not include procreation as one of the prime reticences of life. My mother must have sometimes protested to her, for I can remember extreme patience—and some scorn—on Maa Koo's good black face, and such words as: "The child sees the cock with the hens, the male and female monkeys in the trees, and on trek she sees the buck with the does. Do you think your little daughter was born with an empty skull, mistress? And why should you wish that?"

Mother's reactions to my port of entry into this world were pronounced. I gathered from her quite early in life that "nice" white women "find" their children between clean sheets in a big bed. They peer between the covers and— There you are! You little darling! Bless your heart!

Later I learned from my mother that no woman should ever marry a missionary. No matter what the urgings of love, the prickings of professional ambition, or the fiendish nagging of sheer loneliness— Never! *NEVER!* Never should I marry a missionary! Such a woman's life is torn up by its roots, her husband never gets ahead, and every day is as monotonously like the one which went before it as pearl beads on a string.

Obviously mother had not been "called" to the mission field. She loved my father and, like a good wife, she forsook all else to follow him—but not without a good deal of resentment and self-pity when that led into the heart of Darkest Africa. My father tried to help my mother know and love Africa as he knew and loved it, but he failed. As his sense of failure grew upon him, he made the mistake so many men do in failure. He laughed at her. He laughed out of his helplessness, never loudly, never bitterly. Mother heard only the laughter, without understanding that behind his raillery he was reaching out to her for a companionship she did not give him.

The first trip "home" on furlough that I recall was when I was five years old. Perhaps incidents of that visit stuck in my mind because I heard my father make so many mistakes when trying to explain the customs of black people. Father was an accomplished story-teller; when he intended to amuse, his listeners never failed to explode into laughter. All but mother, that is. There was one tale of which he was very fond about a white woman who, after struggling for years to teach the prenatal practices of her people to the primitive savages of the Congo Territory, "found" her own baby under a trailside bush—curled up like a fat worm on a segment of banana leaf, red and squalling. When I—five years old!—tried to set him right, mother's cheeks burned redder, her lips thinned more tautly, and father's audience howled with glee.

My mother was what is called a "working" missionary wife. That is, she shared teaching and evangelistic responsibilities with my father. She would have said, and have believed she was telling the truth, that she was doing her best to rear me. But it was Maa Koo, not my mother, who was my constant companion. I had begun to imbibe my black nurse's primitive culture even before I spoke English. I was fortunate, for Maa Koo was wise as only those women are wise who, in order to survive, have had to beat back the destructive forces of primordial nature with no weapons other than their bare fists and native cunning. Whenever father shared with any group his colorful version of mother's unorthodox confinement, I always remembered Maa Koo's waggling her head—always as smooth and clean of hair as a melon—and muttering, "Men are for begetting. Not birthing!"

It was on that first trip back to the United States that I met Aunt Bessie. Aunt Bessie was my mother's sister who had married a rich man. It seemed that everything I did "mortified" her. I remember clucking my milk teeth at her on one occasion and warning grimly, as Maa Koo would surely have done, "I should think you would be afraid of Mumbo Jumbo's whip, Aunt Bessie. You grumble too much." Mumbo Jumbo is the jungle god who, in the person of some man delegated to represent him, literally beats refractory wives into a state of domestic tractability. I didn't catch Aunt Bessie's reply for at that instant father choked violently on an apple he was eating, and I had to pound him on the back until he could get his breath.

When, shortly thereafter, we left for Africa again, Aunt Bessie kissed me goodbye and held me tight. I stood locked in her arms as stiffly quiet as a bird charmed by a snake. I felt exactly the way I once felt when a black boy pointed out to me a green vine dangling from a bush. Only it was not a green vine at all, but a mamba, a snake that deals agonizing death in a few seconds.

Then, "I don't see why you won't give the child to me, Ida," Aunt Bessie was saying. "She's a little savage, and she needs training."

Little white-skinned savage that I really was, I knew that children are possessions, like the calves in a farmer's pasture. I believed that it was my father's unquestionable right to sell me for whatever a third person was willing to pay, or to give me to anyone on whom he felt like bestowing a gift. On the train I slipped off the seat facing my parents and stood between his knees. If he had given me away, I would have accepted the transfer as any other little animal must—as African women and children do. Standing there, wedged in between his legs, with his heartbeat thumping in the ear I pressed against his chest, I felt as any pickinin might. I was glad I was still to sleep in his kraal.

When between my twelfth and thirteenth birthdays, my parents again returned to America on furlough, I was that strange sociological hodge-podge which missionary children frequently are at least through adolescence. I was half ashamed of the fact that my skin was the repulsive color of the belly of a dead and rotting fish; but I knew that in some inexplicable way I was a superior and privileged being because of that revolting hue. I felt I was a woman, too, although my body was not yet "ripe for marriage." Since my birth, Maa Koo had striven according to the best dictates of her conscience, to make me a woman who would know her place in the world, and perform her duties in any kraal as a first—fourth—fifth—or even twentieth wife! My mother was dimly conscious of this and combated it rather ineffectually with sporadic lectures which seemed designed to make me feel vaguely guilty of something—I didn't know what.

So I looked upon America wonderingly, with eyes that "saw black" more often and more easily than they "saw white." I was of an age for marriage (African style) although I was still "unripe," and I waited for the men to look me over, particularly the older and richer men—since such acquire the bulk of African virgins. Such men shook hands with me gravely when introduced, and then most of them thumped me on the top of my head with a kindly palm and murmured some such words as, "Well! Well! Well! So this is Sam and Ida Woodbury's little girl!" The only other masculine attention I received was the rough-and-tumble camaraderie of a school playground.

That one year was my sole taste of America's great public school system. Both in the classrooms and out of them, everything about the institution bewildered me. I learned very quickly that I didn't know how to play, that I didn't know how to study, that I was queer, and that my clothes were shabby.

I was also bad. I liked my girl companions and when they whispered questions in my ears, I answered as simply and naturally as Maa Koo had previously answered me. Shortly thereafter I was told that in so doing I had disgraced myself and brought shame on my poor and saintly parents. The mothers of my school playmates had spoken to the teacher. The teacher had spoken to Aunt Bessie. Aunt

Bessie spoke to mother. And mother impressed upon me that no nice, white-skinned little girl ever let her thoughts wander lower than the belt of her dress.

Somehow I could not feel that fault lay with me. Instead, "Tsch! Tsch! Tsch!" I clucked mentally. "So my schoolmates are not nice girls! Else, how could they have asked me the questions they did in the first place?"

But, really, I don't want to paint too dark a picture of my childhood. In fact, I suppose I was about as "nice" a little girl as almost any other little girl of my age. I was just having to do what few adults ever attempt—and most of those fail at! I was compelled by my father's profession to live with, digest, and assimilate into a socially integrated personality two cultures which were continents, races, millennia apart.

All the way back to Africa at the end of that furlough year, a strange canker ate into my child's soul. No man wanted me! So I was to become a spinster, I thought. I was to be like Aunt Bun and Aunt Hallie, and all the other unmarried women workers at our own and neighboring mission stations. All women whom I loved devotedly, and pitied with equal fervor. I didn't speak of this blow to anyone. I simply accepted it with the stoicism Maa Koo had bred into me. I knew I would not marry because there were no unmarried white men at our mission station. I do not know if other denominations differ from ours in this respect, but less than a decade ago we did not send unmarried men to Africa. Unmarried women, yes, lots of them! Spinsters—willing or frustrated—are the backbone of the foreign field. But unmarried men— It was said quite openly that they would be a distraction to the unmarried women workers and might even cause some dissension among these devoted, consecrated, selfless beings. How omniscient! I was to have all this impressed upon me by personal experience a decade later when I, too, returned to Africa one of these devoted, consecrated, completely unmarried, but not entirely selfless beings. Even then I didn't say anything to anyone about the bitter rebellion in my heart.

Never! But the bitterness was there, and more rebellion than resignation. Like every normal woman, black or white, I wanted a husband.

Before I close this chapter on my childhood, I must in fairness to all missionary wives, defend my mother's seeming neglect of me. She was busy all day, every day, with clinics and the mission version of parish calling, but I saw her regularly at meals. There she was a strict disciplinarian, full of advice about the way "white little ladies" eat—and filled with horror and prohibitions of the native delicacies Maa Koo introduced me to whenever we strolled through the jungle.

She taught me, too, using the famed Calvert system of home instruction—which is the mainstay of so many missionary parents. She brought me through the elementary grades and high school. This was a hardship for her, because she was not prepared for teaching, and did not like it. She never told me so in just those words, but my father often mentioned his admiration of her patience and devotion to duty. He admonished me to emulate her admirable qualities.

"It isn't easy for your mother, Laura," he used to say. "You must help her by being a good girl."

I tried. And like so many children trying to be good, I retired into myself from those best fitted to advise me. Is it any wonder then, that having never talked over "white" problems with a white woman, I was more apt to judge by black standards than white? One thing I learned very quickly—it made for an easier, less troubled, certainly a less frequently spanked existence if I watched white folk's social behavior carefully and copied it when among them.

Consequently, when I returned to America to go to college, I believe I must have been as peculiar a human and academic specimen as ever walked through any prissy, ivied hall. Socially I was as keenly observant of life about me as a monkey, as shy as a gazelle, about as talkative as a giraffe—and yet I suffered from the most intense gregarious longings. I would have liked to walk arm and arm down the corridors with other girls—and boys—chattering gaily, but inside I was black, not white. Whenever I opened my mouth, "black" thoughts feathered themselves with strange phrases and darted out in erratic flight. My white companions would stare at me and draw aside. Or they might laugh foolishly as people will when they do not want to be rude but at the same time do not understand and vaguely suspect offense.

CHAPTER
TWO

My parents could not afford to send me to college on their missionaries' salaries, so rich Aunt Bessie nominally carried that responsibility. She arranged for the local college to give me a "missionary scholarship," that is, I thought I was paying no tuition. A state missionary society bought my textbooks for me. Aunt Bessie "gave" me a home, food, clothing and shelter. I had no "spending money"; but I had never learned to bid for a vicarious emotional excitement through the acquisition of trivial possessions, so I didn't miss it.

If, inside of me, I had not been more "savage" than "civilized" I could not have lived through those years in my charitable relative's home. I know she was charitable because she told me so many times. I also heard her tell her minister as much when she explained to him that because she now carried the burden of my support her church contribution must be halved. She told the same story to the Red Cross woman who came to her door, to the Community Chest representative, to the Girl and Boy Scouts, the Veterans' Auxiliary, the Fuller Brush man, and even to a chance hobo who limped up her back porch steps one morning.

I may be black inside, but I am not stupid. In view of the fact that Aunt Bessie had dismissed her maid less than two weeks after I entered her home, and that I made my clothes myself from the garments whose seams had failed to restrain Aunt Bessie's constantly burgeoning body, I knew she was money ahead because of her "charity." Don't think I tell you this because I pitied myself. Far from it. In the African kraal where Maa Koo had grown up, women are never anything but "a pair of hands." And why should I have pitied myself? My days were full. I had a comfortable home. And because my mother had made a clever needlewoman of me and I had much practice on the contents of missionary barrels, and because Aunt Bessie's sole amusement was shopping always in the best stores, I soon became one of the best-dressed girls in school.

Come summer, Aunt Bessie and her husband went north to a resort and I was sent to Aunt Elma's farm. Aunt Elma had much that Aunt Bessie did not dream existed—although there was not much in the way of physical possessions for even the greediest relatives to itemize and quarrel over at her death. Aunt Elma was not a blood relative. Uncle Ben, her husband, was father's oldest brother. He had left school in his early teens "so that the smart ones of the family could get a little book learnin'." However, no one felt any lack of formal education in Uncle Ben's and Aunt Elma's lives. Neither did they.

I loved those summers at Aunt Elma's. Housework was a pleasurable privilege, never a grim duty there. It was a picnic, an adventurous lark to gather fruit, cultivated and wild, and concoct fragrant delicacies from it. They were all something that would be "mighty good when the snow flies." They were mighty good hot and fresh from the kitchen stove, too.

It was at Aunt Elma's that I learned to enjoy leisure—just to sit with my hands in my lap and drink in the beauty of the world about me—and with no sense of guilt on my soul. Or to read a book, not for the improvement of my mind, but because it entertained. I was sitting thus on the front porch half reading, half daydreaming one afternoon when a big, blunt-fingered, work-roughened hand pulled my book away and dropped it on the floor.

"I think it's the Bible that says, 'Of the makin' of books there's no end,'" Uncle Ben murmured as he dropped into a chair beside me. "Now you look at them willows and maples down there along the crick, and them oaks in that woodlot behind them. All that color'ull be gone in a few weeks. I never had time to read many books, but I never found a bunch of words as purty in my mind as them maples in my eyes."

He heaved a sigh of huge contentment, then he turned his head from side to side and sniffed like a black hunter on the trail of game.

"What you and Elma bin doin' in the kitchen t'day?" he demanded. "Smells like grape jelly to me. Hot biscuits and new jelly!" He smacked his lips. I knew that Aunt Elma was listening inside—and that there would be hot biscuits for supper.

"Did you ever buy any perfume off a counter that smelled half as good as that?" Uncle Ben went on.

I didn't know which particular fragrance Uncle Ben meant. There was clematis blooming at one end of the porch, two huge sweetbriar bushes on either side of the steps, more grapes warm on the vine under an August sun, and across the garden an orchard full of ripening fruit. Moreover, I had never bought or owned a bottle of perfume in my life, but Aunt Bessie had given me some of her empty ones to lay uncorked among my handkerchiefs. I knew the poignant delight of sweet smells.

"That horse—you know, old Nellie—is the smartest thing," Uncle Ben was saying. "I almost run over a new-hatched covey o' quails today, but she saw it in time and pulled right up short and stopped until they got out o' the way. Did you ever see a baby quail, Laura? Or notice how the little fellers run ac—"

He broke off as the faint hum of a giant bumblebee resolved into the clacking whirr of a mowing machine. Clark Abelson, a neighbor boy, had gone past the house a quarter of an hour before, mowing the grass and weeds on his father's side of the road. Now he came around the bend, cutting our grass and weeds on the return trip.

Uncle Ben waved to him. "Much obliged, Clark. That'll save me a job."

Clark did not lower the mower blade and start the cutting gear when he had cleared the mailbox post. Instead he climbed off the seat and walked up the path to the house.

"Want a nice cold drink?" Uncle Ben asked. "It's a pretty hot day, 'specially out there in the sun."

I smiled the briefest greeting to Clark and was up and into the house before he could reply. "Get him a handful of cookies, dear," Aunt Elma murmured from the living room couch without even opening her eyes. I filled a pitcher at the kitchen pump, floated the tumbler on the water, and plunged a fist into the cookie jar for a half-dozen of Aunt Elma's saucer-sized confections.

Back on the porch, Clark retrieved the tumbler and held it while I filled it, nodding his head occasionally as though agreeing with Uncle Ben's remarks about the weather, the crops, and market prices. He was standing on the step below me and his eyes were apparently focused on my knees. My dress was not only clean and neat, it was pretty, and I knew it. I was also suddenly conscious of the fact that my body and legs were slender and shapely, and that the hand-crocheted raffia sandals I was wearing were always called "cute" or "darrrrling" by any woman who saw them.

I smiled as Clark set the glass down on the porch railing with slow care, and took the cookies. He selected one for first eating, but eyed it so closely before pushing half of it into his mouth that I, too, bent forward and peered. Clark looked up so suddenly that our heads almost bumped and I took a quick step backward. My face had never been so close to a man's before, and the surge of indescribable emotion which rushed through me left me as tense as a physical blow would have done. The cookies downed, Clark took off his hat and wiped the sweat from his forehead and then from his hatband.

"Yes sir, I think you're right about that," Clark said, and I realized that Uncle Ben was still talking. Then, "I just wondered if you'd like to go to the ice-cream social with me at the community church in town tonight?"

"Who? Me-e-e-e!" Uncle Ben burst out. "Young man, I'm takin' my wife! It's a habit I got into. I bin takin' her places for around forty years now."

I thought I heard a faint chuckle from the living room and Clark and I both laughed out loud. "I'll be over some time around seven-thirty," he said, then turned and walked back to his mowing machine.

That was the first date I ever had, and I spent the rest of the day in a daze. One thought common to womankind the world over, regardless of caste and color, sang through my mind all afternoon: a *man* had found me attractive enough to spend time and money on me. How much Aunt Elma understood of what was seething within me, I don't know, but she helped me dress that evening. Then she combed her rosebushes for a half-dozen late buds and tied them together with a knot of pink ribbon for my shoulder.

Most of that evening is one of my happiest memories. I think for the first time in my life I met young men and women of my own age who accepted me and treated me like one of themselves and not as some paragon of virtue to be looked up to and admired—and left out of the little human intimacies that make life worth living. No one tried to make me feel that I was a lesser god perched up on some kind of churchly pedestal. Nor was there that scarcely subtle sneer on anyone's face for the narrow-minded religious bigot who has escaped to foreign shores where he foments discontent among the mythically happy, though savage children of nature. I was simply a young white girl having an awfully good time. For some reason it seemed deliciously funny just to watch a boy my own age devour cake and ice cream. I wanted to twit him with having the appetite of a locust in a *shamba*—an African garden. But that was the Dark Continent. Another world. Another life. I caught my tongue between my teeth quick and hard.

We played games like children, too. There was a fairly boisterous one in which we skipped and hopped and bounced up and down under the directions of a fellow who sat at one side and bellowed nonsense syllables at us. We joined hands and whirled each other about. I loved it! And nothing could have been further from my mind than the mission field and Africa when a hand touched my shoulder. Clark and I moved out of the circle immediately. I was panting for breath so hard that the words sounded far away and indistinct in my ears. Still, there was no mistaking what the minister's wife was saying.

"My dear . . . your parents are missionaries you know . . . Dr. Fraser and I thoroughly approve of folk dancing . . . wonderful recreation . . . still *I* never dance . . . folk don't expect it of you . . . perhaps . . . Perhaps years from now in Africa you won't want to remember . . ."

"Old hen! Biddy! Cluck!" Clark snorted for me when she was gone.

I don't know how or why, but suddenly all the restraint with which I had put Africa behind me was gone, and I turned to Clark and asked the question my father always asked in every African village he visited, "Are you a Christian?"

"Huh?" he exclaimed in surprise. Then, "I guess so."

His words were light, too light, and the Christian religion had never been a trivial matter in my life. "Are you saved?" I pressed in my father's best professional manner.

He inspected his shoes. They were dusty and he flicked the toes with a crumpled handkerchief. But some perverse imp seemed riding my tongue, and no shoeshine was going to turn the missionary in me aside. "Have you made your peace with God?" I demanded primly.

Clark looked me straight in the eye and answered evenly, "Listen, Laura. I don't run away from a fight, but I don't go around picking them, either. I don't quarrel with people—or God. And I don't have to go around saying, 'I'm sorry,' all the time—to man or God."

No black man had ever answered my father thus, and I didn't know what to say next. For a few seconds I was furious. Why should this boy take advantage of me with that—that unorthodox type of reasoning? Then the imp deserted me and I heard myself babbling apologies, but the rest of the evening was spoiled. The easy camaraderie was gone, and with the sensitiveness of the wretched, I imagined Clark was sorry he had brought me—and that everyone else was sorry for him, too. Then slowly, hate like a

drowning tide rose within me. I hated the minister's wife with all
the primitive intensity that a black woman hates the newer sister-
wife for whom she has been stripped of her arm and leg ornaments.

"Let's go home," Clark murmured.

We were both silent until he pulled up beside Uncle Ben's mailbox. I don't know what I expected, if anything; but it was certainly
not that he should put his arm around my shoulder, draw me close
to him and kiss me. The psychiatrists are right. It is those we love
most in childhood who influence our behavior in moments of stress
forever after. It was surely Maa Koo, wise in the ways of an African
kraal, who spoke through my lips something about my father's
being in Africa, but "Uncle Ben is his oldest brother. He will represent my father. You can speak to him. . . ."

Clark drew his arm back hastily and leaned as far away from
me as he could get. For a moment his lips twitched as though his
mind refused to shape the words he was struggling to utter. Then
he was babbling, "Say, I didn't mean anything! I only asked you
to go tonight because—well, you're kind of cute and pretty. That
Fraser hen! I'm sorry for what happened. I only kissed you because—well, you're kind of cute and pretty. I didn't mean anything!
Understand? Nothing at all!" I have no memory of getting out
of the car and walking up the path to the house.

"Is that you, dear?" Aunt Elma called as I passed the door of her
bedroom. "Don't get up in the morning. You need a good sleep.
Goodnight. It was a nice sociable, wasn't it?"

"Yes. Goodnight," I forced through stiff lips.

Inside my room I lay down across my bed without removing even
my shoes. I hated the minister's wife! I hated the minister's wife!
What was it she had said? ". . . years from now in Africa!" Black
Africa! Africa?

Suddenly I sat up and stared into the darkness as though trying
to see through the dim years ahead. Again I went over what had
been in my mind so often, but never so poignantly as now. Must
I return to Africa? If not, where else should I go, unmarried as I
was? "Home" is a strange word the parents of missionary children

use to describe a still stranger land where everything is topsy-turvy by African standards—where we made regular flying visits filled with long train trips and speaking engagements—where our own relatives exhibited us at teas like prize cattle at an agricultural fair. Home is a land where missionary children become house servants in the name of charity and work harder and with less appreciation than many a black woman in a primitive kraal.

Then I remembered something my father had once said to me, I suppose in one of my troubled moments. "God has many ways of managing us. Sometimes when we do not listen to His quieter words, He simply closes all doors about us except the right one for us to pass through. Then, however grim the outlook, however much we balk, that is the only way we can go."

That is as much of "a call" as I had in the days of my youth to become a missionary. When I went back to college a few weeks later, I knew I would return to Africa. Where else would I have been anything but a misfit? In Africa I knew the social habits of the people I would be among, both native and missionary. I understood the devious workings of their minds, primitive savage and professional religious. I felt very certain they would understand me, and that among Maa Koo's kindred at least I would not be—"queer!"

I was immediately faced with the choice of a profession—what my work on the mission field would be, that is. I couldn't preach, and I didn't want to be a teacher. I had "baby sat" with too many of Aunt Bessie's friends' brats to imagine that a vicarious motherhood could be tolerable. There remained only medical work. I wanted to be a doctor. The nearest medical school was a couple of hundred miles away; and it was when I broached attendance that I discovered Aunt Bessie's charity did not cover any period when I was not physically at hand to iron her linen, wash her china, wax her floors, and dust her precious bric-a-brac.

"Heavens! She thinks we're made of money!" Aunt Bessie squealed. "Well! Beggars can't be choosers. There's many a woman teaching who would rather be doing something else. You're no better than they—just because everything has been given you all your life! You can tell that Mission Board you'll go as a teacher!" So I couldn't become a doctor.

The next best thing was to become a nurse. Possibly that could be arranged. A nurse needed financial backing only for her textbooks and uniforms, I thought, but was informed that ten dollars a month was required "for personal expenditures." The missionary society which bought my college textbooks, again promised books for the period of nurse's training. Uncle Ben " 'lowed as how" a load of corn each year should supply the uniforms. "Kind of 'first fruits to the Lord' like the old prophets done," he joked. Father wrote me that he was sure he could "squeeze ten dollars a month" out of his missionary's pittance. I didn't see how he could. I had never known a time as a child when the enormous sum of ten dollars had been left over at the end of a month. But I had all faith that the Lord would provide, and I accepted his sacrifice.

When I told Aunt Bessie that arrangements had been completed for me to enter a hospital for training, she snorted so violently that her gold pince-nez fell into her potatoes and gravy.

So, at twenty years of age, I felt that life's problems were now solved for me. I had accepted "a call" to the mission field and was preparing myself for foreign service. I believe now that actually I had accepted nothing more than spinsterhood—and that simply because I didn't know how to make myself socially acceptable to a white man. I had never learned by instruction, or observation, those niceties of premarital sex dalliance called "courtship." I was prepared to be a good wife. Maa Koo had seen to that. But I did not know how to get a white husband. In all the charity showered upon me, there was no one—not even my mother!—who helped me with this most vital need.

I was confident of the future, and almost carefree when, a few days before our college graduation exercises the dean called me into his office. He asked me what my plans for the future were, and I told him. He "Hummmm-ed!" several times, and drummed on the desk with the tips of his fingers. Then, "That poses a problem," he murmured.

I could only wait until, with much circumlocution, he explained that my tuition for the past four years had not been a gift as I had supposed, but a loan. I owed the college what seemed to me a vast sum of money. Before I left the dean's office I signed in triplicate a promise to pay all or any part of this sum if and when I could, interest waived. The dean did not suggest that I forget about the debt, but he did encourage me to go ahead with my plans.

Of all the errors into which I have fallen at various times, lack of faith has not been one of them. Something would turn up. Or someone would help me. It has always been so with missionaries and I think that in many ways has crippled us as a professional class. Instead of trying to solve our economic problems, we have simply laid them on the Lord and have struggled to do His work supported, or perhaps I should say hampered, by the meagerest charity.

I actually felt sorry for the dean. He seemed so honestly embarrassed. And why shouldn't he be? In Africa I had seen so many men tied together, two by two; he who had lent foolishly linked with him who had borrowed what he could not pay. And until some third person with wealth heavy on his hands came forward and paid the debt, the two must perform all the functions of living, in the company of each other, and even lie down at night to such rest as is possible when one is disturbed by an unwelcome presence.

"It is the same in America, too," my father said to me once when we passed two such men beside a path. The lender was cutting green vines for a fish trap, and the borrower was never more than a few feet away from his slashing *panga* blade.

"There is one difference in America," my father went on. "The withes are not visible to the naked eye, but they are there just the same. And both men sleep uneasily at night because of them."

Everyone in the hospital was nice to me, nurses, internes, and full-fledged doctors. "Nice" is the right word to use. Most of them paid me a surface-pretty deference, a polite respect without warmth or depth. I had been accepted by our Mission Board for service in Africa, and although there was nothing overt in anyone's behavior, again I could not help sensing that socially I was a creature set apart. At least a momentary hush fell over any group I joined. It was as though the simple friendship of human beings was something too common, too coarse for the elect of God.

There was a curious something about that hospital which the old men and women of an African village would have laughed out of existence as the height of the ridiculous. A hundred young women, and a score of young men, all in the lustiest years of their lives, rubbed shoulders every day and yet were forbidden normal social intercourse. It was as though some psychopath, frosty with age, had laid down injunctions against the primordial wellsprings of life. The rules forbid the nurses and internes dating. They were quite specific, so much so that a nurse usually cast a quick glance about her if an interne offered to get up and fetch her a glass of water or cup of coffee in the cafeteria. Yet, when a group of nurses was graduated, it seemed to me that half the class immediately announced their engagements to young doctors who had left the hospital only days, weeks, or at most months before them.

There was one nurse—curious, isn't it? I can't remember her name or even what she looked like—who was on night duty with me for a few months. Punctually at eleven-fifteen every evening she got a headache. She watched her wristwatch to time its onslaught. At eleven-fourteen-and-a-half, she would whisper in my ear, "I'm going to slip out on the fire escape for a breath of fresh air. This throbbing head of mine, you know! If you see the supervisor coming, just peck on the windowpane. Will you? You're a peach! I'll do something nice for you someday."

She did. When, after graduation, she and one of the handsomest doctors in the hospital were married, I was a bridesmaid. I wore a hat with a wide brim that rippled up and down gently like the edges of a huge banana leaf when the morning sun warms currents of cold night air. My dress was filmy and full and long and touched the grass. It was the color of morning before the sun pushes over the horizon.

When I dressed and stood in front of the mirror I caught my breath. I was beautiful! As beautiful as any woman—prettier than most! Then a twinge twisted my conscience. Would anyone look at the bride with me there? But I needn't have worried, for at the wedding no one looked at me at all. Instead, they stared at the bride. I stared, too, for there was an ethereal beauty in her face which mere clothes, however pretty, can never rival.

Back at the hospital I folded up my dress in tissue paper, boxed my hat, and, when one of the nurses asked if she might borrow my ridiculously beautiful shoes to go dancing, I gave them to her and never saw them again. I have had just two pairs of utterly beautiful shoes in my life, and someone else threw away each pair.

Once every six months the college from which I was graduated sent me a note. The dean or his secretary always assured me that I might have an indefinite period, interest free, in which to discharge the obligation—but they reminded me that I did still owe them four years' tuition. True the bonds were not of twisted bark fibers, and neither of us had to hold up an awkward physical weight as he moved about, but they were there just the same. Stronger than the toughest bark. And—I confess it with shame—I, the debtor, because of my missionary background, was actually less troubled by the obligation than those who had been generous to me.

CHAPTER
THREE

My missionary society, the one which had bought my college and nursing textbooks, outfitted me for Africa. There was everything I needed to last me for six years at least. On the seventh I would be back "home" on furlough, ready to be outfitted again by some good, God-fearing group of Christian women. Please believe me, I am deeply grateful to these women. Many a missionary could not go to the field, and others would go at grave risk of health without their help; but why—Oh, why!—I ask, must charity always be so stark and harsh and ugly?

"Denim underwear! . . . Canvas uniforms! . . . Burlap handkerchiefs!"

That is the merciless way the nurses in the hospital described my outfit when they saw it. There was not a single soft, lace-trimmed, feminine-appearing garment in the lot. The quality of Aunt Bessie's hand-me-downs had been bad medicine for a woman whose thoughts were supposed to be solely on the Lord and His work and the Kingdom of Celestial Perfection to come.

Aunt Bessie, too, contributed to my outfit, but after her own fashion. She gave me a hat, one she herself had worn for only a year. It was a beautiful hat with ribbons and feathers on it. I knew it had cost a good round sum, but it was a hat fashioned for a sixty-five-year-old head rather than one not yet quite twenty-four. There were tears in my heart if not on my cheeks when I kissed Aunt Bessie goodbye at the station. Seated in the train I took off the hat very quickly. The train started with a lurch and the hat slid off the slick, hard coach-cushion and rolled under the seat in front of me. I let it lie there for a long time. Then with the toe of my very sensible shoe, I wedged it out of sight. I left it there when I got off in New York City.

There were two other missionaries of our denomination on my boat, a newly married young couple, James and Esther Grove. She, too, was a nurse, and he was an educator—a teacher with a curious lack of enthusiasm for his work. Not for his calling as a Christian missionary. Not that at all! Like his beautiful, copper-haired wife, he almost seethed with zeal. But when I described African schools in mission compounds and in the bush, he seemed to listen with only half an ear. Perhaps since I am looking back over the past years with full knowledge of what has since happened to all of us, imagination—conscience even—plays fully as large a part in my story as memory.

The second day out of New York I began giving Jimmy and Esther Grove language lessons. It is always so with missionaries. The "old hands" always begin teaching the newcomers before they have finished unpacking. We found much to laugh at in their attempts at tonal inflection and agglutinate sentences, but both of them were keenly interested in everything I could tell them about Africa.

I honestly don't remember too well the quality and subject matter of Esther's questions; but no matter what the task in hand, or the subject under discussion, Jimmy always brought the conversation around to farming: fields, flocks, and gardens. He had been born and reared on a farm, and he was attending an agricultural college when he met Esther. A few belated courses in pedagogy were his sole preparation for the mission field—and love for a beautiful woman, I suppose I must add. Esther's and my work was well established at our mission station. So was the educational work into which Jimmy was to fit himself somehow. But he was born and bred to the soil, and he and his wife were full of such trite old jokes as: You can take a boy out of the country, but you can't take the country out of the boy. One felt that much which was vital in Jimmy would die if such an extraction were made. They

36 ·

were humorless jokes, jokes offered with an air of embarrassment.

Or were they excuses? The thought disturbed me, and I began watching Jimmy. I suppose it was this perpetual habit of watching people, seeking answers in the emotions which flit across their faces, trying to penetrate their thoughts, that first brought me close to Jimmy as a man, a male animal of my own species—creed, caste, and color. He was another woman's husband, but I liked what I saw and—as God is my witness!—there was no tinge of immorality in the liking. The pleasure was as far removed from carnal desire as the memory of a symphony concert or a visit to an art gallery.

Jimmy was a big man, six-feet tall and well proportioned. The muscles rippled under his shirt until I imagined I could see them— like the oiled and scraped shoulders of a black tribesman. He was strong but he never boasted of his strength or otherwise exhibited it. And in spite of all the quips directed at farmer boys, he was neither crude nor gauche. His eyes which were keen and merry enough on occasion often had that faraway look of a man who is seeing the labor of his hands come to fruition in broad fields of grain this year, next year, and all the years to come in a carefully planned life.

But the wise men and women of our Board had decreed that Jimmy was not to turn the black cotton soil of the Congo Territory in endless parallel furrows, plant it with seed, tend its crops, or reap their harvest. Even I, my mind as well as my body once again turned toward Africa, knew that they were right, for husbandry is "woman's work"—in the primitive reaches of the Dark Continent, at least. Jimmy, whose very dreams were rooted in the soil, was destined to stand before groups of the older boys and train them to compute how long it would take them at varying jobs and wages to earn their hut taxes: so many sous per day for so many days must total so many francs, multiplied by the number of wives (each wife always in her own hut) a man had. I knew he would be expected to set similar sums showing that a smaller number of wives would mean a smaller number of francs to be scraped together for the tax collector. Thus he would be using the classroom to point out one of the evils of polygamy and the blessings of Christian monogamy—in a land where human *cattle* are wealth and the size of a man's harem carries as much prestige for the women involved as for their master. And at the same time he must somehow, someway, teach the social therapy of industry!

We transshipped at Southampton to a freighter which carried thirty or forty passengers for Africa. Most of them were traders, usually solitary men returning to their trading stations, and planters, with or without their white families, returning to their plantations. There were more missionaries, too; perhaps a dozen of us all together.

The planters and their wives left us strictly alone. Later, I well knew, when abject loneliness settled down upon these women, they would visit our mission stations and would even invite us to their homes. We, also suffering from loneliness become an occupational disease, would accept their hospitality. But on the boat, fresh out of Europe with its caste-bound teas and *soirées,* we were looked upon as very much a group apart. Nigger lovers! Meddlers! Religious busybodies with our noses deep in native affairs.

Esther and I were walking the deck one morning when we came upon a group of planters' children playing a game familiar to me. A small, thoroughly happy boy was squatting on his haunches and a half-dozen other tots, hands clasped in a circle were dancing about him chanting:

> "Mission'ry in the cooking pot.
> Plenty holy! Plenty hot!"

Esther surprised me by bursting into peals of laughter. She pointed at the boy squatting on the deck and gasped, "Isn't he the merriest pot roast you ever saw?"

For a few seconds I was dumbfounded, and then I knew why Jimmy had given up the lush acres he loved and the fat flocks that were his pride to follow this beautiful creature to one of the social ends of the earth. A man would follow anyone with that spirit if she were—even if she were already—as plain and drab as I knew the jungle would inevitably make her in a short span of years.

As a group we missionaries would have liked to have held a Wednesday evening prayer-meeting, but there was no place on that small boat where we could do so. There were only two rooms large enough. A public lounge from which we could scarcely drive out the other passengers, and the dining room. This had the ship's bar spread across its long, unbroken front wall. An amazing thing about African planters and traders is the unbelievable quantity of whiskey they can and do consume—always strictly after sundown if they are English. Inevitably every one of them speeds the sinking sun with a ritual "sundowner." Even the exceedingly odd man one finds now and then who does not drink, is driven for his social life to sprawling across a bar in awkward, embarrassed abstemiousness.

Sunday morning, however, the bar was deserted and Sabbath breakfast would be late, so we gathered for a worship service. Six denominations were represented in the small group. This brother-hood of the sects is a commonplace of the mission field, at least in our part of Africa.

A curious thing happened that first Sunday morning on shipboard. I was listening with only the fringes of my mind to the sermon— familiar phrases falling on my ears like bits from a memorized passage. After all, what can a preacher say that is fresh and new to a group, half of whom are also preachers? Practically all of whom have voiced identical precepts and platitudes as a professional duty?

The chairs about me creaked and still half dreaming I stood up with my fellow worshipers to sing "Onward Christian Soldiers." The words were as familiar as breathing and I sang without thought or effort. Then the chair legs scraped the floor again. The hymn was ended, but all except the very oldest paused in that first awkward human angle preliminary to sitting down. A planter who apparently had not waited for sunset on the Sabbath had been listening, elbows and forearms spread out on the sill of an open window. Now he was applauding vigorously and shouting, "Bravo! Bravo!" in the best *opéra comique* gallery style.

I glanced quickly at Jimmy and Esther Grove. Jimmy was holding his wife's elbow in firm fingers and staring at her sidewise under lowered lashes. Esther, her nose almost pinched between the pages of her hymnal, was staring with wide-open, unseeing eyes at the outrage-stiffened back in front of her and biting a tense lip above a twitching chin.

Peering sidewise at Esther, I wondered how much and how long she would laugh in Africa—or if the Dark Continent would smother her mirth. I was glad that we were both nurses and would work together. It would be easy for me to help her, and her me. "We have so much in common," I thought at the time. O God! If only I could have known at that moment how much we were to share in common, this lovely, gracious, scintillating, socially gifted woman and I.

"And now may the grace of God descend upon each and every one of you—"

Automatically I lowered my head and closed my eyes. Outside the window there was a scuffle of footsteps and I knew someone was leading the exuberant planter away. Singly and in groups we drifted out of the dining salon to our Sunday morning diversions. Esther Grove and I, with Jimmy between holding an elbow of each, started a circumparade of the deck, with Esther pressing me to "tell them everything, just everything, about Africa."

I tried. I spoke of Maa Koo, of course, because I loved her. And countless others, too, for whom I unconsciously felt varying degrees of affection and respect, African-wise, must have come in for a word picture. What could I say of the customs of the people? Raw, primitive Africa must be seen to be believed, must be lived with to be respected, must be understood by the sensitive heart to be loved.

I remember that Esther laughed in her easy, light-hearted way when I told them that the phrase they would hear in bush villages more often than any other would be: *"Bendele bafa bantu,"* that is, "White men aren't people." I tried to explain that it was a matter of our social customs against theirs, that even in the very largest mission stations we were few and they were many. In the heart of the Dark Continent we were the *ausländers,* the foreigners.

I remember turning to them, intense words on my lips, hoping they would be capable of understanding the Africa in which I had grown up. Esther's face satisfied me for a moment. People were people to her, regardless of race or geography. Loving apparently came easy, and with it the social graces of loving—whether the affection were deep and intense or only cursory and transitory. Jimmy's face troubled me. He was staring into the little waves that seized fragments of sunlight and threw them back into our eyes like a thousand mischievous children with tiny mirrors. It was the same way Uncle Ben looked across his pasture and into a distant woodlot, seeing only what was in his mind to begin with.

Then Esther was pressing me and I was telling her a little story of an old man who had once stopped briefly at our mission compound. He was spry and vigorous and seemingly in good health, yet he was hurrying back to his native village to die. An African tribesman will always do that if he can. On the West Coast at least they had no words for heaven and hell until we, the missionaries, made up the phrases and supplied the concepts for a few of them. To die, however, away from home where one's spirit must forever wander through an unfamiliar jungle, or across an unknown plain, among stranger spirits, that is indeed a grim fate. I chose the tale so that Esther would understand later when her dying patients would be spirited away and painfully, toilsomely, carried back to their own villages however distant. I thought Esther would surely understand—and I wanted someone to understand—how strange a villageful of people content with their own lives find the Jesus-man who suddenly appears among them and asks them to abandon customs, individually and as a group, which countless centuries of famine, plague, and internecine plunder have crystallized into social mores upon which government and even existence hinge.

I remember fragmentarily the old man's actual words: "Dying leaves turn brown and fall. . . ." "Were white people once brown in another life—and are you now dead?"

My mother, a plump little robin of a woman, was standing in front of the man who was squatting on his haunches. Without warning he leaned forward and jabbed a forefinger an inch deep into the fat of her calf. She winced and hopped away. The tribesman had grinned up at her and iterated simply, "Are you already dead? You do not hoe beans as a woman should. And there is not much substance to your flesh. My finger goes through it easily."

We often walked like that, arm in arm, the three of us, Esther laughing easily, Jimmy without much comment on the things I told them about Africa. I suppose I was as much teacher of ethnology and folkways as of language. They learned easily. Perhaps that was what encouraged me to talk. The untouched African is animistic, and everything about him has human qualities—and a folk tale to match. There was the *ngöli,* the tough green vine we used as rope when on trek. Once upon a time, back beyond the memory of the oldest woman, ngöli had been an exceedingly greedy man. He had reached out after everything: after that which his wives earned and which, therefore, was rightfully his, and after that to which he could lay no honest claim. Always that reaching! Reaching! Reaching! Finally he stretched his arms and legs too thin to bear their own weight and he had to twine them around the trunks and branches of trees in order to remain upright. But still he kept on greedily reaching out after what belonged to others, smothering life here, sucking it away there, always taking, taking, taking for his own selfish purposes until he no longer looked in any way like a human being.

Of course I told the tale in a minute or less, but I warned Esther and Jimmy that it would take a tribesman a week to finish the story. I know I babbled on about my Africa like a child. They were easy to talk to, Jimmy and Esther. There was nothing scornful, not then, in Esther's bubbling laughter, nothing repressive in Jimmy's quiet attention. It was Esther who asked the questions that led me on, but I think Jimmy heard more of what I said. Always I felt that in some way he was relating everything to his life as a farmer. Again and again I saw so much of Uncle Ben in his face.

Long before we sighted Africa, and increasingly as we skirted the coast plowing southward, I began to hope with an almost child-like intensity that my father would like and approve of this man and woman. I was very certain they would love him. Who didn't?

It was almost like an answer to prayer when he met us in Léopold-ville. But when I stepped off the boat and threw my arms about my father, fear suddenly drenched the love in my heart and left me shocked, numbed. My arms reached too far. They overlapped. Shockingly. But as always, father was sprightly.

Then I heard Jimmy murmur in his wife's ear, "Wiry old boy, isn't he?"

My eyes sought Esther's. There was no laughter on her lips now. She nodded almost imperceptibly to my unspoken question. Her face was a study in compassion. But when one forgot his thinness, father gave the illusion of health and well-being. I was shocked when Jimmy remarked casually, "Your father will be going home soon, won't he?"

I began figuring when his next furlough was due, but in the middle of my cumbersome mental arithmetic I turned and looked at him carefully, as though I were seeing him for the first time. His physical spryness was an illusion. There was agility of mind and spirit, a brimming, friendly concern for the welfare and com-fort of others that drew a mental veil over his gaunt frame and sere features. Yes, my father was an old man. Others had been retired from the field when younger than he. But standing there on the dock that day, I knew that for my father no place in the world could ever be home but Africa. Then I wondered what had been my mother's reactions to letters from our Governing Board which they always begin sending several years in advance of retirement. True mother was one of those few unfortunate women one finds on every foreign field, a missionary expatriate. But, though she might struggle weakly and emotionally against her fate, when the spirits of the departed beckoned to my parents, she would still be trotting fussily along some jungle path only a step or two behind my father.

On the way upriver Jimmy and Esther fell in love with father, as I had hoped and expected they would. In these latter days I have wondered much if father would not have been considered an exceedingly capable ethnologist if he had had access to scientific circles, and if he had had the time to imprison a due portion of his vast knowledge of the folkways of the Dark Continent between the covers of books.

One doesn't walk the deck much on a Congo river boat. The decks aren't big enough in the first place, and are more apt than not to be piled high with freight and luggage. We sat in small groups, with the newcomers and many of the "old hands" always around father, while he told of new and strange tribes he had visited. Some of those tribes had been so decimated by disease, famine, and the ubiquitous labor recruiter that they had ceased to exist as a people during my father's missionary lifetime. Others—strange as such a statement may sound in these days of airplanes, radios, and all the other paraphernalia of a shrinking world—dwelt in still unmapped areas as large as many American states.

It had been father who discovered—and lost again—what he had always called the Valley of the Bees. So far as I have been able to learn only he and two other white men have ever visited this tiny hidden valley securely walled in on each side by the sheer rock cliffs of one of Africa's many geological rifts. Black travelers who stumbled into the valley were always fed and otherwise cared for, and then sent on their way with a gourdful of honey as food to last until they reached the next village. On the last day of father's stay in the hidden village, he was permitted to visit their fetish hut. There, in their primitive holy of holies, he had found the dry brittle skeleton of a man, an empty watch case the size of a farm woman's biscuit, a pointed knife and two-tined fork, a moldering Testament so frail he dared not turn back the cover to read a possible name on the flyleaf, and a small leather bag holding a handful of pebbles, opaque in color and roughly tetrahedral in shape. The few scraps of clothing lying over the bones were of a cut and texture belonging to another century.

This stranger who had died in the Valley of the Bees had been invested with sainthood by the magic of simple legendry. And because it was obvious to the most casual that my father, too, was a man of peace, he was given one of the small, opaque, tetrahedral pebbles which folk tales said the dead man had treasured above all his other possessions. Father carried that pebble in his pocket for perhaps a decade before he discovered it was a diamond. It sent my oldest brother through medical school.

Father was also one of those few men who had crossed the Hungry Country, which according to him was neither veld, jungle, nor desert, but "a combination of the worst features of all three, if you can imagine that," he would say.

"It wasn't a bad trip," father told us one afternoon. "Not bad at all. Food is there, if you'll eat such as it is. And water, too, if you can smell it out." We all smiled at his use of the African phrase for "discover."

"Charming. Quaint," Esther murmured.

Father went on, tapping a knee with his forefinger for emphasis, "It wasn't such a hard trip. There is no reason why it should be too difficult for one who loves the land." He paused and looked searchingly into Jimmy's face. Then he went on, "Or for one to whom the land is friendly."

There was a small straight furrow between Esther's brows, and her eyes were big and round as she gazed at father. Then her lids dropped, and I was amazed at what I sensed more than saw, a flash of resentment. But at what?

Jimmy, on the other hand, was trading father eye for eye with that air of relaxed detachment which passes for a smile between men who understand each other.

"Beyond the Hungry Country is the land of the People of the Fan," father went on, apparently satisfied with what he saw in Jimmy's face.

Then father was speaking directly to Jimmy with a strange, quiet

· 45

emphasis. "There is so much that is 'known' about Africa that is wrong. All wrong! For instance, you'll run into what are called 'Fang Men' almost everywhere. There is one at our compound right now. The scientific know-it-alls will tell you that they are called 'Fangs' because their front teeth are 'filed' to sharp points. Not at all! We say 'fang' because that is an English word with meaning for us which is obviously applicable to these men. The sound 'fĕng' isn't. But up beyond the Hungry Country, that sound 'fĕng' means 'fan.' A particular kind of fan—strange and terrible!" Father fell silent with that inward look of a man listening to his own thoughts.

Then he broke away from his unseen companions and came back to us. "Now that matter of 'filed' teeth. They aren't filed at all, but chipped. Wait until you see some old man sitting astride a boy's chest, the boy flat on his back on the ground, blood and spittle drooling from the corners of his mouth while the old man with flint chisel and wooden mallet whacks away at the teeth—"

Father had seemingly forgotten the rest of us, for he was talking directly to Jimmy. Esther shuddered violently. I took her by the arm and pulled her away, although she stared backward at her husband until we rounded the wheelhouse and he was out of sight.

CHAPTER

FOUR

From the first time they met, father seemed satisfied with Jimmy Grove as a man. Vaguely I wondered what responsibilities other than so many hours in a classroom he would lay upon the newcomer. It was father who, because of his wide knowledge of Africa and profound understanding of the folkways of the people as much as his position as head of his mission, decided where the new outstations would be located and who would man them. Perhaps it was premonition, perhaps it was that strange look on Jimmy's face which made me wonder vaguely and briefly if father might not sometime send Jimmy out across the Hungry Country to these almost legendary People of the Fan—the "Fangs," as the traders called them.

Now and then father had talked of an outstation there, but nothing had ever been done about it. Not that the distance from our central station mattered. Africa is vaster than the average American ever realizes, and many a missionary pioneering an outstation is located anywhere from fifty to several hundred miles from his nearest professional compatriot. But "Beyond the Hungry Country"—we at our compound had always used those words as one might say, "Across the River Styx."

I tried to shrug the matter out of mind and almost succeeded. But when we left the big river boat we had boarded in Léopoldville and started up our tributary of the Congo in our mission boat, it came back hauntingly. There were old friends among the boys who rowed. There were new faces, too. Among these latter was one whose forehead, cheeks, and chin were so interlaced with cicatrices that portions of his face looked like scraps from an Arabic manuscript. The man was tall. Not so towering as one of the famed Watussi, nor so reed-like in build as the crane-stanced Dinkas, but more perfectly proportioned, like the Masai of East Africa, than any river man I had ever seen.

"How did he get here?" I asked. "Did he come through from East Africa with some expedition: Hunters? Scientists? Explorers?"

Father shook his head. "He says he came from beyond the Hungry Country."

I wanted to ask, "Is he a Fan Man?" but something held me back.

"He just appeared one day and asked to be permitted to pay through labor for initiation into white man's magic," father explained.

"Probably in training to become a super-de-luxe witch doctor," I scoffed. Requests "to be taught everything white men know" are not uncommon from naïve but ambitious young bush boys.

"If he is a novitiate, he will make a witch doctor whose friendship it will be well for missionaries to cultivate," father said slowly and with no trace of humor. Then, "His name is Abu Sayheed. In a sort of degenerate Arabic, that means 'The Father of Wisdom.'"

The boy grinned at me briefly, but long enough to show a row of pointed teeth, apparently sharp as thorns. A Fang Man? I questioned myself silently. I looked Abu Sayheed over carefully. Such ornamental scarring as his face bore can disguise age to the extent of twenty years—either way! Still, from the rounded muscles and smooth skin over his neck and shoulders and hips, he couldn't have been over thirty at the oldest.

"Perhaps he was born 'with an old spirit.'" Father used a Hausa explanation to answer my unspoken wonder at such a dignified name for so young a man.

One other thing father told me about Abu Sayheed that made no impression on me at the time because, perhaps, it was so common to Africa and African folkways. The fellow had been away from his village for a long time and now was looking for something of value to take to his father as a gift upon his return. The African native loves to travel and many a man will refuse a good job near home so that he will have an excuse to trudge a thousand miles elsewhere—anywhere! Also, once having slept a season away from his village, a man does not return to his kraal without gifts for his father and his male in-laws in the pack on his head. His gossip and tales of adventure will be ignored in the palaver hut until he has laid an acceptable token at the feet of his chief.

Father said he had offered Abu Sayheed many things, for the most part trivia a white man discards. But this mission boy, with a face like a fragment of Arabic manuscript, had shaken his head "No," at each item. The fellow was a good workman, steady, flexible and intelligent; and as the weeks went by my father offered other things of greater value, but always the answer was "No."

"He knows exactly what he wants," father told me. "Yet I have asked him point-blank what it is and he hasn't told me. He has worked long enough to pay me well for it, though."

All African "boys," as servants and other workmen are called, expect their employers to give them whatever their hearts desire. Ordinarily even the poverty-stricken missionary is wealthy beyond avarice, as measured by their standards. It can surely be nothing for him to part with whatever their eyes light upon—more will immediately come upriver for the missionary, and apparently without effort on his part.

Abu Sayheed was the exception. Evidently he was not a poor man compelled to accumulate sou by sou and by the sweat of his broad back the hut tax for a father preoccupied with a score or more of wives. A hyrax skin dangled from the belt of the bark-cloth kilt he wore in the mission compound and the G-strap he preferred on trek. In this native purse were cowrie shells, the medium of exchange in many inland villages, and many more sous than I usually carried in my own pocket.

But it was neither coins, nor cowrie shells, nor labor, that Abu Sayheed gave my father in payment for a nebulous gift which he never named or asked the possession of. It was something of far greater value to my father, the Afrophile, who would have gone hungry to acquire any unique ethnological artifact. He gave my father a fan. This fan was circular, about two feet in diameter, and of copper beaten thin by a wooden mallet. So thin, in fact, it bent like paper under its own weight. There was an eight-inch handle, also of copper, roughly pyramidal in shape, measuring maybe an inch through at its larger end, and tapering to a blunt point.

"This is the way it is used," father said when he first showed it to me. He held it, circular portion downward, and swung his arm back and forth in quick arcs. The thin metal whipped past his legs quiveringly and stirred the air about my calves and ankles although I stood halfway across the room.

"Do you mean that they fan their feet with the thing?" I asked.

"No, they fan a fire with it—with two of them. Always two of them," he answered slowly.

An important part of any missionary's introduction to Africa is that short distance after he leaves the last vestige of his own civilization behind and traverses the primeval jungle before reaching the compound in which he will begin his service. For Esther and Jimmy Grove that covered about two hundred miles of Congo River tributary after we had left the big, lumbering old stern-wheeler which had brought us another couple of hundred miles from Léopoldville. We traveled in a native boat called a *shimbeck*. It was really nothing but a monster dugout, covered over in the middle with an awning of green bark.

All through childhood it had been borne in upon me by newcomers to the mission station that this was an exceedingly cumbersome, un-riverworthy, even dangerous craft. I never knew a white man who learned how to manage one. I never knew a river boy who didn't seem as much at home in one as on dry land. Ours was a nice shimbeck. We could sit in the shade of the bark awning, in a deck chair, and sleep or read or daydream away the long hours of jungle travel very pleasantly.

Jimmy hadn't been in our shimbeck more than a half-hour before he insisted on taking his place at the oars. Physically he was as strong as any boy rowing, but could scarcely have been more awkward among them. Our boys struggled hard to keep his frantic lunges with the leaf-shaped oar from whirling the boat about and heading downstream. He was good-natured about his inept efforts, and the boys' frank laughter.

On the other hand, within ten minutes after boarding the shimbeck, his wife had stretched out in the bottom of the boat, her face buried in a bedding roll. I didn't think much about her behavior at first, since many people are violently seasick in a shimbeck. However, when Jimmy sprayed all of us with a sheet of water from his refractory oar, I saw and heard an Esther I hadn't dreamed existed during those pleasant days on the transoceanic liner.

"Oh, for heaven's sake, Jim, come sit where you belong and stop acting like a schoolboy on a picnic," she snarled.

Obediently he handed his oar to a waiting boy and, still in a squatting position, inched his way across the bottom of the boat. Esther raised her head and glared at him. She was trembling When her husband reached her side she turned over with a flop that rocked the shimbeck until we shipped water. "This isn't seasickness," was my first, surprised reaction.

Father, too, was watching Esther over the tops of his reading glasses, his brows and lips straight lines across his face.

Many people are frightened of the great African rivers the first time they are made to feel a torrent's might and their own physical insignificance. Other newcomers to the Dark Continent sit rigid, staring fascinatedly at the great rolling waves that toss a shimbeck up and down as easily, as high and as a low, as a pair of childish feet shove a swing. Some close their eyes and clench their hands. A few write long letters full of bombastic terms trying to describe the swirling floods. These even become proud of the nonchalance with which they later ride our rivers in dugouts so narrow a fat man's hips have to be wedged even into the widest portion.

With a woman's intuition I knew right then that Esther Grove would never accept the Congo or any of its monstrous tributaries as a missionary to Western Africa must—as we ask primitive peoples to accept our God. She would always fear this unbelievably mighty force which preserves or destroys whimsically. Many times during that day I found myself watching this woman with whom I had already spent so many pleasant hours, peering at her as though I had never seen her before. Father, however, kept on calmly reading, seemingly unmindful of the conflict of forces about us. Perhaps it was because of this acceptance on his part of intangibles beyond his ability to alter that he was acknowledged a missionary *par excellence*. In any case, he was much sought out and listened to by black and white alike.

From time to time Esther moaned querulously like a sick child, and Jimmy stroked her beautiful soft hair with a bronzed, work-hardened hand. Once she winced as though he had struck her, and it angered me. Then, because of the emotional turmoil within me, I began imagining the enthusiastic comments of the Committee on Appointments considering Esther Grove: "Charming! Gracious personality! Vitality! Bubbling spirit!" Pat phrases trippingly mouthed! Young as I was, my life in a mission compound had already taught me that "bubbling, vital, gracious charm" is apt to be a parasite, dependent for its very existence on a constant supply of human adulation. The duties of her co-workers are too absorbing, and important, and pressing to let them feed this subtle, ingratiating type of vanity indefinitely.

Later that afternoon I, too, was reading when the shimbeck rocked violently and again we shipped a few splashes of water. Boy after boy from among our oarsmen were laying down their paddles and plunging overboard. Jimmy gasped. Esther raised her head and screamed, understandably. To uninitiated eyes, it simply did not seem possible that anything human could live in that boiling flood. Father and I watched, knowing that the oarsmen had spied some treasure out there. The boys remaining in the shimbeck let it drift slowly downstream as the swimmers converged on one point where a dead fish floated. Father smiled, then closed his eyes and shuddered in exaggerated, mock dread.

When the swimmers returned pushing their prize in front of them, it was broken and ripped into pieces in the water, handed aboard in hunks, and devoured on the spot. It had not been dead nearly so long as other flesh I had often watched black men consume with gusto. Father and I waited indulgently, and we were both honestly surprised when we heard a violent retching sound. Jimmy's face was white, and Esther was being sick in the bottom of the shimbeck.

Jimmy dipped his handkerchief into the river and cleaned her face. Then like a well-intentioned but awkward housewife, he started washing up the bottom of the boat. I moved as though to help him, but father motioned me to stay where I was. Jimmy did not look at either of us as he swabbed and rinsed over the side of the boat and swabbed again. Without knowing why, I was conscious of such embarrassment that my nostrils pinched together and I had to open my mouth in order to breathe, and it would have been painful thereafter even to glance at this man and woman.

It seemed an eternity before the sun touched the horizon and our boys, singing and paddling together with powerful strokes, drove the shimbeck almost its entire length out of the water onto a shallow sandspit. Jimmy was surprised that we stopped at what seemed to him so early in the afternoon. He was to learn that in Africa there is no twilight. There the sun sinks and God draws a velvet mantle over the heavens, festoons the treetops with myriad candles, and it is already night. No dusk or twilight at all.

Again I had to watch Esther make a fool of herself. The boys unloaded the shimbeck completely, hauled it up onto dry sand, tilted it on its side with the bottom to windward, and propped it thus securely with sticks. With a half-dozen small fires in front of it, it would make them a cozy lean-to to sleep in that night. At the moment some of them were busy setting up a sleeping tent for Jimmy and Esther and another one for father and me. Others were heating bath water for us, and the cook was preparing supper.

Everyone knew his work and was getting it done efficiently enough for tropical Africa.

Esther, her feet firmly planted on stable land, was herself once more, being the little housewife, fluttering about, telling everyone what to do—without realizing that in this new and strange environment she had only the vaguest ideas of just what the tasks to be performed were. It was easy to imagine Esther at a school picnic "back home." She would be everywhere at once, telling everyone what to do, doing nothing herself—and getting away with it pleasantly by the magic of her merry laughter and effusive charm.

"So she's one of those!" father muttered.

Suddenly the men began to sing calypso-fashion, with the cook leading. The song was spontaneous, created for the occasion, and to the point. Neither father nor I dared to look at each other lest we burst out laughing. Jimmy and Esther stopped to listen appreciatively. Esther held her head tilted to one side, her eyes on the tree-tops, her lips opened just enough to show the rounded edges of her milk-white teeth, the corners of her mouth curved softly upward. She made an engaging picture—but it was too perfect! Seemingly without even looking at her, the cook caught the pose and sensed the artificiality behind it. Without a break he incorporated a ribald description of it in his song.

Father's laughter broke through, and he jerked out his upper plate and began hawking as though he had something caught in his throat. Even so, he barely disguised his chortle. Most of the boys spoke some English, but they were singing in a very idiomatic Swahili so that neither Jimmy nor his wife understood a word. It would have made no difference if they had. No one is quicker to detect sham than an African tribesman—or to puncture it more mercilessly. Roughly, the cook's song was about a little copper-colored hen whose normal function in life was to lay eggs and hatch out chicks. But she became so engrossed with scratching and clucking and admiring her own reflection in the dew-wet leaves of a morning that she ended in the cooking pot before her time.

"Is it a folk song?" Esther asked sweetly.

"It is folk wise," father temporized.

"Their voices, low and kind of humming that way, they sound sort of like a whippoorwill," Jimmy murmured.

"It's about a—a kind of bird," father admitted. Then, "Whip-'er-well," he whispered almost inaudibly, staring into the fire.

On that trip upriver I began to sense something of the personality problems the head of a mission station must face and deal with. We were finishing supper one evening when Abu Sayheed came up and spoke briefly to father. I heard the black boy's words and glanced involuntarily at Esther. The information that Abu Sayheed had dropped into father's ear was only a minor pebble in the wall of primordial savagery against which this woman must bump her pretty head many times in the coming months.

Father finished his tea deliberately, set the cup down slowly, nodded to me and we both arose. Then as an afterthought he turned to Jimmy. "You may come along if you like," he said. "You'll see a side of Africa you don't read too much about back home, but it's common enough here in the jungle. But— Perhaps Mrs. Grove would like to go to her tent—and—rest," he ended lamely.

I can still see the way Esther bounded out of her camp chair, strangely like the black boys' little bronze hen. Everything which had passed for aggressive leadership in another environment, determination always to be heard, to be in the middle of things, was now painted across her face. One sensed that in the days to come she would be underfoot, full of that quick advice which is born of lack of experience and smug ignorance. She started to say something, but father nodded to Abu Sayheed. The black boy thrust a hastily twisted flambeau into our campfire, twirled it with a movement of his strong fingers, and when it had caught flame, turned and started off along the river bank. We four whites followed silently.

We had covered four or five hundred feet when Abu Sayheed stopped and pointed at an overhanging limb which had partially broken off the parent tree and plunged its bushy end into the water. It formed an effective brake and a sizable pile of debris had wedged up against it. Father and I saw the baby instantly, although its little black arms and legs, sticking out stiffly and grotesquely from its already water-soaked body might have been so many small bits of crooked wood. Father looked about him and finally found what he wanted, a slender pole about seven or eight feet long.

"Now if the current doesn't catch it and take it downstream when I work it loose," he murmured as he stepped ankle-deep into the water and began to prod at the dead wood in front of the infant.

It was not until he touched the bit of human jetsom with his pole that our newcomers saw the child. Esther stifled a scream with both hands over her mouth, but, before anyone could stop him or even shout a warning, Jimmy had plunged into the river. Three short steps, and the water deepened until it came to his hips, and he swayed under the impact of that current like a dandelion at the edge of a gutter during a spring freshet. That time, it was I who screamed. Jimmy's mouth fell open in amazement and then snapped grimly shut as he stood swaying, struggling to keep his balance, to remain upright while he pitted his human strength and cunning against that torrent.

Abu Sayheed leaped forward into the edge of the water, stretched out an arm and seized Jimmy's wrist. Jimmy looked at Abu Sayheed but spoke to father. "Tell him to hold on. Tight. If I bend and stretch, I think I can reach the child," he said evenly.

Again that choked scream from Esther, and I felt her finger tips dig into the muscles of my left arm. Father translated Jimmy's words, although I am sure Abu Sayheed already understood. He merely grunted assent. Slowly Jimmy bent his body at a right angle from his hips, extended his arm rigidly, and strove for balance and distance. I saw his fingers curl about a tiny upflung wrist, saw him pull gently, gently, but always exerting a little more strength. Father and I shot quick looks at each other. How long has the child been dead? was in both of our minds. Then the body of the infant slid out from among the debris.

"Don't try to lift it out of the water. Float it ashore," father commanded. The child on dry land at our feet, Esther let go of my arm and sank to her knees beside it, making little crooning noises. She put out a hand as though to caress the tiny head, fluttered her finger tips against the wet cheek, and withdrew them quickly.

The baby was about six or seven months old, and had been dead anywhere from ten to fifteen hours. "It's a wonder the crocodiles didn't get it," father said to Abu Sayheed.

"Even the loathly ones reject pure evil," the black boy replied.

Father sank to his haunches beside Esther, saw that her knees were pressed into the sand, and sharply ordered her to get up. He didn't at the time say anthing to her about the myriads of African parasites that live in the soil and which attack human beings. Instead he thrust a finger between the tiny blue lips, rubbed the lower gum, then the upper one. As he nodded briefly to me and to Abu Sayheed, Esther murmured in broken tones, as though she herself were the bereaved one, "Some poor mother is grieving tonight."

"It was the baby's mother who threw it into the river," father said calmly.

"What!" she screeched in the cracking tones of a woman whose nerves are beginning to break. "Why?"

"Its lower teeth came in first," he answered. "For many river tribes that is a sign that an evil spirit has taken possession of the child at birth. They believe it must be destroyed before it grows big and strong enough to do great harm to its neighbors."

"Don't you tell them they shouldn't?" she demanded.

"Yes," father answered shortly.

"Then why do they do it? Don't they pay any attention to you?"

You're insolent! I wanted to say to her, but father stopped me with a wave of his hand.

He explained, choosing his words carefully as though speaking to a child: "They keep on doing it because the superstition is generations old and everybody around them believes in it. There are so many of them, and so few of us. We come and go, our ways are strange, and it is evident to all of them that left to ourselves we couldn't survive against the jungle. At best, we're a curious people in their eyes, intruders after a fashion, some of our ways seem good, some of the things we do seem irrational—"

"Do you mean that our Christian teaching has no effect on these people? That they carry their savage superstitions with them into a mission compound?" she interrupted rudely.

"If they come at all, they carry with them what their life has made them. Our Christian teaching has a marvelous, powerful influence on the lives of those it touches, but there are hundreds of thousands, millions we don't even reach—at least for a long enough time for the influence to be lasting," father went on patiently. "As for savage superstition in a mission compound—you still believe that walking under a ladder is bad luck, don't you? Or having a black cat run across your path? Or spilling salt? Or seeing the new moon over your left shoulder? You make a joke of them—and of the counter-fetishes you practice—but you believe them. I don't think any Christian woman would throw her baby into the river—especially if her husband is also Christian. But there are always those among the relatives who are not Christian and who are openly fearful and respectful of the old beliefs. Such children—" he pointed at the little one lying at our feet—"disappear even from a mission compound."

Father's voice had quickened as he spoke, and he finished vehemently. He sounded tired. I think Jimmy understood. "I'll go back to camp and get a spade or something to dig a grave with," he said. But before he could even turn, Abu Sayheed bent forward, scooped the body up in one huge palm, swung his arm in a pendant arc, and tossed the tiny corpse far out into the stream.

"How atrocious!" Esther burst out, and turned on Abu Sayheed angrily. He brushed past her, heading back toward camp. Jimmy put his hands on his wife's shoulders, turned her about, and pushed her after the dancing torchlight. I followed, dropping back gradually until my footsteps did not even fall on their shadows. They were in their sleeping tent when I reached camp, and I went into mine and father's, undressed and went to bed. I was tired and lay awaiting sleep. I had seen other people appalled by the seemingly unfathomable cruelty of Africa, but none of them had ever confused me as Esther Grove did. Perhaps it was only a half-waking thought, maybe I dreamed it. Anyway, I seemed to be sitting on Aunt Elma's porch one fall afternoon and Uncle Ben was saying as we stared into the crimson top of a maple: "Some people are just like leaves, at their brightest and purtiest while the storm's amakin' that's agoin' to blow 'em away."

Father's footsteps—or the sound of a woman sobbing—brought me back to Africa. Father pushed aside the blanket that separated our tent into halves and came and sat on the edge of my cot. Together we listened to the low notes of a man's deep voice and what seemed like the paroxysms of uncontrolled grief.

"She's a coward," father said at length.

"She was frightened in the shimbeck, wasn't she?" I ventured. "And then I suppose the idea of a mother's throwing her baby away—"

"I said she's a coward," father interrupted. "All of us are frightened at times—some of us even run away occasionally. But a coward is frightened all the time and in flight from something all the time."

"I don't understand. What can she be in flight from?" I asked. "What's she afraid of?"

"Life," father answered. "Somebody else has always carried her burdens. She's that kind of woman. And I suppose she has excused herself, to herself, so long by—by being a charming personality that— Well— God help that husband of hers."

I lay quietly, not knowing what, if anything, was expected from me. Father lifted his hand and stroked my face and hair as though I were a child, or kitten.

"Laura, mother and I hoped that while you were at home in school you would find some nice young man and marry him."

Did father realize how much like other young girls I, too, had sincerely wanted a husband? Did he possibly suspect how completely Maa Koo had bred into me acceptance of a primitive woman's place in life? To hoe in a garden? To conceive and bear children?

"But, daughter, you didn't marry. And there's not much chance that you will here on the mission field. The thing you must do now, Laura, is put the thought of a husband and children—your own children, that is—out of mind. Even if it takes a lot of doing. And it may!"

I felt my throat tighten and my feet and legs grow cold under the blanket, in spite of the tropic night.

"There are worse things in this world than being an old maid, daughter," father went on. "Giving thought to another woman's husband is one of those things. I had meant that you should work in the hospital at the central station. We always need nurses, but—" He stopped and glanced in the direction of the other tent. The sound of the sobbing had died away now. "She will have to go into the hospital although, as a young married woman, I had hoped she might organize prenatal schools in the near-by villages. You will have to do that now—and explain—your—single blessedness as best you can to those who will scoff at you. Perhaps that is best. You know a half-dozen dialects perfectly. You will understand what is said to you—innuendo and all; and you will be able to answer as you never could through a translator. You can get along without much help in the jungle."

I swallowed and tried to speak naturally, but my voice sounded thin and squeaky in my ears. And I have no idea why I said what I did.

"Perhaps you will send me—up beyond the Hungry Country? You have always said someone should start work there. Perhaps now is the time?"

"Now is always the time for God's work," he answered, and there was an unmistakable sigh of relief in his words that I had not indulged in any silly, childish, futile denials that Jimmy Grove had peopled my thoughts often. Perhaps too often.

"But you are not the right person for the work in that field," father was saying. "Perhaps in the future it may be laid upon you, but—the will of God is always made manifest in good time."

He bent over and kissed me, and I returned his kiss like a little girl.

60 ·

CHAPTER
FIVE

It was good to be back at the mission and I stood up in the shim-beck after we had rounded the last curve in the river peering through cupped hands—like a horse between blinders—in order to help my eyes pick out the folk I knew were waiting for us at our boat landing. They were all there, white workers and native Africans.

There was mother and my brother Norman and his wife Blanche, and Auntie Bun and Auntie Hallie—only I mustn't call them "Auntie" any more since I was now grown and a full-fledged missionary like themselves. And pressing to the forefront, in danger of falling into the water, if not pushed in by those behind her, was old Maa Koo. She didn't seize me and kiss me and maul me as the others did. Instead, when I was finally shoved along to her, the fingers of our four hands tangled themselves in a tight knot, and we leaned forward, resting our shoulders against each other, the sweat of our two cheeks mingling. Ordinarily Maa Koo was as full of words as any other black woman; but now after seven years' separation, we simply stood silently, loving each other from the bottoms of our hearts, until someone pulled us apart.

There was tea for the entire white staff at mother's cottage, of course, and much chatter and good will and decorous gaiety. It was almost like a lecture-hall demonstration in polite usage to watch Esther charm everyone present. It did seem to me that my mother, our hostess, was pushed somewhat into the background, but I'm sure she never noticed that. She, too, hung on Esther's words, as did every other woman present. So did my brother's wife, and Sister

Hallie, and Auntie Bun—who had refused to let me call her "Sister."

"I've been your Auntie for so long— Well, I like being your Auntie. Don't you try to 'Sister' me, you skinny, half-baked puddin' of a missionary!" she had said, lapsing into what had been her most affectionate term of endearment for me as a child.

A kind, soft smile perpetually creased Aunt Bun's round face, which in turn rested like a bronzed apple on the three rolls of fat which passed for her neck. Her eyes seemed squinting, pushed in from the outer corners. Her glasses needed changing—but that would have to wait until her next furlough.

"I'm going to do absolutely nothing the first week but sleep about twenty-four hours a day!"

Esther's lilting tones covered the social chatter in the room and drowned it with the same ease that a sudden spring rain lays the dust on a country road. There was a moment of shocked, embarrassed silence. Mother stood with the tea kettle in her hand, dribbling hot water down the front of her dress and, fortunately, between her feet.

Norman had been talking to Jimmy. When I looked at the two of them, my brother was saying something slowly, looking straight in front of himself. Jimmy, too, was looking straight ahead, hearing nothing. I was to learn in the days to come that there is little in this world more pathetic than a loving husband whose charming wife contrives to embarrass him.

Father clapped his hands to call everyone's attention to himself, but he was watching me with an unwavering glance. A stern glance? I felt hot blood flood my neck and creep up my cheeks. I drew a deep breath, smiled briefly, and gave him just the faintest nod. The muscles of his jaws relaxed, and he returned my nod. We understood each other, father and I.

"Listen, everybody. We brought two missionary barrels up the river with us. Now is as good a time as any to open them, isn't it?" he began.

There are always things in missionary barrels at which we laugh.

There are bound to be, since those who pack them are only human beings, and since the barrels are destined for a land of which the packers know little or nothing—or are full of erroneous knowledge. And then, as everyone well knows, those for whom the barrels are intended "can find a use for anything and everything. Poor dears!" And they are so right! In all my years as a missionary child and working staff member, I have watched and helped at the unpacking of literally hundreds of such barrels, and I can count on the fingers of one hand the items which had to be thrown away as completely useless.

There are many immediately useful things, too. Almost on top of the first barrel which brother Norman pried open for us was a quilt. Its top was a gray-hued confusion of interlocking rings pieced together from scraps of calico. The stitches were unbelievably tiny and precise. The quilting itself was an intricate design of twining stems and ruffling leaves. It was beautiful and all of us women bent our heads over it and stroked the cloth on which patient, loving fingers had stitched away so many hours for our sakes.

Sister Hallie hugged the quilt in her arms like an oversized infant. "I want this," she exclaimed, half defiantly, half pleadingly. There were many nods of quick and free consent.

Then her face softened and she went on hesitantly, as though she were sharing a secret—and uncertain of the wisdom of doing so. "It's the wedding-ring pattern. The double-wedding-ring! And— that's—as close to a wedding ring as I—as I'll ever get, I guess."

Sister Hallie was tall and even more slender than I. In fact, she was gaunt. She was bumping sixty awfully close, and was the kind of perfectionist who inevitably irritates—other perfectionists. There were those on the mission staff who had more than once guessed anxiously and exasperatedly at the number of years before Sister Hallie would be sent home, to remain home permanently, retired. But every now and then the woman said or did something "that makes you love her even when you're right on the verge of wringing her scrawny neck," as Aunt Bun described it.

"Now who wants these?" father demanded, effectively shattering the embarrassed silence which was threatening to smother us. On the palm of one hand he balanced a shoe box that was completely full of huge, tortoise-shell spectacle frames without lenses. He took off his own glasses and donned a pair. They made him look like an owl whose eyes have unaccountably slipped out of position. We howled.

It was Esther who cut into our mirth with, "Oh gracious! How stupid to send things like that!"

Father's lips never lost their smile, but those of us who knew him heard the rebuke in his reply, "Mrs. Grove, if I were a betting man, I'd lay you good odds that we find a use for these."

An unbelievable amount of *oddenda*—as we used to call it—can be wedged into a missionary barrel, but the next bundle I remember was made up of flour and feed sacks. They had been ripped apart, washed and partially bleached, but one could still read on many of them: Purina, Rabbit Pellets, Oyster Shell, and similar legends. Some showed ghostly checker-boarded squares of red and green except for a circle in the middle of what had been one side of the sack.

"Now those! I need those," Aunt Bun spoke up. "Perhaps I shouldn't speak of it in mixed company, but my—uh—unmentionables are also almost unusables."

We laughed again. There was not a one of us there—excepting Esther Grove, of course—who had not worn panties and petticoats and nightgowns made of similar feed sacks.

"If there are more than Bun needs, may I have two or three?" mother piped up. "I read somewhere that if you cut them into squares and dye the squares and hemstitch them together again, they make a very pretty luncheon cloth."

There were many other things in the two barrels we unpacked, of course. Some beautiful, most of them sturdy, and all of them used eventually one way or another. Even the pill-roller—especially the pill-roller! At the time, however, there wasn't a single one of us on the staff, including Dr. Dick (Richard Burton, the head of our mission medical work) who knew what the thing was when

64 ·

father pulled it up out of the depths of a barrel. It was in a shallow flat chest which might have been meant for small tools or cutlery and showed age in spite of meticulous care. Fortunately there was a note inside of the contraption, written on several sheets of ruled paper torn from a ten-cent tablet.

The writer was an elderly man, too. His script was stiffly upright, his curves now jagged angles, and the long strokes of the letters staggered somewhat. The pen had been held by fingers that trembled slightly. The *s*'s (*f*) and the *t*'s (*z*) belonged to a style of penmanship taught three-quarters of a century ago, and the *r*'s were all upside down (*r*).

The writer, who signed himself simply, H. L. Wilson, told us that he was giving us his pill-roller, which was the first piece of equipment he had bought as an apprentice apothecary (druggist to you) sixty-eight years ago. He apologized for the fact that it was a small one, it rolled only twenty-four pills at a time, but he estimated that he had rolled several hundred thousand medicated pellets in his day. Then followed careful instructions:

Make a stiff paste of some easily digestible, cohesive material. White flour was recommended as excellent for the purpose. Impregnate it with a proportionate weight or bulk of the desired drug. Press this into a thin sheet and place in the middle of the pill-roller, which opened up and, seen from the top lid, really looked somewhat like the inside of a waffle iron. Then close the pill-roller, press the lever at the side firmly, raise the lid, and lift the extra paste up and off the bottom plate. The pills would be the size and shape of aspirin tablets and could be left to dry on the pill-roller as they were. Or they could be twirled to perfect spheres between the tips of one's fingers—or novices might use the palms of their hands.

When father stopped reading most of us gaped a wordless "Now I've seen and heard everything!"

Not Dr. Dick, however. He held out his hands eagerly for the small chest. "This is for me, I guess," he said.

Father cleared his throat and started clowning a speech of presentation.

"It may be that this is really a valuable gift," Dr. Dick interrupted him. "You know how it is over at the hospital. We never have enough medicine—particularly for the itinerant workers—and for the folk who love the importance of being dosed. You know any African loves medicine. Half the people who line up and hold out their hands haven't anything wrong with them; it's just fun to be in a queue—and to have someone listen to their symptoms. Then a lot of those who are really sick we can't do anything for, except psychologically. If anything will save our precious drugs for those who really need them, and those we can help—"

He spread out his hands in that gesture of helplessness common to all missionary doctors faced with the overwhelming need of a disease- and superstition-ridden continent.

"Let's go make a batch of pills, Dick," father said.

A half-dozen of us followed them into mother's kitchen, but not Esther Grove. At the door I looked back and this new medical worker was staring after us, incredulity in her eyes.

In the kitchen we were stymied for a moment, but only for a moment. What would we use for the basic paste? White flour was out of the question for us. But someone found a gourdful of boiled manioc set aside for the cook's breakfast. Here was a leathery, cohesive, harmless paste ready to hand.

We meant to make just one batch, twenty-four pills, but we didn't stop until the bowl of manioc had been scraped clean. Like children we couldn't wait for them to dry. Brother Norman built a fire in the oven and we baked them. Most of the new pills we left looking like dirty gray flat pebbles, but a few we rolled. Dr. Dick, always dexterous, was turning out gray perfect spheres before the manioc gave out and our fun was ended.

"Let's see how they work," he exclaimed as the last batch came from the oven. He walked to the door and called in a carefully noncommittal manner to a pickinin loitering on the step, "How are you feeling today, Imogee?"

The child immediately clapped his hands to his stomach and

rolled his eyes as pickinins always do when there is the possibility of anything so delightful as medicine in the offing.

"Here, take one of these," Dr. Dick invited, offering him a bit of baked manioc.

There was an eager hand outstretched, a flash of white teeth, and a rolling movement of the child's throat muscles. Then a smile spread over the pickinin's face.

"You see, he feels better already," Dr. Dick remarked. "Right diagnosis. Correct medication."

"Dr. *Bwana,* the medicine isn't strong enough," the child's voice cut into his smug satisfaction. Dr. Dick hesitated while he peered at the pickinin sternly. Then he relented, doled out another home-made pill while he exclaimed, "That's enough! Run along now."

Turning back to us he explained with a laugh, "I'll have to dust them with something to make them taste sufficiently bad, else I'll lose my reputation as a big and powerful white witch doctor."

We filled one of mother's biggest stewpans with his pills and handed them over for him to carry home. In turn he held the pill-roller out to me.

"Clean this, will you, Sister Laura. And take good care of it. I still believe somebody sent us—*SOMETHING!* I shall write a personal letter of thanks to this H. L. Wilson, whoever he may be."

He was the first one on the mission staff to call me "Sister," as a working term, and I knew my face glowed with pride. It would be pleasant serving with him, personally pleasant and professionally a great privilege, for Dr. Dick was an excellent physician and surgeon.

Then I remembered. I was not to work with Dr. Dick. Because I had returned to Africa unmarried, and because there was a young farmer my own age on the staff, a married man with a beautiful, accomplished wife, I must traipse up and down the river, through jungle and swamp, across veld and desert. I would miss the chance visitors who mark the high social days of our missionary years. Never looking like a woman! Never feeling like a woman! That was to be my service.

By the time I crawled into my cot that night I was as angry as I had ever been in my life. Angry with father, at Dr. Dick, at Esther, at Jimmy. Especially at Jimmy! If the man had ever looked at me with more than the most diffident politeness, there might have been reason for my exile, I muttered into my pillow. Then because I was a woman, and because the only luxury no one could take from me was tears, I sobbed myself to sleep. Sobbed as helplessly as I had the night the neighbor boy at Aunt Elma's assured me in vehement, almost frightened tones that he "hadn't meant anything at all!"

The next morning I joined mother and father at family prayers. As usual that little house of native brick and thatch was an oasis of peace and calm in the teeming, lush, and noisy African life about it. There was a rote pattern to father's prayers. He remembered each and every one of us in a specific order and then he always managed to weave a little sermon into his morning talk with God. There was a time when as a child I had looked upon these prayers as father's report to a heavenly judge upon our behavior of the previous day. I was sure that each one of us had an individual Book of Life, in a Celestial Library. I was certain that God and an innumerable corps of angels listened to every family prayer and recorded on alternate pages our deeds of the previous day, good and bad. I was positive that when my naked soul stood shivering before God's throne, *My Book* would be placed upon my Heavenly Father's knee and that page after page would be flipped and their contents noted before divine judgment was pronounced upon me.

But as I knelt beside my mother that morning, my mind was full of the countless billions who have been born, struggled, and died before me. I knew without benefit of tutored precept, that each and every one of them, by thought if not by deed, had broken the Commandments.

I dipped my head deeper into my hands for I was mindful of Maa Koo, kneeling somewhere in the room behind me. Maa Koo was Christian, but nevertheless retained a wholesome respect for the mores of her people which had taken shape and crystallized in their millennia-old struggle for survival. She had assured me often that my father wasted his time and eloquent ministerial ability in calling upon Mu'ungu the greatest of all the gods, in such mild, soft tones. Long, long ago, eons backward in time beyond the memory of the older woman, Mu'ungu had tired of the stupid, stubborn iniquities of man, and had gone far away to escape the chorus of their perpetual, intolerable whining. It took a voice of thunder to reach him now. No wonder Mu'ungu had fled. What were the pages of every individual Book of Life filled with if not error, sin, rationalization, and error again?

Father was in the middle of his daily prayerful sermon, discussing the sin of covetousness with God, outlining what, in his mortal mind, it consisted of. Or was he trying to instruct me? "Covetousness is like the tiny seed which falls from the beak of a guinea hen and lands in a crevice of a rotting log. There, on the sunless floor of the jungle, unseen, unnoted, it sprouts and struggles for life. When it puts out its first rootlets and tendrils, it is so tiny and frail a thing that a handful of leaves fluttering down to cover it will smother out life completely."

I pulled my hands away from my face so I could watch my father. He went on to tell God—or was it me?—how the seed of error growing in the human heart can, like the jungle vine, smother everything it dominates.

"Have you ever heard your father pray more beautifully?" my mother whispered in my ear. "Sometimes I think he is just casually conversing with God." But I knew that once again he was admonishing me, gently but firmly: "Thou shalt not covet thy neighbor's house, thou shalt not covet thy neighbor's wife, nor his manservant, nor his ox, nor his ass, nor anything that *is* thy neighbor's"—including thy neighbor's husband.

At breakfast I turned to father and asked, "Have you decided where I am to go and what I am to do?"

"Dr. Dick has asked that you help him in the hospital for a few days at least. Mrs. Grove has the language to learn and—she has to become accustomed to mission routine."

Mother stared at both of us, turning her eyes from father to me and back again. Apparently she, too, had taken it for granted that I would live in the mission compound and work at the hospital. Apparently, too, whatever father suspected or feared about me, he shared with no one but himself.

"Dick raised cain last night when I told him I'm going to put you on the trail," he said, and then turned to a discussion of other mission matters with mother.

I was a little late when I reached the hospital that first morning. There were a good many folk among the outpatients lined up in front of the dispensary who remembered me as a gangling girl. Now I had become another *mama,* as so many white missionaries are called. A great many shouted greetings, some came over to jerk my thumb, that is, shake hands, and a few of the women bumped my shoulders with their own, the equivalent of a friendly embrace. It took time, and when I entered the dispensary Dr. Dick held out the stewpan full of home-made manioc pills by way of good morning. "Here, dust these with something awful-tasting," he commanded briefly.

My eyes turned to the small row of glass bottles on the single drug shelf. As a child I had been proud of our hospital. Many a time I had hung around the door of our dispensary like a pickinin on clinic mornings, awed by Dr. Dick's bottles and instruments. Now, fresh from a well-equipped, modern hospital I gaped at the pathetic display of drugs—or lack of them, rather. I cast a quick glance at Dr. Dick's instrument table, too. I had seen more and better equipment thrown into the wastebasket after a single operation "back home."

"Pills ready, sister?" His voice was crisp and he was peering over my shoulder as I read, "Bitter aloes—"

"That's it, the bitter aloes," he exclaimed. "I never use it anyway —they've got cathartics of their own that strip the intestinal tract of its mucous lining. The things these people do to themselves!

And that reminds me, when the bitter aloes is gone, we'll drench our pills with quasia. You never heard of it, I know. It's an old-time tonic, and as bitter as they come. Some drug firm back in the States cleaned house a few years ago and sent us a case of the stuff. But one thing a missionary doctor can't fool with is doling out tonics however excellent. I've never even opened the box. It's around somewhere."

Then, "Where's Sister Grove? She could be doing that while you help me with the mob outside." But neither of us saw anything of Esther that morning, while all the sick, sad, and suffering of Africa —with a liberal sprinkling of the curious—crept past us. Several times he murmured something about my running over after Esther. But each time we were too busy at the moment for me to leave just then.

First among the patients was an old man who hobbled up and asked plaintively if we couldn't do something to make his "guts behave." He was holding a great bulge of something against his stomach with his palms and forearms. When he raised his fists to flutter his fingers in a vague numbering of the days he had traveled and the kilometers he had covered in order to reach the mission, a loop of intestine fell to his knees, the most enormous hernia I have ever seen. The old man winced and then gathered up his "insides" as casually as one of his wives might have picked up a chicken or a pickinin.

"Go over there under that tree," Dr. Dick pointed with the scalpel he held in preparation for the next patient. "Sit down with the people there, and this afternoon I'll cut the devils out of your belly." As casually as that! It would be a major operation, I knew. But then, only God knew how many major operations lay ahead for this afternoon and the morrow.

"Did you recognize him?" Dr. Dick asked.

I only had time to murmur, "No. I never saw him before that I remember. I've been gone a long time, you know," before a young girl turned her backside to us and slid the tassel which normally hung between the crease of her hips around in front of her.

The tassel was the same to her as a wedding ring to a white woman, bestowed upon her by her husband after the consummation of her marriage. She was not native to the Congo Territory; this custom did not belong to West Africa. We knew that her husband had bought her far to the east, probably when he worked on some plantation or mine there.

"You know him, all right. That was M'Buto," Dr. Dick was saying as he bent over to peer at the woman's protruding hips and count the abscesses and scars which knobbed and furrowed her skin.

"M'Buto!" I exclaimed. "No! It couldn't be. Why, M'Buto—" M'Buto was scarcely older than myself. He had been a houseboy for my mother for several years, and my father had had great hopes of him as a Christian. "That fellow's sixty if he's a day."

"You carry your guts in your hands for four years and see if you don't look sixty, too. Sterilize, nurse."

Dr. Dick pushed the woman around so that the sunlight struck her hips at the best angle.

"Four years! Why didn't he come to the hospital before," I demanded as I swabbed hard at the hips in front of me. Heaven only knew what had to come off of that skin before Dr. Dick could use his scalpel on it. The girl never even winced. She merely steadied herself with the knuckles of her two hands in the dust in front of her like an animal standing tensely on all fours.

"You were born in Africa. You tell me why he didn't come in before," was all Dr. Dick replied.

Carefully, methodically he opened and cleansed the largest of the abscesses. Then he cauterized the small wounds and told the woman to go home, and come back the next day. The girl didn't budge.

"Cut all the evil out," she commanded in even tones. "I can be away from my village only one morning. This afternoon I must hoe in my garden, and tonight I must cook my husband's supper and await his convenience in his kraal."

Dr. Dick heaved a small sigh, but once again bent over the

woman's rump, lanced and cleansed every abscess and cauterized every incision. Then he hesitated.

"It really ought to be bandaged, or at least taped, but how would she look?" He turned to me with something very close to a boyish smile on his face. "But then, I haven't the bandage and the tape, enough that is to risk its being torn off and thrown under a bush ten minutes from now.

He spoke to the girl who gave a push with her knuckles on the ground and began straightening up slowly, in little jerks, like an oversized mechanical doll. Once erect she pulled a length of bamboo out of one of her ear lobes, picked a wad of grass out of one end, and emptied two eggs out of it onto our table among the sterilized instruments. They were tiny, pigeon-sized, and almost green with age. Dr. Dick scooped them up with a quick hand and laid them in the dust under the table, and motioned to an old woman who was next in line.

The girl gave her body a jerk and twist which slid her marriage tassel back into place and stalked off. I stared after the child-wife. In the past seven years I had forgotten much about my unbelievable Africa—or perhaps I had learned so much about the ways of white people that I, too, was beginning to appreciate the gulf separating two eras in the evolution of the human race.

"Just the pain alone would have put a white man or woman in bed for a week, wouldn't it?" Dr. Dick murmured. He, too, was staring after the girl. "She'll be back again. Yaws aren't that easily disposed of."

There was a slapping noise and we turned back to the next patient. That old woman, never having visited a clinic before, probably thought all females presented their rumps to the white witch doctor, and she was on all fours as the girl with the yaws had been. Her breasts like those of many elderly African women, were absolutely flat and strap-like and so elongated that the dugs were dragging in the dust between her two hands. Nonchalantly, just as though she were hoeing in the village garden, she threw her breasts back over her shoulders in order to get them out of the dirt.

Her skin was clean of blemishes, and the keen eyes, combined with a toothless grin, with which she watched us over a shoulder did not indicate any inward "devils." Dr. Dick tapped her in the ribs and ordered her to stand up and turn around. Her ridiculous breasts slid off her shoulders and slapped against her stomach as she obeyed. Her ear lobes, now barren of ornaments, lay like leather thongs on her shoulders. The hole in each would have carried an eight-inch plate. One knew that in her youth their capacity must have been a matter of great pride. Her sole article of clothing was a string of braided palm fiber around her neck from which dangled a small, tarnished silver comb with no more than a half-dozen teeth left in its back.

"Where are the devils that are tearing at you?" Dr. Dick asked.

The old woman began a shrill recital of such human misery as no one individual could ever endure, grinning happily all the while. It was obvious there was nothing the matter with her. Dr. Dick turned to the gourdful of home-made pills resting on the edge of our instrument table. Slowly and soberly he counted out three.

"I am fearful of cutting a hole in your skin and letting such horrible devils escape into the world. I must kill them inside of you," he said handing her the manioc pellets and telling her to take them: one now, one after the evening meal, one next morning.

The patient seized the pills and threw all three into her mouth at once as we had known she would do. We watched her wallowing them about with her tongue against her toothless gums. Her eyes gleamed, but the bitter aloes could not pucker her mouth any tighter than her many years had already done.

"The devils are dying," she announced cheerfully, and along the queue of patients ran an admiring grunt. She held out her hand again. "Give her one more," Dr. Dick ordered. "The old beldam's having the time of her life."

I stirred the pills in the gourd with a parsimonious finger and finally picked out a small, imperfectly shaped one. Then sternly both Dr. Dick and I waggled our forefingers: No! No more!

The old woman shrugged her shoulders and strutted off, conscious of the admiring glances from the line of patients behind her. No one would ever know how many devils had been exterminated in her that day—and the number would certainly not shrink with her retelling of the adventure.

The next patient was a young buck of eighteen or twenty, a fellow who knew he was handsome and cut quite a figure. He had taken time before coming to us to don every ornament of fur, claw, and feather he possessed. On his head like a helmet, he wore a white enamel saucepan, the handle sticking out jauntily over one ear. He turned slightly and I saw that from the other ear, down past his shoulder, his skin was caked with dried blood. Dr. Dick put me at cleaning up the fellow's neck and shoulder so we could see what damage lay beneath.

I took him to one side while Dr. Dick beckoned to the next in line. As I worked with hot water and cotton, he lanced boils, cleaned ulcers, laid on bandages, and every now and then I could hear him mutter, "Drat that Grove woman!"

I laid bare three parallel gashes which looked as though they had been made by a razor. The young buck told me that while walking a jungle path he had heard a noise and had leaped aside just as Old Twitchy Nose (a leopard) had fallen on him from a limb. The big cat, its aim spoiled, had twisted in mid-air, a companion said, slashed out with one paw, and caught him just below the ear. Then snarling like all the devils imprisoned in a magic *lokole,* that is, a drum in front of a chieftain's hut, it had bounded into the bushes and disappeared.

Such wounds are usually a welter of gangrene before they reach a mission doctor, but this one was remarkably clean and the flesh underneath the severed skin showed signs of knitting together. I remarked upon this fact, and the young fellow curled his thick lip noseward in a supercilious grin. The stewpan waggled rakishly and slid over one eye.

"I have eaten of the heart of *tembo* [elephant] and of the entrails of *ngana* [hippopotamus]. With the spirits of such huge, strong beasts within me, what devils do I need fear?" he boasted.

I grinned at him and he evidently took it for admiration, for he tossed his head and the saucepan slid over both eyes.

"Your patient is ready, doctor," I called to Dr. Dick.

"Sew him up yourself," he answered, and I saw that he was working on an ulcer which had eaten a hole clear through a man's foot, exposing the radial bones. I gasped in pity at the sight and Dr. Dick raised his head to look at me sharply. "You can, can't you?" he commanded more than questioned. I nodded and went to work, although I never before had sewn up human flesh.

I did other things that morning, too, I had never done before, things which no one in the American hospital "back home" had ever trained me for. I helped Dr. Dick deliver a woman of a dead foetus. The old women, the midwives of her village, had tried to deliver her and only God in heaven knows what they had done to the poor suffering creature before she crawled to us literally on her hands and knees.

And the woman lived.

Somewhere around noon Dr. Dick pulled off his rubber gloves and motioned me to untie his white coat.

"Go get some lunch," he ordered. "And find out where Sister Grove is, will you? And why she isn't here?" Then, "Just think, I didn't have any nurse at all yesterday morning," he ended with a short laugh.

I wondered as I crossed the mission compound to the neat little three-roomed cottage of sun-dried brick and tin roof assigned to the Groves, just how he could have gotten through such mornings without a nurse.

"Come in," a sweet voice called out cordially when I knocked on the Groves' door.

"In here, darling," came the same tones from the bedroom when I stopped just inside the front door. And then, "Oh, it's you," when I opened the bedroom door.

Whom had she been expecting, I wondered. Did her own husband knock on his own door?

Esther was sitting in a chair, befeathered slippers on her feet, filmy negligee over her nightgown, and hair brush in her hand. Her glorious copper-colored hair lay in ripples over her shoulders.

"What do *you* want?" she demanded, and yawned prodigiously.

"Dr. Dick—" I began. "At the hospital—"

I broke off and stared. Esther had begun dressing and even at Aunt Bessie's I had never seen such panties as she casually kicked her legs into. Four-inch lace caught up in frothy ripples with knots of satin ribbon and tiny artificial flowers. One afternoon's sweat in our tropical jungle and no laundry boy in the world could ever make that garment fresh again, flashed through my mind, and yet I wanted, almost desperately, like a yearning child, to touch those panties, just to run the tips of my fingers across that silken lace.

"Oh, for heaven's sake!" I heard Esther exclaim. She shook out a petticoat of the same kind, literally in my face. And then, "Oh, it's hot! Patients are tiresome this kind of weather, aren't they?"

Unconsciously I put my hand to my middle. I was sore there from the retching I had suffered after the delivery of the baby. Then I heard a step behind me, a man's step. I turned and ran, brushing past Jimmy at his front door.

That afternoon Esther came to the hospital looking like what a poet has called "a vision of delight." We had the hernia patient on the table in the grass hut which was our operating theatre. Esther paused just inside the door. She was not wearing a uniform. Dr. Dick raised his head and looked at her for a long minute, taking in every detail of her beautiful costume.

Then he said slowly, "I should like to show you around, Mrs. Grove, and even give you a spot of tea. But as you can see, I'm busy, and shall be for the next hour or so." He bent over his patient again.

The words were quiet and even. There was no reason for it, but I felt as though he had slapped me across the face with the back of his hand. Esther must have felt so, too, for first her neck, then her cheeks, and finally her forehead crimsoned until they rivaled the violent glory of her flaming hair.

CHAPTER
SIX

Esther hated Africa from the very first and I doubt that anyone ever knew exactly why. She had been so full of life and vivacity and eagerness "to learn everything about Africa," on the boat; "to help these poor, poor people."

Father and mother called on the Groves in their cottage that first night, and the next morning Esther came to work only a half-hour late. She was beautifully shod, coiffeured, manicured, perfumed, and clad in a silk poplin uniform. Dr. Dick was busy and I told her of the surgery cases coming up in the next two hours and asked her to prepare the trays. "Who are you to give me orders?" she asked impudently.

I looked up in amazement and, at that instant, her lips curved into a charming smile. Her eyes, however, bored into me defiantly. Then they too twinkled, and her whole face dimpled. "Good morning, doctor," she cooed.

Dr. Dick had stepped into the doorway. He had been making the rounds of patients not sick enough for a pallet in our tiny hospital hut, but too ill or weak to return home. They and the wife, father, or son who had brought each one to us slept in small lean-tos near by. There the relatives fed the patients and gave them whatever care we could impress upon them as being necessary. Dr. Dick made the rounds every morning with three questions always in mind: How many had died during the night? Who was stronger —who worse? And had any patients been spirited away by his people who had lost faith in the ability of this white witch doctor?

"Morning, nurse. Six surgery trays, please."

"Ooooh! Six surgery trays coming up!"

It was flip! It was like a half-dozen notes from a child's carefree song—a child who has not yet learned that the world and everything in it does not belong to her exclusively.

Dr. Dick stared across her head at me, and I looked from first one to the other of them stupidly, confused, feeling somehow put in the wrong for nothing at all. Then I was suddenly, furiously angry and thoughts too fast—thank God!—for words raced through my mind. Who was I—she had sneered. Like a medieval Christian I beat myself cruelly across my soul with the answers: Nobody. A nobody! I would never be anything but a complete nobody! A nonentity in Africa. A misfit in America. A woman without her own home or family; in my soul neither black nor white. A female animal neither possessed nor possessing—

Dr. Dick was tapping me on the shoulder and the tinkle of the beakers in my trembling hands was in my ears before I heard his words. Dumbly I followed him out of the door and into the hut that served him as office and consulting room. How long we sat there, I don't know, but presently I found myself with my hands over my face and tears dripping through my fingers. I heard them fall with distant *spats* onto the starched cloth of my sturdy uniform. Finally I dried my eyes, blew my nose, rubbed my wet palms up and down my thighs and looked up at Dr. Dick. He didn't make banal remarks but waited for me to speak, if that was what I wanted.

At last I stammered, "She has so much—everything—doesn't she—"

Suddenly, unaccountably, we grinned. Then Dr. Dick leaned far over until our foreheads almost touched and spoke with the mischievous air of a gossip pretending her confidence is—just what it really is—nothing at all.

"Laura, don't ever tell anyone I said such a thing. If it got back home, I'd be reprimanded by the Board. But I sometimes read other books than the Bible and medical tomes. One of those books—Saint Thomas Aquinas pops into my mind but I can't be sure who it was about or just how he said it. Anyway, it was to the effect that it is easier to be a good practicing Christian if one is comparatively rich."

He leaned back in his chair at that. While his eyes twinkled, I saw that he was watching me keenly. I had expected to laugh at some joke, but I was bewildered. Then for the next few seconds, although my body remained waiting in a split-bamboo chair in a grass hut deep in an African jungle my spirit was suddenly "back home." I lived through an evening in a parsonage when both the minister and his wife ordered me about unceremoniously: "Do this!" "Do that!" "Haven't you got that done yet!" "Hurry up, finish it. Then come here." I saw Aunt Bessie—who never even bothered with grace before meat unless she had company—walking about majestically with nothing in her hands and had her advice asked repeatedly on such weighty matters as: "Do you think the tablecloth should be pulled this way just a little further?" "Are those flowers best on the mantel or should they be on the hall table?"

Dr. Dick's kind voice cut across my memories: "It takes different kinds of wealth for different situations. You don't carry money with you on itinerary do you? It takes salt to buy what you need here. Just how far would a pocketful of salt get you in a department store in America?" I had to laugh along with him at the thought.

"You're rich—even in the things of this world—here! And your resources of the spirit are—" he spread out his hands in a boundless gesture—"unlimited."

I felt my lips tighten, and then sag again in amazement at his next words. "Mrs. Grove is—a beautiful—cultured—savage. And out of her element. Back home, in America— Well, I don't know very much about how life is lived in America now. Your father and I have lived among our—our gentle savages for so long we're sometimes unable to judge white folk. Here, that Grove woman, is—just a beautiful savage, but not the same kind your father and I work with. Better begin your outstation work immediately, Laura.

Talk with your father about it, and plan your first itinerary right away."

"So—you know?" I faltered.

His next words left me further puzzled. "You're a woman, a young woman, Laura—and rich! Don't forget that! Your father and I quarreled over you last night, dear girl. I called him a fool. I've called him a fool before, and I've been proven wrong before."

He said other things to me. Some of them sounded strange at the time, others intensified the rebelliousness within me. Maybe he knew that. He had grown old in Africa, and in his years of service he had seen missionaries come and go. He used to say laughingly to my father, "You polish up their souls, and I patch up their bodies." But he wasn't too bad at polishing up a soul himself. In any case, he understood the therapy of the sound of kind words whether they were listened to or not. And he was not unaware of the fact that the vagaries of a woman's heart frightened and enticed her spirit down strange bypaths.

That evening at supper father began outlining the work he had in mind for me. Villages to the north and east where clinics should be established were to be visited, with perhaps especial effort put forth in the outstations where medical work of a more intensive nature should later be set up.

Within a few days I started out into the jungle and for almost a year I traipsed through swamp, across veld, over rocky ledge, and back again. I fought superstition and ignorance, disease and filth, flies and fleas and mosquitoes and innumerable other pests. I lifted up my faint voice in the wilderness in the name of Christ and prayed. And all the time I struggled against a sense of futility which blanketed my spirit like a pall. Sometimes I was frightened —not of Africa! But of the questions which tormented my mind because I could not clothe them with words and give them voice. I think that was because I knew the answers— No! not the answers, but the quick, easy, pat replies another would have given me if I had spoken aloud of the turmoil within.

Don't think that the year was not profitable, or that it was devoid of what I suppose many folk would call the spice of life. Sometime I would like to tell you in more detail about two villages I visited regularly. One was ruled over by Hylo, a chief so wealthy that he housed his slaves in a separate, near-by village. Hatango, the master of the slaves, himself a slave, ruled over the second village. Hylo himself never visited the slave village, for there, by primitive tribal law, he would have been subservient to Hatango. Both were "savages," but strong men, fine characters, and likable. I cut a huge round hard knob off the second finger on Hylo's right hand, and he always insisted, thereafter, with a twinkle in his eyes, that I had ruined the peace of his idle moments. It had been real entertainment, he assured me, to drum with that knobbed finger on the shaven skulls of his wives.

Hatango, in his turn, rescued me from an elephant. Having sent my porters ahead, I had been walking along a path alone one day when I rounded a bush and found myself face to face with one of these monsters. I think the beast was as much surprised as I, for he just stood there, flapping his immense ears back and forth, his trunk dangling like a broken vine, and his little pig's eyes blinking. For a second I was paralyzed, then I turned and fled back along the way I had come, into a small, less densely wooded glade. I made for the nearest tree of sapling proportions and shinnied up it with the frantic strength of fear in my arms and legs.

I did not look down until I was what seemed, at least, twenty-five feet high among the first branches. Then I screamed in terror, for below me I saw tembo place his huge forehead against the trunk of my sapling and give a little experimental shove. I heard the top of the sapling swish through the air above me. Where I was, the trunk swayed a good five feet. I twined my arms and legs about the tree like the small lemur we call a "bush baby," to keep from being snapped off. Then tembo put his head to the trunk again and pushed, and I knew it was only a matter of time until the tree would be uprooted or the bole snapped. I held my breath, and the sapling came to rest against the outflung limb of an immense old silk-cotton tree. I stepped onto that limb and clung with my hands to the branch above me.

The second I was safe, the beast below stopped playing with the sapling. Slowly and deliberately, as though this were mere idle entertainment and nothing at all important, he waddled over until he stood directly underneath me. Then he raised up on his hind feet, and finally uncurled his trunk straight upward. I know the helpless hypnotic terror a bird feels when it watches a snake slither along a limb toward its nest. At that moment I could have died as unresistingly, as apathetically as any savage "smelled out" by a witch doctor. But the trunk stopped when it was a short three feet below me. Then I saw the big body push itself upward, and the trunk stretch until there was no sign of a wrinkle in all its hideous length. The breath from the small nostrils shot up beneath my skirt. But the trunk stopped six inches below my feet, and push and tense and strain as tembo would, it came no closer.

The beast dropped to the ground, and idly stirred up little eddies of leaves and dust with his trunk. I had a silly, hysterical desire to laugh derisively. My weak feeling of triumph was premature, however. Up came the great body again, upward uncurled the trunk. Again that heave and strain, and again that absurd, awful truncated nose within six inches of my feet.

And then—*WHOOOOSH!* My heavy skirts were blown up to my armpits and I was enveloped in a cloud of dust and jungle debris. I sneezed and coughed and choked, and I would have suffocated or fallen had tembo kept up this mischievous play. There was only the one puff, however; I suppose an elephantine snort of contempt. Then he walked over and leaned up against the trunk of my silk-cotton tree as nonchalantly as a farmer boy against a fence post.

I don't know how long I clung to my limb, but presently I was crying, and then I heard dry leaves rustle and a stick snap below me. Through tear-blurred eyes I saw what looked like a mahogany gnome below. Tembo saw the gnome, too, a gnome that was shouting, stamping and flailing its arms about. Unbelievably, but meekly, tembo pulled his huge hulk together and shambled off into deep jungle. It was like some two hundred and fifty pound minister quailing before the choler of a bantam-weight deacon.

Finally I closed my gaping mouth, and then reopened it with the plea, "Get me down out of here. *Que'teer! Que'teer!* Quickly! Quickly!"

"How did you get up there?" came an equally astonished query. "Was your father an Old Man?" (That is, a gorilla.)

"Nonsense!" I snapped. "I climbed that tree," pointing, "when tembo was chasing me, and he pushed it against this limb. How— However did you frighten tembo away?"

The gnome squinted at me. "I did not frighten him," he answered. "I merely told my big brother that he should be ashamed of himself to so frighten the white mama whom my master, Hylo, is waiting to see."

"Push that tree over here again so I can step back into it and climb down," I half commanded, half pled with what dignity I could manage.

The gnome drew himself up and puffed out his chest and enunciated pompously, "I am Hatango, master of Chief Hylo's slaves. I was elevated to this position because of my great wit. It is evident to anyone before whom you stir your lips and waggle your tongue that when the Lion of the Heavens [the sun] bleached out your skin, he also leached out your brains." The gnome laid a hand against the trunk of the sapling and gave a languid shove.

I waited while he climbed the sapling, noticing that he wore a hyrax skin purse, or treasure bag, strangely full and plump. It fell between his legs and the tree occasionally, hampering him awkwardly. But up he came until he reached the limb where I had stood, and on upward fifteen feet or more above my head. Then he swung his body toward me and began a rhythmical series of jerking movements. The sapling shivered and swayed toward me, a bit at a time, until finally I could throw my arms about its bole and step back among its branches. A moment later, Hatango, the master of the slaves, and I stood facing each other on the soft jungle mold.

"I have nothing of value with which to pay you, but you have undoubtedly saved my life—" I faltered to a stop before the peculiar expression on his face. His eyes were narrowed, and his brow furrowed, yet he seemed to be grinning impishly. Then slowly, as he did everything, he untied the drawstring of the hyrax purse and pulled out a crudely carved, grotesque, greasy little figurine of a being part human, part beast.

Still grinning he pushed the object into my hands with the words: "If you take this, mama, and keep it hidden from all black men's eyes, you will do me a great service."

"But it is I who should be giving to you," I began, although my hands trembled with eagerness. My father would, if necessary, have gone hungry in order to possess such a piece of primitive Africana. "Why give this to me? It must be of value to you."

But the little old man continued to push the phallic figurine toward me. "Hide it! Hide it well!" Before I knew what he was about, he had hooked a skinny finger into the neck of my uniform, pulled me toward him, and forced his greasy god into my bosom.

I laughed, but the little old man was clenching his fists and shouting at me: "Who is it that has the right to beat the slaves?" It was a rhetorical question and I waited for the answer.

"Is it King Hylo?" the gnome demanded. Obviously the answer was "No."

"But King Hylo is idle. Since the white man says with the thunder of guns that he may no longer make war, time passes too slowly in his kraal. He wanders onto the veld and sees five or six herdsmen sleeping, and he buries his toes in the fat of their ribs. Why shouldn't the herdboys sleep so long as one among them watches? It takes only one voice to shout, 'SIMBA! LION!'"

When a West African chief is so wealthy that he houses his slaves in a village of their own, and appoints a master of slaves to rule over them, he automatically relinquishes many of his physical rights over his *cattle*. After a fashion, they become serfs attached to the soil rather than slaves. It is to the master of slaves they must answer for their misdeeds and not their owner. The old man had a real grievance.

"Should a king follow the women to the gardens and pace off the length of the rows each cultivates in a morning? Who decides which woman shall be beaten? Who picks up a stick and lays about their heads and shoulders until they scream like hungry leopards?"

He supplied the answer himself, a resounding "I, Hatango!" But the thought of this little fellow trying to beat a group of husky, malingering women was ridiculous. Laughter bubbled within me, but the outrage in his words kept my eyes steady and my lips straight. Then his anger faded, and a sly twinkle rippled the wrinkles about his mouth. He took a step forward and patted my now hard and knobby bosom. "I have given King Hylo something to think about that will take his mind off his slaves."

So! The gnome in front of me had stolen his master's personal and private god! The theft might not be discovered for weeks or even months, certainly not until some emergency needing the intervention of a god arose in Hylo's life. But when discovered, Hylo's village would be in an uproar; and if the thief were ever uncovered, all the gods of the jungle could not save this fierce little old gnome's life. And this man, whose life was in danger, had made me a receiver of stolen goods. What was I, a Christian missionary, to do? Before I could open my mouth to ask, Hatango had vanished.

I settled the little god inside my blouse until his presence was not too obvious. But what should I do with the thing ultimately? To approach King Hylo's fetish house for any purpose—even to return his private god—would give offense. To try to return it to Hatango would give equal offense. Its custody was payment exacted for having in all probability saved my life. To report the little old man's misdeed would have been to sign his death warrant.

Before darkness fell, my hands were further tied in the matter. King Hylo met me at the edge of his village with a gift of food for myself and my porters. As I talked with him, and later as I administered pills, cleaned ulcers, and gave sage medical advice, I saw no sign that he had discovered the loss of his god. But when I left in the afternoon to go on to the next village, he gave me another gift of food for the evening meal. A parting gift is unusual in Africa, but Hylo was an unusual man and I did not think much about his strange generosity until he himself placed one parcel, wrapped in a segment of banana leaf and tied with a bit of braided grass, in my own hands.

I am glad I undid that parcel in the privacy of my tent, for out of it, into my lap tumbled a second, grotesque, crudely phallic figurine. It was almost identical to the one Hatango had given me, except that this one had a forked twig thrust against its neck and secured by a thin fragment of rawhide—the traditional slave stick. There was no slightest doubt that this was the personal and private god of the master of the slaves. I could almost hear King Hylo chuckling in his kraal that night, and I knew exactly what his reasoning had been! Since the master of the slaves had grown arrogant, he, Hylo, would reduce his swollen spirit by the theft of his god. And I, the missionary, would not betray him, for with a mere wave of his hand, Hylo could close a territory as large as the state of Indiana to further Christian work.

So, because I didn't know what to do with two stolen gods, I did nothing, although I rationalized much from various religious and social angles. Today the little gods face each other from opposite ends of my desk. The god of a black king leers at the god of his slave, and the god of a slave trades him sneer for sneer without the shadow of a tremor.

That year, always on the move in the jungle, I tasted a primitive Africa even more completely than as a child I had absorbed it from the best of old black nurses. It takes wit and brute strength to survive in the deep forest, and many a Christian missionary finds that the picture of Christ, whip in hand, driving the money-thangers out of the Temple remains longer and more forcefully in the native mind than eulogies of the gentle, loving Jesus. The Old Testament, literally interpreted, is accepted more easily than the gospels of love and forbearance; and many a village elder most sincerely believes he can improve upon the grim prohibitions of the Mosaic Code and the Ten Commandments by attaching riders of punishments awful beyond the modern Christian's conception.

I had heard my father speak of having seen a man on his way to be crucified—on living saplings, their tops crossed and bent to the ground, which, when released sprang upright ripping human flesh to shreds and flinging the fragments skyward.

I myself once came upon a completely deserted village and when I followed the sound of happy shouts and merry laughter, found men and women kicking a skull about. The bone was a pure white, the man had not been dead long enough for it to dry out and turn ashen. Why had he been killed? Who had done it? And how?

No one bothered to answer my first question. That was unimportant now, since the man was dead and his evil ended. *No one* had killed him. No one whom a white man could seize and drag off to a mine or labor camp for the rest of his life. It was the little red ants that were the criminals. Could the labor recruiter use them to dig his gold or build his roads?

But ants do not kill a strong, healthy man without help. Many hands had dug the hole in which the victim had been buried up to his neck. Who could say what knife had sheered off his eyelids? Or had dribbled honey from the crown of his head to the edge of an anthill so that the voracious creatures would find him in the shortest time possible? It had been great sport to watch the little red devils swarm over the defenceless poll and into the screaming mouth. No terrible detail was spared me—the occasion had been too entertaining not to share. The eyes had been devoured first, the breath was choked off in the nostrils and the screams had been stifled by a rapidly swelling tongue. One of these "simple, happy children of nature," a girl perhaps fourteen or fifteen years old, told me that the head had been completely stripped of all vestiges of flesh, brain and cartilage, inside and out, and had rolled away from the neck of its own weight before her small baby had satisfied its hunger and fallen asleep at her breast.

I encountered the ridiculous, too. One afternoon I was holding a clinic in a village when a man came hurrying down the one street and beckoned to a woman standing in line. She tossed her head in impatience and muttered things I did not catch but which provoked her friends to laughter. Then she followed the man into a hut. Almost immediately the air was rent with the screams of a tortured animal. Was the man killing his wife? I demanded. Only the younger women tittered lightly, the older crones scowled uneasily and one beldam volunteered the information that what went on in a man's kraal after the palm-fiber matting has dropped in place is his own concern and nobody else's business.

I knew that well. Still the screams were so agonizing I think I would have committed an extreme breach of native etiquette and have brushed the matting to one side and entered had not the man and woman fairly erupted from the door. I climbed up on my chair so I could see over the heads of the women about me—all interest in me and the show I had been was now directed elsewhere. The man held a club, a sort of knobkerrie in his hand, and whenever he could catch up with the fleeing woman, he rained blows upon her back and head. Twice they circled the village, everyone gaping and turning to follow them with her eyes, and my weak screams were completely drowned out by the woman's calliope screechings.

Then the man stopped chasing the woman, threw his knobkerrie through the door of his hut, and trotted back into the jungle without a word. The woman, her back and shaven head a mass of bruises and rapidly swelling welts, shouldered her body back into exactly the same place she had previously held in line. Between gasps for breath, and as noncommittally as though she were speaking of someone else, she told her avidly curious sisters that her husband had been hunting elephants. Many heads nodded vigorously, other husbands were in the same hunting party. The men had found tembo but before a spear could be hurled, a bull had charged.

Past many men much nearer him the beast had thundered, and had made straight for the man we had just seen. There was a shout of merry laughter among the women. Then someone, noticing my amazement explained that for a bull elephant to so single out one particular man of a hunting party is sure sign that the man's wife is at that moment committing adultery. Such an erring woman must be punished; and as was expected of him, the man had left his companion hunters, returned to the village and administered the sound beating we had just witnessed.

"But you weren't committing adultery. You were standing here in line before me. I saw you. All these other women saw you. Why didn't you tell your husband so? He would have had to believe you when there were so many witnesses to prove your honesty," I spluttered indignantly.

For a moment there was thick silence, every woman staring at me with amazed eyes. Then one old hag sidled up to me and patted me on an arm as though I had been a child.

"If tembo says the woman was committing adultery, who are you, mama, to call the greatest and strongest and wisest of all beasts a liar? Are you alone possessed of all wisdom, beyond that of our countless ancestors and the immeasurable jungle?"

Sometimes a woman who is much alone in the jungle will do silly things, particularly if she feels, without any mental and emotional stops, that the women about her are her sisters regardless of race, creed, or caste. I did, not once but often. I mean such things as honoring native customs, little things that did not violate my religion but made my co-workers raise their eyebrows and smile.

For instance, there was the Tree of Rags. When I returned to Africa, Maa Koo again attached herself to me—to my joy! When I was sent out on itinerant clinical work, Maa Koo sometimes went with me. I was riding along one day on my bush-car with Maa Koo seated behind me on something like a luggage carrier which my brother Norman had rigged up for that purpose. A bush-car is a "pusher bike." It has two wheels for narrow paths and a third wheel which can be attached for paths that are wide enough and

where the going is somewhat rough. Maa Koo and I were far ahead
of the porters when we came up to a dead tree whose stark branches
were alive with fluttering strips of cloth.

"Foor goodness' sake, what's that?" I exclaimed.

"That is the Walenyi women's Tree of Rags" my old nurse
answered and went on to explain: "Sometimes a Walenyi woman's
husband is so greedy that he takes every bit of money she receives
in the market for her vegetables and chickens and will not give her
even a sou for the cheapest, smallest strip of cloth. But she doesn't
return to the goatskin or cowhide cape across her shoulders, which
was the only garment her mother ever wore. Indeed, whenever she
passes this tree she tears a fragment from her ragged *kanzu* [skirt]
and ties it on to a branch. There it flutters to the disgrace of her
husband. She believes that before it rots and drops to the ground
she will have a new garment."

I laughed—Maa Koo could be so funny. And then I sobered.
Thoughts which I did not welcome were pushing themselves into
my mind. And Maa Koo was no help at all. "The mama with hair
like the dying Lion of the Heavens [that is a sunset] has garments
which are no good for the jungle. But if you want an inside kanzu
[petticoat] like hers, tie a rag on the tree, daughter."

There were hundreds of fragments of a cheap calico we call
merikani on the lower branches. Some were newly tied, no dew
had wilted the knots, no rain had leached out the color. Of others
there were only tangled threads left. Then because I was a woman, I
suppose, and young, it seemed to me that every coarse thread in my
underwear rasped across every nerve in my body like the underside
of the eeysöe leaf in the hands of a man polishing a drum. I lifted
my skirt and looked at my petticoat and then dropped my skirt
again. Only God knew how long that denim garment must last me.

Maa Koo was chuckling. "I told the washboy to hang the lazy
mama's leg kanzus [panties] under a ylalti tree."

"Under a ylalti tree! Why, Maa Koo?" As though I didn't
know! But being a woman, I pretended ignorance.

"The little oomoi lives on the leaves of the ylalti tree and lays its eggs on whatever is hung below them." The old woman burst into a toothless guffaw. Before I could join her she went on: "The oomoi is a gnat, and its eggs hatch out into tiny worms. These worms crawl under the skin of whatever animal they touch. One does not feel them boring their way in, but after they are curled up under one's hide, they grow and fester and if they are not picked out with a bamboo splinter, they itch worse than any lice until they crawl out of the skin, newly hatched tiny white oomoi flies, hungry for the leaves of a ylalti tree. The lazy one will jump more quickly when her rump begins to itch."

I tried to look severe, indignant, but I laughed in spite of myself. Maa Koo crawled off the bush-car and came over to stand beside me. Then carelessly she ripped a strip off her hem and tied it to the Tree of Rags.

"Perhaps you will buy me a new kanzu, daughter?" she murmured with a sly glance in my direction.

"And perhaps somebody will buy me a new kanzu," I said suddenly. Using my teeth I ripped the hem off one side of my canvas handkerchief and tied it to a twig. Then like a whimsical child, I ripped off another strip of hem and muttered bitterly as I knotted it to a twig also, "A beautiful new kanzu—the kind a woman puts on because she wants to and not because—because she has to cover up her nakedness."

When I returned to the mission station from that trip, my mother had a shocking tale to tell me.

"Laura, you can't imagine what happened! The washboy hung Esther's laundry under a ylalti tree! Dr. Dick had to take twenty-six little oomoi worms out of her—her hips. Why, the poor girl, she could hardly sit down for a week! That washboy! I never knew him to be so careless before. I gave him a sound talking to, believe me."

Again I tried to look severe, and then mother and I both laughed. Neither of us would ever betray old Maa Koo.

CHAPTER
SEVEN

After a year in the bush my itinerant work came to an end. Father informed me one evening when I touched home base that Sister Esther was unhappy in the hospital. I knew that, for on my brief visits to the mission station I always spent a few hours with Dr. Dick in the hospital, and of course I saw Esther there. As a child I had absorbed too much of the African woman's phlegmatic acceptance of what she cannot alter to be shocked at what I saw in Esther.

"What you cannot explain you may laugh at, or fear—but remember you may have to live with it, little worm," Maa Koo had said more than once.

All black Africans immediately give the whites who live among them a name which may be descriptive of character as well as physical attributes. Esther was called The-Mama-without-Respect. We missionaries always ignored a derisive name bestowed upon a newcomer because we knew it would be changed when a better one was earned. Twelve months can be a long time in the jungle—long enough to test any man or woman—and it was obvious that Esther still had earned no one's sincere regard.

When she first came to Africa I once saw Dr. Dick lay an infant, only seconds old, in Esther's arms. She shrank back involuntarily from the tiny purplish creature, its arms and legs doubled up tight against its body, and twitching convulsively. She would have dropped the child had Dr. Dick's broad palm been withdrawn. Then, before the look in his face, she had seized the child and pressed it tight to her bosom, blood, birth serum and all, with a fierce light of determination in her eyes.

A year later that spark of determination which carried her through those first days was gone. That ember was dead, and its ash was a cold gray smudge across her soul. She passed on slow, unwilling feet from patient to patient. The sick awaited her stoically. There was no love in her heart for those to whom she must minister. She received no thanks in return from a normally garrulous, grateful people. Truly, she was "The-Mama-without-Respect."

I never understood Esther. But I lived with her closely for almost a year. And I could do it because of Maa Koo's training. I might have been a little fearful of her once; but as the days wore on what Maa Koo would have called the fear resolved into contempt and pity. But I lived and worked with her. And I am glad I had that year. Deeply grateful to God, and for three reasons: I think I began to perceive the great wisdom back of the biblical injunction, "Judge not!" I saw more of Jimmy and I sensed how much he was coming to love Africa, the land. And I saw and played my small part in Esther's one missionary triumph.

Esther was to leave the hospital, I was told, and I knew it was just as well. Few tribal Africans on the West Coast, at least, come to a white man's hospital. They love the ministrations of white witch doctors, but only if such help is a relatively social matter. That is, we clinical workers, itinerant and otherwise, are something in the nature of a vaudeville show in which they too can participate and from which they can walk away laughing, whenever they choose. The hospital cases do not come to us until their own witch doctors have admitted failure to them, and they are in desperate straits.

Greatly as these people needed—and some of them appreciated—help, they turned their faces away when Esther walked among them. More than once I watched Esther covertly, wondering at the speed and completeness with which her charm had been vanquished by the impact of another culture—frayed into ugly fragments by the

94 ·

attrition of the social mores of another stage in the evolution of civilization.

I have thought many times since that Esther was like a house plant which must have a sunny southern window, constant temperature, the right degree of moisture at its feet, no water on its leaves, and artificial feeding. The rest of us missionary squash vines had to be able to put down roots into any kind of soil, to clamber up and over whatever lay about us, and to produce fruit regardless of sun, drought, mildew, or rot. Father, as was his painful duty, had written to the Governing Board "back home," telling them that Mrs. Grove was obviously unfitted for missionary work and unhappy in it. He had suggested that she—and her husband because of her, of course—be recalled. The President of the Board himself had replied to father in substance that it was equally obvious to him that we missionary sobersides needed Sister Grove's gaiety, that anyone as charming as she could fit into any group, that she had been the most popular nurse with the doctors in charge of the hospital where she had trained, and that such a creature as she could not fail. Had the missionaries on the field given her the fullest co-operation? he asked. Had we helped her in making the necessary adjustments? If she were a round peg in a square hole, would it not be a Christian service to help her find a round hole into which to fit?

That was why I was taken off my work and brought back to the mission station, to try to help Esther find a round hole into which she might settle herself acceptably.

"Why me?" I wailed.

Father's reply was direct and blunt, "Because your work can be interrupted with less upset to mission routine than that of anyone else."

"You mean I'm least important," I snapped at him, but dropped my eyes before his unwavering gaze.

"You haven't done a half-bad job this last year, daughter—in spite of being a round peg in a square hole yourself. Will a few more months matter?" Then he laid an arm across my shoulders and pinched my cheek the way he used to do when mother had insisted that he take me to task for some childish infraction.

"Oh, father, she—she—she is such a burden," I wailed. I rebelled at putting into words for him that Jimmy was now out of my mind, that I was at peace within myself, that I dreaded and doubted my strength to face a reawakening of what was buried deep under twelve full months of satisfying activity.

"Do you know what Abu Sayheed told me the last time we went downriver together? A little tale of his people. There was a man who was constantly complaining that his troubles were too great. He complained so long and loudly and bitterly that Mu'ungu got tired of hearing him. There was a flash of lightning and a loud clap of thunder and Mu'ungu stood before the man and asked him if he didn't know that each man at birth has a burden bound to his shoulders and that the measure of his manhood is the manner in which he carries that burden through life? The man knew all that, but complained that God had bound too big a burden upon his shoulders. So Mu'ungu took the man to the Valley of Burdens, which was completely filled with what looked like stones, some big as huts, other like grains of sand.

There Mu'ungu unbound the man's personal burden, and as it went rolling back down the hill into the valley instead of the roar of a landslide, he could hear only a tiny, tinkling whisper of a sound. Then Mu'ungu told him that since no man can go through life without a burden on his shoulders, he should choose one to his own liking.

The man spent days in the valley, always looking for a smaller and still smaller stone. At last he found one so tiny that he had to carry it in a hollow tooth for fear of losing it. When he finally laid it, all wet with his spittle, in Mu'ungu's hand, he halfway expected to be reprimanded, but God only stared at him in wonder. Then slowly he asked, "Foolish man, do you not know that this is exactly the same burden I just unbound from your shoulders?"

Most decisions about staff members at a mission station are made in conference with the member concerned participating. There was a conference which concerned Esther, and it was decided that from now on she was to be an itinerant educational worker. I don't know whether or not the girl held any degree other than her R.N., or had had any training in pedagogy. I know she never understood my exile, but instead seemingly envied what she called, "Laura's freedom to move about."

She openly sneered at Sister Hallie and dear Aunt Bun. But whether she knew it, Esther was envious of these women too. Sister Hallie was called by her students The-Overripe-Coconut—a great compliment implying that her head was so full of meat (information that is) that if she should fall and give it ever so slight a bump, it would burst wide open. Aunt Bun, on the other hand, was frequently The-Custard-Apple-on-the-Topmost-Branch—that is, she was sweet enough to eat if one could but reach and bite into her.

Both women were loved enthusiastically by their pupils, and more than once I surprised Esther's envious eyes following them as they went about their work. For my part, I wondered just what the adoration-hungry Esther would do if a child, its hands gummy with ripe plantain meat, or greasy with fish oil, should embrace her silk-clad knees in its loving arms.

I think those who really made the decisions at our mission compound agreed that Esther was not being helpful in the hospital. But I believe it must have been she alone who decided that somehow she would have what Sister Hallie's and Aunt Bun's big hearts and hard work brought them, plus what small advantages I enjoyed. She would be an itinerant educator.

"It is only fair to let her try," father explained wearily. "It may be a little hard on you, daughter, for you must take her on trips upriver and help Dr. Dick in the hospital at the same time."

"What villages will she visit?" I asked, envisaging a circuit. And, "How many days a week?"

A brief glance passed between father and mother, the kind which means a man and his wife have given the matter confidential consideration and have arrived at conclusions which will not always stand impartial critical discussion.

"We thought we'd let her try her hand at N'tacke," father answered with the ghost of a smile on his lips. "If she succeeds there—"

N'tacke was a dying village, perhaps the home of a dying tribe. It lay a half-day's journey away by shimbeck. In my father's lifetime he had seen it dwindle from a thousand huts to perhaps no more than a couple of hundred persons. No one could adequately explain the melting away of the village. True, there had been slave raids in the old days, internecine warfare, epidemics, and periodic famine; but these calamities befell other villages which somehow managed to survive.

For some reason the WaN'tacke were simply dying out as a people, and like all jungle creatures which recognize and accept helplessness when it is a condition of life, they had become shy and exceedingly timorous. Father used to stop in their village as a matter of duty; and I have heard him say that in a dozen visits he failed to catch a glimpse of that many souls.

If Esther, who so badly wanted the praise and admiration of others without bothering to earn them—if Esther succeeded in N'tacke, my father had said— But like him, I didn't finish even the thought.

So for five days a week I helped Dr. Dick in the hospital. On the sixth day, since Esther was too inexperienced to travel alone, I took her up the river to the village of N'tacke. I had planned to spend the shimbeck hours translating. Dr. Dick had piled a heap of medical journals into my arms the evening before our first trip. In each he had marked one or more articles or passages which he wanted me to read, digest, and translate in abbreviated form for use in the classes where he trained his native medical helpers.

"I would do it, nurse, only—" he didn't say, "I haven't time," but "—only one born to African language and the thought patterns of a primitive mind can make sense instead of nonsense of these— these learned, mental meanderings."

As the weeks went by, I got a good deal of work done for Dr. Dick. But on that first trip upriver Esther was exhilarated by the new experience and she chattered like her old self. Evanescent plans ran through her mind constantly. "Sometime I'd like to lecture on the primitive customs here," she'd say. Or, "But 'one-night-stands' in America can be so wearing, can't they? Maybe I shall write and give only an occasional lecture. To paint a scene like that!" pointing at the ordinary jungle river bank with a sigh of aesthetic rapture "—in broad, bold strokes and colors— Words, I mean, Laura. You understand, de-e-e-ear?—with a public always breathless at my sensitiveness of perception and constantly urging me to produce more. And more!"

It was a relief when our boatmen pushed the mission shimbeck up onto the little barren, hard-packed space of clay where the women of N'tacke came to bathe and fill their water pots. I pointed out to Esther a narrow path running back through the trees and told her that about four or five hundred feet away she would find the village of N'tacke. I was careful to say, "the village," not "the people."

"My N'tackians!" she exclaimed airily. I'm not sure that she meant to satirize the manner in which missionaries so often speak of the people to whom they minister. There was one white-haired man, as old in the service of Africa as my father, who visited our mission station about once a year. Just to hear him say, "My Kavirondo" was like God's benediction—but a benediction without censure of beings who had somehow managed to slither out from under the divine thumb.

Without replying, I clamped the leaves of a medical journal open with a hairpin.

"Oh! I suppose you want me to say, 'My WaN'tacke,'" Esther went on, using the correct plural. "You see, I've picked up a few linguistic fine points."

I tried for a smile and managed a grumpy "Father says you're quite a linguist." Then on impulse alone, I held up crossed fingers and gave her a cheery "Good luck!"

I'm glad I did that, for the cunning glint which had sharpened her glance faded swiftly and a child-like wistfulness took its place.

The woman knew that as a missionary she was a failure, and this attempt at educational work out and away from supervision—and comparison with successful women!—was sheer bravado. "If you need me, give a whoop and I'll come," I added.

"Why should I need you?" she snapped defiantly.

I dropped my eyes to my own work, while she gathered up the books she had brought with her, stepped out of the shimbeck and started up the path. Ten minutes later I heard Esther halloo-ing, but she was not calling me. She was calling *her* WaN'tacke, for she had found what my father and a half-dozen other missionaries had always found in this curious village: empty huts, chickens scratching in the dust of the one street, dogs sleeping in the sun, stools in the palaver hut still warm from the impress of human rumps, cooking pots bubbling over dancing fires—but no human beings. I waited, listening, pitying. Then all was silence.

Suddenly I jerked my tense body erect in horror. Had the woman in her anger and desperation and stupidity run into the jungle in search of the WaN'tacke? There were places where, if she forced her way through the vines and underbrush for as little as ten feet, she would be helplessly lost.

I stood up and called to Abu Sayheed who was bathing. He stepped out of the water and shook himself like a puppy while I explained my fears to him briefly. He nodded, and together we hurried up the path.

It was Abu Sayheed who saw Esther first. He laid one hand on my shoulder and pointed with the other. We both stood stock-still and stared. Esther was squatting beside a hut on her haunches, native fashion—perhaps for the first time in her life!—a flounce of lacy petticoat sweeping the dust behind her. Beside her was an old, old man. Perhaps he had been asleep when his relatives and neighbors fled. Perhaps he was just too old and feeble or weak even to care any longer if some white ogre caught him. But Esther—I shake my head in wonder even now as I think of it— Esther was holding a primer up before the old man's bleared eyes and was expounding to him the vague intricacies of alphabet and syllables.

I looked at Abu Sayheed and he smiled. Together we turned and went back to the shimbeck, each walking as silently as he could.

A half-hour later Esther came down the path. She was tired, one could see that from far away. But defiance had faded out of her eyes, and in its place— It was not quite enthusiasm. I can't describe her expression.

"How did things go?" I asked, lest she should take note of my saying nothing.

"Oh, I had a class," she answered casually.

Presently Abu Sayheed began to sing about Esther and what had happened in the village of N'tacke. Not because their hearts were in it, but because as father used to say of his parishioners at worship, "They like to make a joyful noise unto the Lord," the other boatmen joined in the chorus.

"They are singing about *you*," I told Esther.

She looked startled, and then wary, and then pricked up her ears, but her knowledge of the language was not yet sure enough of the highly idiomatic phrases of the boatmen.

"They respect a teacher highly," I explained, "And they are saying that you—that you must be very wise."

Actually, they were expressing some wonder at her smooth clear skin and glorious hair when within her skull reposed the knowledge of a wrinkled, hairless hag. Perhaps I should have tried to explain to her that the women who train the young girls for marriage and motherhood in tribal bush schools are always old, and that the men who preside over the boys' initiation rites in "devil bush" carry their strength only in their skulls. But could she have understood a song based on such ritual? And not take offense where only highest praise was meant? But Esther was sound asleep. Teaching like nursing can be exhausting work.

I really didn't expect Esther to want to go to N'tacke again, but she reminded me several times before our next visit was due. In the bottom of the shimbeck as we stepped aboard that day, lay an armful of sugar cane. Abu Sayheed grinned and explained, "Learning is a dry labor. The musty meat of wisdom is swallowed easier when washed down with the juice of sugar cane."

Esther eyed the long stalks dubiously, while thoughts of her one pupil, undoubtedly perpetually hungry because of his toothless gums, flashed through my head.

When we landed at the WaN'tacke's laundry and bath pool, Esther stepped out of the shimbeck and Abu Sayheed picked up the sugar cane to carry it for her. But where the path entered the jungle, Esther turned and held out her arms. "I will carry it. I don't need any help," she said in sharp, brittle tones.

But Abu Sayheed picked up a stalk of the cane and was saying to her, "This is the way I peel it, mama." He plunged his pointed teeth into the hard shell-like outer casing and ripped strip after strip away until the sweet wet pith was clean and bare. "But the jaws of children are weak and their teeth are tender and cannot always pierce this hard bark. Perhaps you will want to peel the cane for them." And Abu Sayheed drew his hunting knife and laid it upon the pile of sugar cane in Esther's arms.

I know my mouth must have fallen open, literally. Not because I have never seen a pickinin unable to get at the pith in sugar cane by one means or another. But because I had never known an African black man to let a woman, any woman, touch his weapons. Awkwardly dragging the tips of sugar cane behind her, Esther strode into the jungle and Abu Sayheed, after nonchalantly shedding his G-string, plunged into the river. Fifteen minutes later he came up to the shimbeck where I sat working and crooked a finger at me.

"Come," he said. "Let us see if the Little-Mama-Who-Is-Earning-Respect has again captured her one pupil."

Together Abu Sayheed and I stood hidden in the bushes beside the path watching Esther labor as she had probably never labored before. And then, when the last cud of dry sugar-cane pith rolled from the old man's slack lips, she would lay down her primer, pick up Abu Sayheed's huge knife, hack off a joint of cane and peel it for the dotard.

Then Abu Sayheed lifted an arm and pointed silently across my shoulder. Following his rigid finger with my eyes, I saw the head of a child, perhaps ten, twelve, or thirteen years old peering around the curved wall of a hut. "The-Little-Mama-Who-Admires-Herself will have her class yet," he murmured and chuckled so deep within his throat that it sounded like pebbles grinding together under water.

Several weeks later Esther asked me what made native children "stink so bad."

"Mothers rub their children with the oil that rises from a potful of rotten fish, or the oil they express from castor beans," I answered. I explained that these oils keep the skin from chafing and cracking in the sun, and help keep down scabies and lice. But Esther was scarcely listening.

"Castor Bean!" she exclaimed. "That's what I'll call him. Castor Bean."

"Who?"

"A boy—a little fellow—oh, just one of the kids, you know." It was a brave attempt at nonchalance. And then she wrinkled up her nose in a spasm of genuine disgust. "Phe-e-e-e-w! He leans over my shoulder while I'm trying to teach—to teach some other student, and he smells to high heaven of castor oil. Sometimes I've thought I couldn't stand him another minute."

Her last words were an attempt at imitating Aun Bun, from whose lips one sensed all the love of a missionary-teacher-mother in the most personally derogatory of statements.

I could finish this incident in Esther's unhappy life for you, native fashion—and take a month in the telling! That is, I would leave out not one second of time or item of detail no matter how repetitious or monotonously uninteresting. But briefly, one day Grandpop, as Abu Sayheed and I called Esther's senile pupil, was gone. Either he had died a natural death, or some relative had led him off into the jungle. We would never know what had become of him since one does not mention the dead by name lest the spirit be listening and, hearing its name, feel itself invited to rejoin the living. And that is a calamity if the spirit is inclined to malice.

But Esther was not left without a class. Castor Bean, who until that time had never done anything but lean over her shoulder and demand a share of the sugar cane, took the primer out of her hands and read. She had taught him well although he had given no sign of learning while her efforts had been directed elsewhere. She told my father later—somewhat airily—that she had merely explained the purpose of missionary education to Castor Bean, and immediately he had corraled a class of other youngsters for her. We think she may have threatened the withdrawal of the weekly sugar-cane feast.

My father went to the village of N'tacke with Esther after the real class had been going on for several months. I had long since stopped accompanying her up the river, and I had no idea how her work there was progressing other than as she let triumphant phrases drop now and then. It was a very real triumph for her. No one ever told her that it had hinged upon the accident of her stumbling upon an old man too feeble, too tired, too sleepy, too sick, too near death to run away or to care. She had succeeded where everyone else before her had failed. It was not the accidental opening wedge, but the end result that mattered.

My father saw and talked with the WaN'tacke, these shy, dying people who had always eluded him before. He brought Castor Bean back to the mission with him for broader training than Esther could give. He paid the boy's parents two pounds of salt per season —an exorbitant price—for "the possession of their son."

Castor Bean, too, demanded a gift before he would accompany father. If he was to live among white men and cram his head full of the strange things they knew and thought important, he must possess that which set them apart from all the black people he had ever known. He must have a pair of eyes which he could put on and take off. Spectacles! Father promised them to him as soon as he should arrive at the mission compound.

I myself saw father open the box of lenseless horn rims and stir about in its contents until he found a pair which fit the child's face and ears. Castor Bean accepted the gift like a diploma. The last time I saw the boy he was still wearing those lenseless rims as proudly as any Knight of the Garter ever displays his blue ribbon.

And not only Castor Bean! Such rims, the heavier and gaudier the better, are worn by every N'tacke who learns to read. We may have to order more from the United States, by the way; for the village of N'tacke is no longer dying. There are new huts there now, and thriving shambas. Esther's work was good.

CHAPTER
EIGHT

It would be hard to define the hope that Esther's spurt of energy and enthusiasm and success engendered in all of us. The change in Jimmy was marked. He whistled sometimes. He surprised us all by bringing out a mouth organ and entertaining us with everything from mournful oratorios to snatches of light opera. Then, before we knew it, he had a—I don't know whether it should be called a band or an orchestra. Both the xylophone and marimba are native to Africa and from time to time as the fame of Jimmy's band grew among the black people around us we saw and heard instruments we had never seen or heard before. There was one marimba at least eight feet long. It took four men to carry the frame, and two others lugged the gourds which hung below the keys. And those gourds! Some were four feet long and six inches across the top. Others were no more than the length and width of one's little finger. When the mood to make music was upon the player of this instrument we had to get out of the room, pushed out by the volume of sound he hammered out of his keys with his sledge-like fists. That fellow and the friends who helped him transport his huge instrument, stayed at the mission compound as long as Jimmy was there. When Jimmy left, I'm told they gathered up their marimba, and like the Arabs of the poem, stole silently into the jungle.

We also saw and heard all sorts of shepherds' pipes. We saw them in the making, too, for every boy in the compound made himself a set of pipes. Each instrument when it was finished was as different as the personalities of the boys who blew their love of sweet sounds into them.

Drums we had galore. Some of the drums were of high quality; some of the drummers were artists. Others simply beat out exotic rhythms and wild cacophonies that defied Jimmy's loudest, most energetic attempts at conducting.

And Aunt Bun—another unexpected musician among us—always said that she wasn't much better. Years ago when Aunt Bun had been preparing to come to the mission field she had learned to play an accordion. In the two decades following that time, however, she had somehow become wedged into one of the niches of our music-less academic system. She had kept the instrument all these years wrapped in oilcloth against tropical damp and locked in a tin trunk against termites. Now, "We're both getting old!" Aunt Bun cried out when we greeted her first stiff-fingered, wheezing notes with shouts of laughter. Aunt Bun would have become discouraged by herself—but no one was happier than she when Jimmy refused to play without her music, lugubrious though it was.

It's hard for me now to recall very many of the musicians who came to our compound and stayed to play and work and learn for varying periods of time, or those who simply visited us briefly because of our music. There is one among the latter, however, who stands out sharp and clear in my memory. We whites did not know he was in or near the compound until Jimmy's musicians began to forgather one evening. Then he stalked into our midst and assumed a position of prominence as though by inherent right. The black boys made way for him so respectfully that we whites gave him more attention than we usually bestowed upon such temporary visitors.

The stranger's face was heavily scarred, and father and I had no more than caught a glimpse of it before we involuntarily turned to look for Abu Sayheed. He stood lolling against a tree in the far fringes of our lantern's light. We could not see his face clearly in the shadows, but we did not need to—his tribal cicatrices and this stranger's were the same. That meant they shared a common homeland. But Abu Sayheed gave no sign at that time that he knew the man. When we first tried to ask any of our mission boys or girls who the man was, we didn't exactly get a "Ssssh!" for our pains, but something close to that.

Three wives followed the man. Each bore on her head a small bundle wrapped in the kind of cloth they weave with their hands and feet up north toward Timbuctoo and Fort-Lamy, and sometimes further to the east and along the Shari-Ubangi River. But, according to our mission folk, the man was not from Timbuctoo, or Fort-Lamy, or Shari-Ubangi Country.

The man immediately sank to his haunches facing Jimmy, our "Music Witch Doctor," as the mission boys were now affectionately calling him. The three women squatted behind their husband— the proper place for female *cattle*. Each woman took her bundle off her head and laid it in front of her. Out of the first two came the fairly familiar one-stringed violins we had often seen and heard in various parts of Africa. The third woman unrolled a small drum, the kind Egyptian fellahin strum on lightly with their finger tips. The woman immediately tucked it under one arm and caressed it gently as though testing its pitch. Then she turned back another fold of her cloth and disclosed a tangle of thongs and thin slabs of polished wood suspended from an arc of ivory that might have been a huge boar's tusk.

The man held out his left hand for this last instrument, and with a quick motion threw a loop of rawhide from which it hung suspended over the stump of his right arm. It was not until then we saw that his right hand was gone, neatly severed at the wrist. The scars were those of a clean cut, cauterized from having been plunged into boiling fat. The man was a convicted thief! Maimed and exiled.

Without a glance at anyone, without waiting for Jimmy to clear his throat and murmur: "Are we all here? Everybody ready? Okay, let's begin," the man began to perform on his instrument. He played the thin dangling slabs of wood with his left hand like an upright keyboard, sometimes patting them lightly with the fleshy portion of his finger tips, sometimes hitting them sharply with his fingernails. On his little finger he wore a woman's thimble. When he struck the thin polished keys with that, the notes rang out like bells. They cut through the gentle pulsation of the drum and the resigned wail of the one-stringed violins like the notes of a triangle in an orchestra.

To us whites, the man's tunes were mostly unfamiliar. What they were to our mission people I can't say. There was one air that was repeated like the orchestrated variations on a theme. It can't be reproduced by our system of music because the finest distinction that we provide for, is the half-tone. Our ears reject all else as dissonance. I don't know whether it would take a Mozart or a Wagner to capture and imprison such tunes on paper for other musicians; the cultural world is aesthetically the poorer because it has never been done. Of all the missionaries I have known, only one has been a great musician, and he has carried the music of his homeland with him. A handful of travelers, explorers, scientists have made a few records of the bastard tunes—neither African nor anything else—which are hummed near the coast. It is so much easier perhaps to pose with a foot on a dead lion's head or with a puny arm resting nonchalantly on an elephant's immense skull than it is to invent a new system of musical notation required to capture the phantom scales of primitive music.

None of us looked at our watches that night, none of us tilted our chins so that our eyes might note the flight of the stars across the heavens, marking time in the most ancient manner. I don't know what hour it was when the man stopped playing and with a backward sweep of his arm handed his instrument to the wife with the drum. It was then he looked about him as though for the first time he were conscious of his audience. There was no applause from anyone. I don't know why, but it didn't belong.

Then we whites sighed and stirred in our chairs, and our mission folk spat between their knees. But still none of us spoke, for the stranger's eyes had found the face of Abu Sayheed. There was no sign of recognition between the two men, but they stared unblinkingly at each other for an interminable minute. It was Abu Sayheed who looked away first.

He stepped up behind the chair in which my father sat and said in a low voice but clearly enough to be heard by all of us, "Bwana, you will send a goat and a handful of hens to the camp at the foot of the mahogany tree which Mu'ungu split with his spear [lightning] during the last rains. It stands at the bend of the river just beyond the sandspit where the crocodiles sleep in the sun."

Then Abu Sayheed faded into the night and we turned back to the center of the circle. But the man and his three wives were also gone.

Father's voice rose plaintively through the still night. "A goat and a handful of hens! Apparently I am to pay dearly for my evening—at the opera."

He meant to be funny, and to break the tension which still vibrated about us.

Then came Jimmy's voice, as low and as clear as Abu Sayheed's had been, "Let me pay for the goat and hens, Mr. Woodbury. It was great music."

Esther tittered as though a child had said something foolish. No one paid any attention to her, but the spell was broken. We turned to the mission boys about us, full of questions.

"He is The-Spirit-of-Music," they answered shortly.

"Many men hear him in the jungle."

"Few men ever see him. None see him often."

"I do believe they actually think he was a spirit," Jimmy said as he helped Aunt Bun fold her accordion and tuck it away in its tin case.

"Of course they do!" father and Dr. Dick chorused in unison.

Several things happened in the next few months that I remember well for one reason or another, but which I must pass over quickly.

Word came to father late one night that a planter, a Monsieur Floheur was dying. Father thanked the messenger, and went back to bed. It was not that father was callous to the sufferings of others;

it was simply that he was well acquainted with the planters in our jungle, a dozen or more of whom were scattered about us. All of them had come to Africa with the intention of hacking a plantation out of the wilderness, their heads bursting with dreams of quick and immense wealth. Most of them lived only for that time, ten, fifteen, twenty years hence, when they would return to their homeland, "rich as a lord," and ready to ape the munificence of a Renaissance prince. Everyone of them knew that it meant work, heartbreaking, unremitting toil.

What none of them knew to begin with is that physical vigor melts like snow under a tropical sun. That the torture of insect pests, disease, and sheer, overpowering loneliness eats away the very soul of any but iron-willed men. It was no uncommon thing for a rough, bluff, colonial planter to appear at our mission compound unannounced, and say: "I've just got to look at a white face. A white woman." No offense was intended. None taken.

They never stayed more than a day or two. These were hard-working men, the best of the lot, fellows who, barring disease and accident, would return home in due time with at least a comfortable competence. If they were garrulous, they talked to whoever was within sound of their voices—about nothing for the most part! All of them, talkative and taciturn, stared at any white woman within eye-range as though she were a seven-legged wonder from another world, regardless of age and the possession or lack of feminine charm. Quite often we enjoyed the visits of these men, but it is difficult for any woman—even a missionary—to walk naturally when passing starved eyes. Some of these men worshiped with us as though it were a privilege. All of them sat through prayers with their hands tightly clasped between their knees or their arms rigidly folded across their chests and peeked out of the corners of their eyes to be sure they bowed their heads at the right time.

There were some planters, however, whom the jungle had beaten, almost from the very start. When a missionary, following a jungle trail, comes upon the cottage of such a man, he recognizes it immediately. There is always an arc of empty bottles fanning out before and behind the house, the heavier arc depending upon whether the planter had used the front or back door most often when disposing of his empties.

These men seldom visited our mission compound, but it was not uncommon for them to send word that they were dying. Sometimes they were. But in any case, they were sure of a few hours' visit with father at least.

Monsieur Floheur was one of these wretched men. I knew him only by name and gossip. I took it for granted that he had never visited our mission compound, and he had never before sent word that he was dying.

As I have said, father went back to bed when word came from Monsieur Floheur since it so obviously followed a jungle pattern with which he was pathetically familiar. I was helping in the hospital the next morning when a boy brought Dr. Dick a note. Dr. Dick read it through slowly and then he shook his head, murmuring, "Poor Bun! Poor Bun!"

"What's the matter with Aunt Bun?" I asked. I knew from his tone and manner that she was not sick. But why his "Poor Bun!"? She was one of the jolliest, most self-reliant, self-sufficient, and least to be pitied members of our mission staff.

He was still shaking his head as he said to me, "Your father wants you. Hang up your lab apron. You won't be coming back today." And still there was no sense of distress or urgency in his voice. Only warm, human pity. My own steps were slow, almost laggard as I walked over to my parents' cottage. In the living room were father, mother and Aunt Bun.

"I think you should go, Elizabeth," mother was saying. When mother refused to use the childhood nickname I had given Aunt Bun, and snipped off "Elizabeth" between firm teeth as though she were biting off a thread, I knew she was laboring under emotional stress. And then, "It's your Christian duty, Elizabeth," she added.

Aunt Bun's sweet round face was a picture of quivering hesitation, doubt, and misery. She turned pleading, questioning eyes to father. "I don't know what is the right thing for you to do, Bun," father answered the silent appeal. Much of the tension eased out of her face as though the fact that he shared her doubt was a comfort.

"If you feel you should go," father went on, speaking ever more slowly, "if it will be a comfort for you to remember that you—did all you could, then—I'd come! Laura will come along, too, if—as a woman—you need her. But Bun, if you'd rather not come, then don't. There's no sense in harrowing one's soul simply for the sake of adding fresh pain to an old misery." His final words were surprisingly energetic.

"I think there are Christian duties that—" mother began. Father stared at her sternly as though she were a child, and she lapsed into silence. But it was an indignant, self-righteous silence. Bun felt it, and shivered.

"I—I think I should go," she said quickly.

A half-hour later we were trekking off into the jungle, father, Aunt Bun, and I, and a handful of porters with food for two days and our bedding on their heads. By mid-afternoon we had reached Monsieur Floheur's tumbled-down hovel. As we walked along, father had found occasion, when Aunt Bun was out of hearing ahead of or behind us, to tell me the brief, pitiful tale.

Monsieur Floheur had come to Africa about the time Bun herself had arrived. There had been a girl at home in Belgium who had promised to wait until he had carved a home out of the jungle for her. But in less than a year Monsieur had received a newspaper clipping giving an account of the girl's wedding. Following a romantic pattern, which Monsieur in his youth had accepted without question apparently, he had broken open the case of cognac intended strictly for snake bite.

"I probably saved his life that time," father said. "A storm drove me into his cottage one day when I was on an outstation trip. I found him scarcely breathing—'out cold' I think they call it. His boys had simply taken whatever of his possessions they could carry, including all that was left of the cognac, and walked off into the bush. He was wheezing and coughing in his stupor, and I was afraid of pneumonia; so I brought him back to the mission with me.

There he saw your Aunt Bun and promptly fell in love with her. Bun was—younger, in those days. Pretty, too. When he returned to his plantation he ordered up another case of cognac from Léopoldville—for snake bite, I suppose—but when it finally arrived, he went on another binge to celebrate his engagement to her.

"It was like that for several years, and Bun stuck to him loyally until finally he didn't need any excuse to get drunk. In fact he was seldom sober. He created a disturbance at the mission once or twice, and then I told Bun I had to ask him to stay away. She understood.

"Curious, but so far as I know, they have never broken off that engagement—formally, that is; but I don't think she's seen him for the last ten years. I don't think she should have come along now, and I don't think Bun really wanted to come, but— Well, your mother has curious notions sometimes, Laura. She's meek enough in her way, but she can dominate."

From then on until we reached Monsieur Floheur's hut, I found myself repeatedly staring at Bun's plump back. Had she, too, been a little rebellious that "God's work," had meant she must renounce the love of a man and the mothering of his children? Was that why she gave every one of her jungle pupils immeasurable care—and unstinted love? Aunt Bun never protested her Christianity, but I never saw the scrap of human flotsam that could not drift into some sheltered niche in her big heart.

I suppose Monsieur's hut—I can't call that structure a cottage—was the very hastily erected, temporary shelter most planters throw up at first. He had never built a permanent home although he had been in Africa—I don't know how long. Fifteen, twenty years? As a child I had never known of Aunt Bun's love affair and heartbreak.

Monsieur lay on an old cot, his limbs tangled in ragged dirty blankets, the kind the government issues to labor recruits and convicts. He was on his back when we entered, his mouth wide open, and flies buzzing over the spittle-drenched beard.

He was breathing and father tried to speak to him. After a

minute or two he opened his eyes. The whites were saffron-colored, like his few remaining teeth. His irises slid aimlessly back and forth not always focusing, until they came to rest on Bun's face. I don't know whether he recognized her as Bun, or merely as a human being who had come to help him. In any case, his eyes remained fixed on her stupidly like those of a flayed sheep hanging under the butcher's tree at a village market, staring in stupid surprise at nothing.

Father touched my shoulder and motioned me to follow him. We went out, leaving Bun behind, and walked here and there among the empty bottles around this lair. We talked a little about nothing much. A wild profusion of old-fashioned European flowers which someone had sown years before was tangled among the debris— mignonette, candytuft, carnations. Towering over what had once been some kind of building was a twenty-foot rosebush. "Beauty triumphant, trampling man's grossness underfoot," father murmured. He pulled down a thorny limb and smelled a shell-pink, four-inch bud.

When Bun called to us and we went back into the hut, Monsieur was dead. Father and I both looked at Bun quickly but her face was as gentle, as serene as always. She had made a pillow of an old coat of Monsieur's, and by pushing his chin against his chest had closed the man's awful mouth. She had also pressed his eyes shut and brushed back his limp, straggling hair.

This time father took Bun by the arm and led her out. I prepared Monsieur's body for burial as best I could. He was rotten with syphilis. I'm glad Aunt Bun didn't see that.

Father stirred about among the trash in the hut and found a rusted shovel with a bit of handle left on it. Two of our porters dug a grave for Monsieur under his giant rosebush, but it took much persuasion from father to get them to do it. They grumbled, and more than once reminded us that Monsieur was not worthy the dignity of interment—let the jackals have him! Brave Bun! She took their estimate of the man who had squandered her dreams along with his own life without wincing. Father read the burial service from memory.

I don't think any one of us uttered a half-dozen words on the long way home. We were within sight of the mission compound when Aunt Bun dropped back beside me. It was evident that she wanted to say something. Father considerately hurried on ahead.

Finally, "If the time ever comes when some good man wants to marry you, Laura, marry him! No matter what others say or how they argue."

Her eyes were defiant and I wondered if she expected me to argue. Bun knew, as all missionaries among primitive peoples know, that the man who does not respect his own manhood will not accountably be metamorphosed into a strong, upright character simply because some woman undertakes to fetch and carry for him. Bun parted her lips as though she meant to say more. Then she smiled suddenly and walked ahead of me quickly. Aunt Bun truly loved human beings—and without being an emotional parasite herself.

A few days later our regular monthly mission staff meeting took place. There was nothing much to discuss that evening except the fact that within the current year Aunt Bun was due to go "home" on furlough. Should her work be stopped during her absence? Or was it possible that others among us could absorb her duties and carry on for her? To me it seemed the most normal and natural thing in the world that since Esther Grove had succeeded as a teacher—and magnificently as a missionary at N'tacke where everyone else had failed—she should take Bun's place in the classroom. It was a heaven-sent solution for us, and for Esther who was patently unhappy as a nurse.

But the next day Esther brushed against me in the dispensary and whispered in my ear, "I've got the problem licked. I'm going to have a baby!"

I almost dropped the tray I was holding in my surprise. "Oh, Esther! How nice! When?" Then before she could answer: "What problem are you licking?"

"Well, I can't work if I'm pregnant, can I? And I can't give all day to a bunch of stinking brats if I have one of my own. Now, can I?"

So Esther thought having a child of her own would free her from mission duties! I looked down at the tray in my hands in order to hide my amazement. Because I felt I must say something, I murmured, "Mission babies are always wonderful. When is yours due?"

"Oh, I don't know," she answered airily. "Maybe a year from now. Yes, a year from now would be just about right I think. Certainly not any sooner."

"You mean you're not pregnant now?" I gasped.

"Oh, you ninny," she laughed. Then with an exaggerated air of superiority, "Give me that tray before you spill everything on it. Wherever in the world did you take your nurse's training!"

I did not gossip—not even to father and mother—but a confused Jimmy Grove was receiving congratulations on his approaching fatherhood before his wife had conceived.

CHAPTER
NINE

Within the next few weeks I came as close to hating Esther Grove as the strict Christian training I had received from my parents would permit me to admit of hating anyone. She chattered to me almost incessantly about her child, and the imagined advantages which would accrue to her from it.

It is a terrible thing for one woman to have to remember another as I remember Esther. Many times I have awakened in the middle of the night feeling as guilty as a child with a hidden kitten in its bed—and without the comfort of being able to caress a soft ball of down. Then I have remembered my father's face and words when, unable to bear the burden of the woman's egomaniacal selfishness any longer alone, I opened my heart to him.

"She's a missionary mistake, Laura," he said. "Oh, yes. Mistakes are made on the mission field, and by governing boards, the same as with any other profession. Elsewhere Esther— Well, perhaps life would be more like what she wants it to be. Here, mere prettiness, vivacity, and charm aren't enough and she can't dominate others by using the ordinary feminine weaknesses. She can't bend either her white co-workers or force our black parishioners to her will. And then another thing that is hard to take, that is bewildering for anyone who likes herself as well as Sister Grove does, she's The-Little-Mama-without-Respect. Remember that! She also knows that Bun—whose clothes make her look like a pillow with a string tied around the middle—that Bun is frequently called The-Fat-One-with-Soft-Guts, that is, Loving-and-Tender. Sister Hallie? She's The-Mama-Burdened-Down-by-the-Weight-of-Her-Mind."

Father's translation of Sister Hallie's native nickname always amused me. Sister Hallie had two college degrees and a gold Phi Beta Kappa key. They were the only preferment Sister Hallie had ever been able to wring out of life, and they grew in importance in her mind as the years piled up.

"Now you! You know what every villager calls you," my father laughed.

Indeed I knew. The-Little-Black-Inside-White-Outside-Mama. And I knew why I had that enigmatic name. I was Maa Koo's daughter although born of another woman and another race.

"Even Sister Grove's husband is called, The-Beloved-of-the-Merry-Spirits."

I knew why Jimmy was called that. One way or another he would and could do any task at which he was set, and difficulties only broadened his pleasant smile. He loved the native music and seemed to understand it better than the rest of us. He learned the native games his pupils played in their own villages, and he laughed at himself as a perpetual loser in them. And he could laugh without giving offense at the ludicrous excuses a group of mission boys can use to cover up their lack of any understanding of what baseball is all about.

But at the name our people had given Jimmy, a chill never failed to cross my heart. The merry spirits are, in many ways, the village African's counterpart of the white man's Lady Luck. They are equally fickle. And in the back of every black man's mind is the certain knowledge that sooner or later the merry spirits will tire of their erstwhile darling and move on to another. When that time comes most men cease to be pleasant companions. Were the spirits only playing with Jimmy now?

"But, father, how can Esther suppose that having a child will mean that she will be freed of all mission responsibilities?" I asked. I remembered so many mission wives who had come, borne children, served, and gone. Others had been here when I was born, and had grown old with my parents.

"Did you tell her you were born under a trailside bush?" father teased me.

"There's Mrs. Dr. Dick—" I began.

"She's reared six children and buried two here in Africa," father recounted for me. "And she'd still put an old-fashioned circuit rider to shame." We smiled at each other indulgently. Everyone loved the doctor's wife—and was personally a little appalled by her immense energy.

"But can't Esther Grove see—" I began coming back to my problem.

"Esther Grove is one of those women who have always manipulated life for their own shoddy convenience. Such women *won't* see." Then father patted me on the shoulder lightly, but his words, like his face, were serious: "Daughter, there aren't many times left to me when I shall give you fatherly advice, so listen to me carefully now. *Live your own life.* Don't let anyone else live it for you. No matter how well-intentioned or how big-mouthed they may be. You know right from wrong; that's basic. And you've got a mind. Use it. I don't mean that you should be a sore thumb in any community—that's floating along on your emotions, not using your mind. And equally important, don't ever try to live anybody else's life for her. Pity if possible. Help if your help is honestly wanted, and try to understand a situation for what it is. Otherwise, keep your heart—and your skirts—clean. That Grove baggage is a thorn in everybody's flesh here. Thorns rankle at first, then they fester and push themselves out. Give her time and she'll relieve us of herself."

But how much time I wondered. And could I bear to see her stare at sweet, kindly Aunt Bun with that superior half-sneer on her face while Bun tried to share the wisdom of her many years of missionary experience with the upstart? "Father, I enjoyed the itinerant work," I started out, feeling my way toward what might be a solution. "Couldn't I possibly go back to it? Just for a little while, at least, until—"

"No!" His abrupt refusal had the force of a blow. He went on more gently, "I've had worse problems than Esther Grove to live with in my time. And I have lived through my difficult times. So can you. If it's any comfort to you, Laura, you never have to live more than one day at a time, you know. One second for that matter. And you can stand any irritation—anything for one second."

The irritation was there, and more than once it inflamed into pain. I was in Bun's schoolroom one morning carrying coals to Newcastle: that is, I was giving the usual periodic talk on the necessity of brushing one's teeth to children who are perpetually scouring their entire mouths with the twigs they chew up into brushes for that purpose. They agreed with me that toothache is a terrible nuisance, that the removal of food particles from between teeth is a pleasant matter, and one bright little fellow added for me, "If your fingers are buried among your teeth, you cannot be playing knucklebones. Jesus says, '*GOOD!*' and God nods, *YES.*" I nodded too. Indeed it was good, since at least half of black Africa's income changes hands at knucklebones, a gambling game which is the primitive counterpart of jackstones.

Aunt Bun, in order to help me, admitted that as a child she had not liked to brush her teeth and sometimes failed to do so. She pulled out a partial plate to show the awful consequences. African peoples are as a rule sensitive and sympathetic to a fine degree. The children knew they were supposed to be appalled, and they responded beautifully. Ludicrously.

But there were also two sniggers. One was from a tall child whose parents' village lay many days' journey to the south of our station. He informed Bun that she looked like a boy of his own tribe who had just been initiated into manhood—a part of which ceremony was having his two front upper teeth knocked out so he could spit between them like a man.

The other titter came from Esther, who drew her lips back in an exaggerated smile, a smile that lasted too long. She was showing the children that her own teeth were perfectly formed and healthy. If Esther expected Oh's of admiration, she was disappointed. After a solemn stare at The-Mama-without-Respect, the runt of the class stood up and solemnly addressed pointed questions at Bun.

Why was she, whose heart was big enough to hold every child in Africa, planning on leaving them, he asked, not simply, but with all the verbal flourishes of an old-time orator. Why was she leaving in her place the mama who loved no one, he went on. Did she imagine that feeble knowledge could push its way into a mind already filled with strong distrust and dislike? Good questions! But how could Bun explain to them that life in the only land they had ever known was supposed to be so wearing that she must "rest" one year out of every seven?

Then another child arose and bluntly asked Bun if she was returning to the kraal of her parents in the hope that they might somehow secure a husband for her. With the legendary wisdom and solemnity of an owl he assured her it was wasting time and effort. She was already undoubtedly too old to serve a man in any capacity other than as a back-warmer on a cold night. Of course, she would make a really good back-warmer, because there was plenty of her, and it was all soft. He marched up to her and snuggled against her bulging tummy to show how pleasant that could be.

Again there was a titter from Esther, this time hard, metallic, like the tinkle of dead bamboo leaves in a wind. Then her voice, "Tell them, Bun dear, whether you are going home after a husband? If you snare one, I promise you whatever you ask for a wedding present."

If life and my father had not schooled me to the restraint they have, I would have bashed Esther Grove over the head with whatever first came to hand.

Then that razor-edged voice of her again, "Ho hum! How boring can life be? I guess I'll go see what *my* husband is doing." She didn't have much in the way of hips to swing, but she flipped them like a chorus girl as she strolled out the door.

"The slut!" Aunt Bun said. I turned in amazement to her. "Don't mind me," she whispered. "I'm only—only—being—a woman."

Her eyes were snapping and her cheeks were as pink as the petals of a damask rose. I wanted to cry out, "Aunt Bun, you're beautiful!" But I didn't need to, for while I hesitated a child marched up in front of her and announced solemnly, "Mama, I want to touch your forehead with mine."

Bun sank on one knee, gathered the child in her arms, and as solemnly as two African sisters meeting unexpectedly and greeting each other lovingly on some jungle trail, laid her forehead against the child's. Her class waited in respectful silence. My Aunt Bun was well named The-Fat-Mama-with-the-Soft-Guts.

Esther became pregnant in due time and talked about her "condition" so incessantly that mother once admonished her tartly, "*You* carry the child, Sister Grove. *We'll* all love it when it is born."

Then mother did what I suppose the female head of every mission station does on such occasions. She brought out from her boxes the odds and ends she had gleaned from various missionary barrels from which a layette might be fashioned. Esther squeaked like a mouse in a trap when mother laid before her some red and green checker-boarded feed sacks intended for diapers. She stirred the heap with shrinking, disdainful finger tips and would have none of it.

Instead she must make the long trip downriver to Léopoldville for the things she wanted for her baby. And I must go with her, since in her "condition" she could not travel alone. Father said, "No!" The mission was short-staffed as it was, and to cripple the work further simply to indulge a capricious whim was not only absurd but would be maladministration on his part. But in the end I went. Mission babies are truly special beyond the lot of ordinary newcomers to this earth.

I carried with me somewhere around twenty-five dollars with which to buy necessities and the few indulgences a dozen people allowed themselves. I made my purchases in less than two hours, choosing each item carefully as I must do. We were supposed to stay in Léopoldville only two or three days, since this was not a vacation trip. We stayed almost three weeks. For financial reasons

I had to leave the hotel at which we stopped the first two nights and ask hospitality from the wife of one of the local ministers.

Esther bought many things for her new baby, beautiful things. She made a few purchases for Jimmy, too. That was taken care of the first afternoon. She breakfasted in bed; miraculously in so short a time got herself invited to teas; even dined out with young and middle-aged men who had never before to my knowledge shown even the slightest interest in missionaries or their work. It was a temptation to forget my father's injunction to "keep my skirts clean" and I tried to remonstrate with her. She laughed at me and exclaimed with a theatrical up-toss of her arms, "Oh, to live again. But, of course, you wouldn't know what that means."

She arched her ankles, stood on the tips of her toes, and started to stretch her arms above her head. "My best slimming exercise," she called this gesture. But she was standing in front of a full-length mirror and her arms came down quickly this time. With repeated little gasps of horror, she stared at her reflection. She was no longer as willowy and lithe as she had been, and no amount of "curling in her tail," she called it, or "sucking in you-know-what" could alter that fact. Moreover, there were long months ahead when this situation would inexorably grow worse. Her face was a study in consternation, as though she realized this fact for the first time.

Nevertheless for almost three weeks, Esther enjoyed herself socially as few missionaries do, at least while on the field. She bought many things, beautiful things, for herself. The kind of things every woman loves and most of us missionaries dream about occasionally. Our thoughts may be on God and the eternal things of the spirit, but we remain women to the end of the most self-abnegating life. Without a cent in my pocket, other than what was absolutely required for travel back to the mission station, I watched Esther buy things she would never have occasion to use in Africa. I don't know how much money she had or spent, but several times I went with her to the bank that handled our mission funds. There I saw her draw out from some private source what seemed like fabulous sums to me.

"Jimmy will raise Hail Columbia!" she whispered to me once with a half-guilty and at the same time lightly boasting air as we walked away from the teller's window. My spirit raged, but most of the time I managed to breathe through my nose and not across a yapping tongue.

Oh yes, I kept my skirts clean in a way to please father. But the next time Dr. Dick and I were called out to a village to meet an epidemic outbreak, I remembered Esther's shopping spree with all the strength of starved emotion. I remembered it because our trek took us past the native Walenyi women's Tree of Rags. I'm not superstitious—naturally!—so I can only say sudden inspiration struck me and I peddled my bush-car off onto the grassy sward surrounding the dead branches festooned with fluttering scraps of rotting cloth.

"Go ahead," I called out to Dr. Dick who had stopped to watch me. "I'll catch up with you in a minute."

I took it for granted that he obeyed me and without thought jerked up my skirt and, with the help of my teeth, tore a strip off the hem of my iron petticoat. I was straining upward toward a branch when a guffaw brought me back to earth again. Dr. Dick was calmly sitting in his bush-car where I had left the trail, and trying to blow his nose between chortles.

"For heaven's sake, what now?" he finally managed to gasp out.

I gathered up what shreds of dignity I could and explained the magic of the Tree of Rags.

Again he roared with laughter and then sobered sufficiently to get out, "I hope you get your petticoat. Yes indeed, I hope you get your petticoat."

That evening, after dinner, Mrs. Dr. Dick brought over to me a neat little bundle. Being the kindly, tactful soul she was, she followed me to my room before presenting it. "The doctor says you need underwear," she began.

Drat that man! was my first reaction. After a quick glance over her shoulder to be sure the door was closed, Mrs. Doctor laughed at me. "He told me about the Tree of Rags, and at your age it's exactly what I would have done," she whispered. "None of us have too much, dear, I'm not going to pretend that we do," Mrs. Dick was explaining. "I can understand that you might not want to trouble your mother, too. And, thank goodness, I have enough to share—and a few of the things I've scarcely worn at all."

I surely thanked her, that being a normal thing to do. And we must have exchanged a few pleasantries and then said goodnight. All I remember, however, is that she was gone and I was sitting on the edge of my cot unwrapping the bundle with trembling fingers. I remember, too, exactly what was in the bundle: two slips, two nightgowns, two pairs of panties—made of feed sacking imperfectly bleached, like those offered Esther for diapers. Across the stomach of one of the nightgowns, six letters could be read easily: *PURINA*. The sacks had not been big enough to make full-length nightgowns, of course, and Mrs. Dick had added flounces with ghostly red and green checks.

One thing which is never missing from missionary barrels—fortunately!—is quantities of sewing thread. Mrs. Dr. Dick liked to crochet, and there were filmy edgings of what she called "hairpin lace" on each garment. She had used the weight and color of sewing thread available. There was purple and green lace on the panties, pink and blue on the slips, and yellow and brown on the night-gowns.

Dutifully, as the child of good missionary parents must, I tried to whisper at least token gratitude: "Bless her heart. Bless her dear heart." But my lips were stiff.

I don't know why it is, but life on the mission field seems to go by seasons. Maybe it is simply that the train of incidents of one's daily existence, like thoughts, falls into a rut. This is true of the big as well as the little things. During the wet season, it rained every day for three months. During the dry season, the skies were cloudless daily for three months. Four seasons in the year, two wet, two dry.

There were days at a time when I believe nine out of every ten patients waiting for Dr. Dick of a morning had a broken bone somewhere in his or her body. Other times there would be a plethora of ulcers. Then we would be snowed under by maternity cases. "You'd think that pregnancy was something contagious," I've heard Dr. Dick exclaim more than once. But again we might go for a season without a single expectant mother coming to us. Contrary to popular opinion in America, native African women have their contraceptives, crude but effective. But whether the seasonal crops of babies was intentional or otherwise, I can't say.

It was the same in the schools. Children seemed to learn *en masse,* or the teachers complained that they labored to the best of their abilities before normally bright students who apparently had pulled some sort of veil over their minds. And in the workshops, too. More than once I've heard some instructor burst out in bewildered frustration: "Nothing done! Not a thing accomplished all week!"

I've seen father, trying to make up his monthly report to send to our Governing Board "back home," turn through the pages of his journal unbelievingly. Last month, the month before that, and the month before that, too, father, a wonderful evangelist, undoubtedly the most successful in our area, had written of his accomplishments: "Nothing! Nothing done! And yet I've worked just as hard."

No one of us could ever explain how these things happened. Our black folk, as usual, had a folk tale to fit the occasion, concerning a race between, not a tortoise and a hare, but an elephant and a lizard. According to jungle logic, neither beast won nor lost. Nor was the race a draw. It was simply an allegorical tale illustrating the unpredictable nature of the rewards man enjoys or suffers as a result of his wisdom—and misdeeds. In a season of good fortune our mission folk say: "Many lizards dwell in your thatch. May they never desert you." Or if it is misfortune, one will hear a simple, pitying: "Tembo stalks through your garden."

One morning we white folk on the staff awoke, looked elsewhere than into each other's eyes, and admitted what we had heard so often: Tembo was stalking through our garden.

CHAPTER
TEN

Our season of misfortune was heralded, if not by the scream of an elephant, at least by the hysterical words of an angry woman. For a short while after our return from Léopoldville, Esther did what she called "play along." That is, she lent half an ear to Bun's earnest, patient attempts to ease her into the pedagogical field. She made a bid for popularity by showering gifts upon her pupils, and at the same time she berated them for not knowing the uses for the knicknacks she imagined they should treasure. She brought out boxes of candy for them that none of the rest of us knew she possessed. She had not shared them with us when we opened up our little boxes of cheap stale cookies as a special treat. The children devoured the candy, not delicately, a piece at a time, savoring each tiny nibble, but crammed it into their mouths, foil wrappers and all, by the handsful. In turn they brought her what they thought she should enjoy: fried caterpillars, roasted locusts, pressed gnat cakes with the mildew scorched off them by a quick bath of flame, boiled monkey's hands, "mellowed" fish. I will not repeat the names she called the children, or describe the gestures with which she refused their offerings.

I heard one youngster demand of her, "How do you know your ways are better, when no one seeks your company for pleasure of it?"

I saw her slap him—a thing I never knew Aunt Bun or Sister Hallie to do to a child, no matter how tired or how great the provocation.

Esther informed my father one evening at our regular staff meeting that she was going down to Léopoldville again. Patiently, oh so patiently, she explained to all of us that she was going into *a real hospital* there to have her baby. I don't know how many hundreds, how many thousands of babies Dr. Dick had delivered, how many native mothers given up for dead he had saved. I know that every white planter living within a good many miles of our station depended on him, or some other missionary doctor when their wives were confined. He never said a word at Esther's declaration. The only movement he made was to lay a hand on his wife's knee when Mrs. Dick gasped audibly—as all of us did in spirit.

Moreover, Esther was explaining, a woman needs her husband at such a time, and Jimmy was going with her. It was evident that these arrangements were as much a surprise to James Grove as they were to the rest of us.

There didn't seem much that anyone of us could say, and we certainly were glad when father cleared his throat. But even he seemed waiting for some sort of guidance. After all, what can be said to a misfit who seems hell-bent on obtruding her maladjustment into every phase of her neighbors' life? I wish I could remember my father's words. He was a wise man. And he was no weakling. He could and would do, or say, whatever was required of him, however unpleasant.

"I thought I said *a real hospital*," Esther interrupted him petulantly with an exaggerated shrug of the shoulder nearest Dr. Dick. "Not this—this—nigger haven."

That was the first, the only time I have ever heard that inexcusably, senselessly offensive term in an African mission station. Father did not finish his sentence. He had been standing beside a small table. He moved it aside as carefully as a housewife handling a fragile antique. Then he pulled up a carved mahogany stool some chief had given him and sat down on it, all his movements slow and careful.

As my father gave himself this time in which to frame his next words, there was a triumphant, an almost savage look on Esther's face. But father never got his reproof out. And Esther's sneer gave place to surprise and then bewilderment when Jimmy took hold of her arm and started to get up. She attempted to shrug him loose, but he only tightened his fingers. Slowly he arose, dragging Esther up with him. He pushed her in front of him toward the door and through it. As she passed me I looked up squarely into her eyes and saw that mixture of helpless fright and as yet unplaced anger that spreads over the face of an animal when it has been stopped short in a charge by a big, mushrooming bullet expertly placed by a hunter.

There was heavy silence for a few seconds after they had left— both inside the room and out. Then a woman's complaining voice and a few rumbles of baritone. Again the woman's voice, shriller this time and growing shriller by the second. Finally a crescendo shriek and I swear the rhythmic spat! spat! spat! of a palm being forcefully applied.

"He ought to break her neck," mother announced with strange cheerfulness.

Father looked up from his low stool and the corners of his mouth quivered as though he were trying to suppress a laugh. Perhaps he was remembering times when mother, too, had found it difficult to be a missionary's wife. Perhaps amusement won out over solemnity, for he dropped his hands between his knees and stared at them fixedly.

"I think," Sister Hallie spoke up with a nervous twitch that traveled the entire length of her thin body, "I think we should ask divine guidance at this dif—at this time."

All heads turned to Sister Hallie in amazement and then dutifully—for who can refuse to pray?—we crooked our necks and waited like a flock of Quakers on a First Day Morning. We knew God would bless us. He had already done so! But not being Quakers, the silence grew uneasy, strained. How could one pray in a situation like this? Openly thank God because a man has spanked his wife—although she had needed it for some time past?

"Our Father Who art in heaven," Dr. Dick's kind voice scarcely ruffled the silence but it soothed each and every one of us like a loving caress.

"Hallowed be Thy name," Mrs. Dick's voice joined her husband's.

"Thy kingdom come"—father and Aunt Bun in unison.

"Thy will be done on earth as it is in heaven!" Sister Hallie's voice was stronger, clearer than anyone else's, but less certain of itself by virtue of its vague stridency.

One by one we joined in until a solid chorus of voices surrendered to God, ". . . the kingdom, the power, and the glory forever."

There was peace in the room again, and we looked into each other's smiling faces with full confidence in our ability to meet collectively any problem facing us. But never before or since have I known prayer to be such a merry matter, and yet so devoid of any sanctimonious hypocrisy.

Six weeks later Esther was confined. Hers was an uncomplicated, but a long and tedious labor. I don't know whether it killed her child, or whether she simply lacked the will and ability to give life. In any case her baby—a perfectly formed little girl—never breathed although Dr. Dick labored over it as hard as he had labored over Esther. Its tiny body grew cold in his hands.

Esther lay on one side, her face turned away from us. She did not scream or otherwise rebel at her physical agony. And she never saw her child, for less than an hour after Dr. Dick laid it down, unthinkingly, mechanically as though she had been a native woman, he pinched her nostrils shut and drew a sheet up over her face.

Father led Jimmy away, somewhere down by the river. Brother Norman, Abu Sayheed, and the other mission boys made her a coffin. They covered over the rough boards with strips of our beautiful, locally woven cloth. Inside they lined it with the down-filled comforters she had brought back from Léopoldville for her baby's crib. Mother and Mrs. Dick dressed her in her wedding clothes and pillowed her head on a frothy boudoir cushion she had brought from the United States. Truly America had always been Esther's rightful home whether or not it became a make-believe land for the rest of us. Aunt Bun, Sister Hallie and I denuded our mission gardens of flowers, and wove a fragrant blanket that covered half her coffin.

The law, and tropical necessity, compelled Esther's burial before sunset. As I sat in our chapel and stared at her still face, I thought I had never seen her look more beautiful. No wonder Jimmy had loved her in spite of her emotional immaturity and social maladjustment. She had been meant for love, and for all the little niceties of courtly behavior.

All of us women wept. We would have continued to hate Esther, each in her own way, had she lived. Now, inexplicably, our grief was honest and real. She was so very beautiful.

The shock of her death was still heavy upon me when Aunt Bun started down the river to begin her furlough year. Pious and prissy as Sister Hallie, I recoiled when Bun threw her arms about my neck at our boat landing and whispered in my ear, "Don't you let that man get away from you."

I knew what she meant, but refused to recognize fact. My air of stupidity—hypocrisy!—infuriated the usually placid Bun. She grasped my shoulders and shook me hard. "Grow up! Wake up! I was a fool. Don't you be! There's nothing—wonderful—about a squandered life—even if you do fill it with good works!"

For a few seconds I was as terrified as a child lest God strike Bun dead for her impiousness. Then I was equally frightened that the others should hear and understand, and I looked over my shoulder quickly. But she had chosen her time well. They were loading the shimbeck with the odds and ends she was taking to America. I turned back to her, strangely eager to hear more. But she laughed at me and then kissed me lightly on the cheek, as one sister kisses another, and went from me to Sister Hallie, her arms widespread.

I took over a couple of Bun's classes and learned from my pupils that "The-Fat-Little-Mama-with-the-Tender-Heart does it this way. No! No! Mama Lolla [the "r" in Laura being an impossible sound for them to mouth], The-Fat-Little-Mama-with-the-Big-Heart does it This Way! *THIS WAY!*" Blunderingly we did it *THIS WAY!*

Strangely, turning points in our lives are seldom recognized for what they are when they first appear. Certainly the woman who materialized out of the jungle one day did not look unusual in any way. Her head was shaven clean as a bean until the sunlight reflected from it in glimmering highlights. She wore very little: a twig of leaves suspended below her navel from a thong of braided grass fibers which cut across her stomach, and a partially tanned cowhide across her shoulders. In a fold of this noisome cape nestled a baby. It was several months old but as scrawny as a crippled hen which must forage for itself among the strong and vigorous.

The woman stood on the lowest step of my parents' cottage and demanded food in loud and vigorous tones. None of us recognized her, and she was obviously frightened in spite of her bold manner. But, just as though her skin had been white, she tried to hide her uneasiness with glaring looks and bluster. The baby opened its mouth in a feeble wail, and mother stepped forward. But the woman whirled to face mother as though expecting attack, at the same time shoving the infant deeper into the cowhide.

It was a common enough story the woman told. She and her sister-wives and the other women of her village far north and to the east, had planted their gardens at the right time and in the age-old way. That is, they had waited until the rainy season was past, and had dropped in the furrowed earth grain enough for rotting, grain for the little earth people which will live whether or not men do (that is, grubs and insects) and grain for sprouting, growing, fruiting and eventually feeding those who planted. Always, when a garden has been planted, a few mice creep out from beneath jungle leaves and steal a few seeds from the grubs and other earth peoples. But this past season there had been many mice, and they had devoured all the seeds dropped for any purpose.

This happens occasionally and the wise wife keeps back a supply of seed for a second planting—and for a third also. Three times the women of this village had planted their gardens, and three times the ravenous mice had crept out of the jungle by night and devoured the seed until there was not one grain left in the earth for sprouting. So a season had passed when no beans or yams or manioc had simmered in the women's cooking pots. They had lived on the game the men had brought home from the hunt and the fat grubs the women had pried out of the rotting bark of dead logs. But the men had hunted too long and too often, and the game had become exceedingly wary or had fled. And there was now no bark left on the dead logs surrounding the village. True, there was still wild spinach and celery under the trees, and the women filled their cooking pots with these. But they are good food for gorillas, not for men. One could eat until his belly swelled out before him like a growing gourd and still be hungry. The woman must have grain food and flesh food to take back with her. So many had already died in her village that the jackals who dispose of the dead had begun to sniff daintily at the corpses dragged out onto the veld instead of falling upon them like the spirit of famine. If the woman returned to her village empty-handed, more would die. As though to prove her words, the infant in the cowhide again wailed fretfully. And again mother took a step forward, quick words of sympathy on her lips.

I wish I could translate for you, word for word yet without violating the spirit of it in any way, the tirade the woman loosed upon mother. In many ways, it was a courageous thing for her to do. She was far from home, among strange people, and possibly looking upon the first white men she had ever seen.

"Fool! Nitwit! Nanny goat! Stupid calf! Crook-necked hen!" These and worse, much worse, she called mother.

"But the child is hungry," mother protested stoutly.

It was Maa Koo who explained to all of us in matter-of-fact, blunt terms that the woman was interested in keeping her husband alive so that he could father more children upon her and her sister-wives. Only in that way could her village survive.

But what about the child she carried in her cowhide?

"Pooh!" Maa Koo snapped her fingers to show that it was a thing of no account. It had less than a fifty-fifty chance of survival. And even if it did live, stunted and a weakling, the years would be many before it reached manhood. And in the meantime children must be sired season after season so there would be no gap between the generations if a people were to continue to exist.

Father promised the woman food for herself and her people, seed when the next planting time should come around, and porters to carry it to her village. Then he sent her off to the native compound to eat and to spend the night. Mother bustled into the kitchen, found milk, and hastily stirred up barley water for the infant. These she put in Maa Koo's hands with strict injunctions to the old woman that she must make sure the child swallowed them.

"No *posho!*" mother ordered. "Absolutely no *posho!*" Posho is a sort of half-cooked mush, hard to digest by even a healthy adult stomach.

I went along with Maa Koo to see if the child needed my services as a nurse. When we reached the native quarters the woman's own stomach was already round and tight with food, and she was rolling chunks of posho into pellets the size of a walnut and pushing them down the child's gullet with a determined forefinger. She looked at mother's barley water, tasted a sip of it cautiously, and spat it scornfully into the fire.

Then she turned back to the pot of posho, scooped up a chunk on her thumbnail, rolled it into a ball with a few deft movements of her fingers, and when her baby opened its mouth to wail, choked off its expression of helpless misery with the heavy indigestible mass. I looked at Maa Koo, and the old woman nodded at me. In spite of the mother's solicitude we both knew that when she started back toward her village in the morning that corner of her cowhide which had been a cradle would be flapping free.

We returned to my parents' cottage, and Jimmy Grove was there, talking earnestly with father about agricultural instruction in our schools, and the needless hungry days which are never more than a few seasons off in any African villager's life. I sat down beside mother and dipped my fingers into her sewing basket. I threaded a needle and punched my finger into a thimble, but I didn't take any stitches. As Jimmy argued and I listened and looked at him, I remembered the peace on Uncle Ben's face as he sat on his porch and looked across his meadows and grain fields toward the flaming swamp maples along the creek. I remembered the eager intensity in Jimmy's face when father had once spoken to him of the land's liking a man. Father turned to say something to mother, but stopped when he saw my face. I fell to sewing furiously.

But, "Oh no! No, dear, not tan cotton in a black sock! Whatever are you thinking of?"

It was mother's voice, and she was taking my darning gourd away from me. I could feel the hot blood flooding my neck and rushing up into my cheeks while she snipped and picked at my hasty stitches. When I could look up again, it was straight into father's eyes, keen, curious, and smiling. Jimmy was staring at the palm of one hand and rubbing an exploring thumb over the tendons padded with the heavy calluses which had been there since childhood.

"Agricultural work would be quite an innovation for a religious mission, but then so were the medical and the academic works when they were introduced. You're young blood, Laura, what is your opinion of the wisdom of such a venture?" father asked.

I turned to Jimmy. His face was eager, something like Clark Abelson's when he had asked me to go to the church social with him. I remembered, and with all the intensity of the physical experience, how pleasant it had been to hop and jump and swing around with my fingers locked in Clark Abelson's—before the minister's wife had tapped me on the shoulder. I remembered her words, too, and I felt like laughing in silly abandon. I felt like sharing a good joke with someone—*She said it would be a memory to be ashamed of!* Silly thing.

"I think it was wonderful!" I heard myself saying.

Jimmy's face glowed. Father caught the slip of tense, peered at me a moment, and then took off his glasses and meticulously polished the already glistening lenses. I could have kissed mother when she thrust the sock back into my hands with a righteous

136 ·

"There now!" and my needle threaded with the right shade of cotton.

A few minutes later Jimmy and I were walking across our compound lawn. He was talking and I was listening. What he rambled on about didn't make very much sense to me at the time: contour cultivation, erosion dams, selective logging—or maybe it was selective breeding and scientific lumber cutting—*bearcats* and *caterpillars*. Poor Jimmy! He had seen what greedy, stupid men had done to the soil of his own land, he understood what they are already doing to the Dark Continent in those accessible regions near the coasts. He dreamed of a time when tractors would furrow the rich dirt beneath his feet, and the jungle's lush growth would be controlled and directed to the filling of men's granaries and stomachs.

It seemed to me we had no more than called goodnight to father and mother before we were standing on the steps of the cottage Sister Hallie and I occupied.

"I'm going to send you over things to read," Jimmy said. "I take *The Farm Journal* and *Country Gentleman,* and I have stacks of Government Bulletins."

"That'll be nice," is all I knew how to say.

He hesitated as though making up his mind about something, and suddenly I was frightened. Would he, like that other boy, "back home," kiss me? And then run from me in fright?

And then, "You know, I sent and got an Afrikaans grammar and dictionary and I've started studying them. There're some awfully good farm magazines published in South Africa, by African farmers for African farmers. I'd like to read them." His tone was confidential, almost pleading like the little boy whose whole body quivers with the wordless question: Do you approve of me?

"Oh, that would be nice," I managed again.

Then Jimmy was walking across the compound lawn and I myself went into the house and my bedroom and started to undress. Anyway I next remember holding a shoe in my hand and staring at it as though I had never seen footgear before in my life. I had just been wondering if Afrikaans is very difficult to learn. Not to speak, but just to read. I dropped the shoe and walked lopsidedly to my dresser and stirred around in a drawer with an impatient hand until I found my purse. Yes, I believed I had enough money with which to buy an Afrikaans grammar.

I know that if this book were a proper work of fiction, following the evolved pattern for such, I would now devote the next two or three hundred pages to detailing a courtship which would have very little in common with the simple mating of a man and a woman. If I may digress, I believe we have become a race of courtship psychopaths. We demand that our vicarious lovers must caress, fight, make up, and beat off unbelievable competition for as nearly one hundred thousand words as can be managed. Then, the promised physical consummation of marriage only a few unprinted pages off, we pretend that a life with no more difficulties, or problems, or mistakes lies ahead.

Jimmy's and my courtship did not follow the pattern of romantic fiction. Most of it was very calm and rational not to say sedate—but pleasant. Father and mother had been mildly disappointed when I brought no husband back to Africa with me. I saw in their faces often what quickened within my heart like a dormant plant brought into the sunshine and watered. Jimmy had become an unattached male, the only eligible one within hundreds of miles. We were both perfectly normal flesh and blood. What more natural than that we should turn to each other?

I was not the only unmarried white female on our staff. There was Sister Hallie, of course. But a difference of at least thirty years lay between her and Jimmy's ages—on the wrong side of the ledger for Hallie. Still I know, as I remember things overlooked then, that long stifled yearnings stirred vaguely in Hallie's heart. Perhaps the maternal instinct can be enfeebled by enforced celibacy; but it never dies in any woman until that woman herself is dead. I came in from the hospital one noon and found her scanning her face in the mirror as carefully as she would the countenance of some former pupil whom she felt honorbound to recognize and couldn't.

"Find a white hair?" Vacuous! But I meant it as light humor.

Sister Hallie turned, smiled, and tucked a lock of her iron-gray hair behind an ear. As she did so—she did not mean me to see it, but there was the mirror—she slid a book the size and color of my Afrikaans grammar into a drawer with her other hand. That evening the grammar was on my bedside table under my Bible—where I had never placed it.

A few evenings later Jimmy knocked at our door and when I opened it he heaped my arms full of farm magazines—and the overflow into Sister Hallie's hands. Until he pushed me aside so he could do so, I hadn't realized that she was right behind me. When he left two or three hours later, Sister Hallie was sitting staring fixedly into one of Jimmy's pamphlets. I glanced across her shoulder, and into an almost life-sized, red and white, carefully combed and curled, pictured face of a Hereford bull. It wore the same calm, bovinely patient look as "Mrs. Dr. Dick—when she's very tired!" Hallie almost shouted at me. Her eyes were gleaming as I had never seen them gleam before. Then she turned a few pages and showed me a picture of a farm hand leading a team of Belgian mares into a barn. Their unbelievably—impossibly rotund hips—

"See! See!" Sister Hallie was jabbing at the mares with her forefinger. "Their tails, curled up in the exact middle—in the same kind of hair-do Sister Bun always wears!" We squealed with laughter like children.

And then we broke off suddenly to listen. Faintly we heard Jimmy whistling. It sounded as though he were trying to capture some air of the thief-musician; he was not succeeding very well. Sister Hallie looked down at the pamphlet clenched in her hand. When she glanced up the merriment was gone, and her words were prim as usual when she spoke. "After all, Sister Grove is—scarcely cold in her grave. Tell— Tell your farmer boy, Sister Laura, that—that—the proprieties—" She turned, stalked into the bedroom and closed the door behind her.

Sister Hallie was not a rival—whatever the quality of her memories and longings.

CHAPTER

ELEVEN

I wouldn't say that Jimmy was a man of the soil before he was a missionary, but he was among us because that was where the stumbling footsteps of a wilful, copper-haired beauty had led him. I do not say this in criticism—how could I? I was there too, you remember, because I had no other home. The only people I really understood, or who understood me, were jungle dwellers. I have wondered often if, had we been situated differently, Jimmy would have paid any more attention to me than other men had done. Not that that mattered really! No altar-bent girl ever had more help, subtle and otherwise, from loving, eager, anxious relatives and friends. Romantically, Jimmy was a sitting duck; and a man as domestic as James Groves was—as domestic as one of the dairy cows of his youth—doesn't struggle against a fate that follows the already accepted pattern of his life.

I did not act on Sister Hallie's advice—to speak to Jimmy about "the proprieties" that is. Someone else did, however. It could have been any one of a half-dozen different people—or all of them! Consequently he did not propose until— Well, I began to wonder if someone had not been more zealous than helpful. But as the days and weeks lengthened out into the punctiliously correct year of mourning for Jimmy, the mission staff courted him assiduously on my behalf, and he made a farmer of me.

In fact, I think we all became the most crop-and-flock conscious group of missionaries ever to swap dreams in the middle of a jungle. The Governing Board at home must have wondered at the plethora of agricultural data with which we swamped them, tales which harped upon the fact that a saved soul and educated mind dwell together most harmoniously—and predictably—in a healthy, well-fed body. And complete truth was on our side, give or take a little excusable exaggeration. Your poet's savage, carefully nurtured on wishful thinking, is a happy, carefree child of nature; the missionary's is more apt to be disease-ridden and hungry. I remember once penning a sententious "Diseases of the mind and soul as well as those of the body strike deep and vigorous roots in weakened, undernourished flesh."

We had such a wealth of material from which to draw to support our statements. The locust swarms that denuded village gardens and the glades where wild game pastured. With grain food and flesh food gone, we suspected but could never quite pin down orgiastic sacrifices to the god of man's belly. Or those seasons when mice appeared as though created spontaneously out of the earth, eating the seeds in the women's gardens and the roots on God's veld—more orgies. Perhaps human sacrifices? Or in a time of prolonged drought men died because their flesh weakened and failed—as did the newly confessed faith of many Christian headmen. We labored prodigiously to do God's work, but we were only frail, human flesh, prone to error—

The Governing Board hadn't a chance before the onslaughts of a family determined to snag a husband for a loved daughter! Jimmy was appointed a pioneer agricultural worker since he had the right background and some scientific training and was already on the field. But, so the Board wrote, it was too bad that he was a widower since married men lead more settled lives and accomplish more lasting work.

As Mrs. Grundy's proscribed year of propriety neared its end, I and all my family began to nudge Jimmy for a formal declaration. I did not attempt flirting with other men in order to arouse jealousy —there were no other unmarried white men within flirting distance. With that single exception, however, and on the very best of advice from women, those who had as well as those who had not succeeded in getting husbands, I tried all the time-tested, acclaimed foolproof recipes for forcing a man to speak that portion of his mind which was to my specific need and liking. I did his mending, sewed buttons on his shirts, turned the collars and cuffs, patched his underwear, darned his socks, embroidered big *G*'s on father's best handkerchiefs and gave them to him. I cooked for him. I remember a green coconut milk pie which I made—with much overseeing from mother. He was impressed with my tale of the number of bad eggs we had had to discard before we got enough good ones for the recipe. He ate a generous portion of the pie, disposing of it with farmer-sized bites so he could show me a picture of a milk cow and point out to me the three triangles in the build of the perfect show animal. Sister Hallie took one look over my shoulder and—I suppose remembering the Hereford bull or the Belgian mares— bolted unceremoniously.

I walked with Jimmy in the moonlight, and both of us flailed the air with our arms beating off mosquitoes. I strolled with him in the sunlight, and we mopped the sweat from our faces—and I squirmed to ease the itch of those sodden portions of my body I dared not mop or scratch. I was ready to melt into his arms at any given moment. But tell me, just where can a woman melt to when a man's hands are full of switches and knives and he is busy demonstrating bud- and lateral-grafting, and—oh, what not! Once Mrs. Dick gave me her last precious drop of French perfume to rub behind my ears, and the man— No, the farmer I had snuggled up to paused in the middle of a dissertation on what cross-pollination would do for the native maize to sniff and ask, "What's that peculiar odor? Do you smell it?"

I complained helplessly to mother, and she consoled me with the formal "Give the man time. After all, Sister Esther is—"

"Scarcely cold in her grave," I finished for her.

"Don't you think that after all these months she ought to be getting pretty cool?" It was father standing in the doorway laughing at us. "I'm wondering if I oughtn't ask the man if his intentions are honorable."

"Do *his* intentions matter? That is if he has any conscious ones?" Mrs. Dick asked.

"Tsch! Tsch! Tsch!" mother clucked at all of us, but I interrupted her, "Don't worry about *his* intentions. They're too—too—darned honorable."

"Well, now, I don't know," father went on. "He eats half his meals with the girls nowadays. He spends all of his free time with them. What is there left for him to do but pack his clothes and move in? If I didn't trust Sister Hallie completely—"

Then one morning, just like every other morning, a messenger from a near-by village reported an infestation of baboons. These animals, ordinarily harmless if left alone, were up to age-old deviltry. At night, when everyone was asleep, they watched the kids until they had nursed, the man said. Then they swung over the thorn-bush fences, snatched up the kids, and with their powerful fingers and dagger-like incisors ripped open the stomachs of the tiny goats to get at the fresh curds and whey inside. Would The-Big-Man-Whose-Mouth-Said-Little-but-Whose-Gun-Said-Much come and shoot the yellow fiends? Especially one old devil who had actually taken to nursing the nannies?

Jimmy had not yet returned from this pest clearance excursion when Dr. Dick sent me off in the same general direction. In another near-by village an exceedingly strong devil had entered the body of a man through a tiny puncture on his arm. It was tearing the man to pieces with fiendish claw and fang from the inside. Would some white witch doctor help him before his skin held together only a riddled mass of flesh and scarified bone? Dr. Dick could not go without serious inconvenience to others, but he gave me careful instructions, looked over my packed bag, and chucked in a few more handfuls of the home-made pills we were never without nowadays. Then as he and father always did on such occasions, he laid an arm across my shoulder and, like one individual making a simple request of another, asked God to be with me in my work, to give me wisdom and my fingers skill, to bring me back safely, and to bless me always according to His divine plan.

I set off in my bush-car without even taking a boy with me. I arrived in good time and routed the devil who had come to bay in a deep-seated abscess between two muscles of the forearm. I expressed and swabbed out at least a half-cupful of foul-smelling, greenish yellow pus—excreta left behind by the devil in its flight, I was told. The relief of my patient was pathetic and gratifying. But my success meant no loss of face or prestige for the local native witch doctor because of the size of the devil involved. I knew quite well that if the abscess had not been layered in between two muscles, the witch doctor would have handled the case quite capably, and we would never have known anything about it.

I had not expected to, but in the end I stayed overnight in the village, sleeping on a pile of skins—after first dusting them liberally with insect powder—in what I suppose might be called the throne room of the chief. Before I went to bed I cleaned a few ulcers, pared an enormous corn off the palm of a woman's hand, advised a few younger wives to come to the mission hospital for their confinements, and dispensed liberal quantities of home-made pills to the attention-seeking, curious, and eager ones.

The swelling had gone out of my first patient's arm the next morning and he had no fever, so I left a package of Epsom-salts with him for compressing and a few crystals of permanganate to color the solution so its efficiency would be appreciated, and started for home.

I was almost there when I looked up and saw in a crotch where the stump of a dead limb branched out from a tree trunk, a big, thrifty-looking orchid plant, and I stopped immediately. Not that orchid plants are anything unusual for us. We see them on every trip through the jungle, sometimes literally by the dozens. Ordinarily orchids are shy plants that root at heights where climbing is dangerous for anyone but the spryest of young black boys. Many a time Mrs. Dick, who had an orchid garden, called an urchin back from the dizzy height to which he had already scrambled when she saw branches sway beneath him and the coveted plant still seemed as far away from his willing hands as ever. But this plant was so close to the ground I thought I could walk up to the tree, stretch up my arms, and lift the mass of roots out of the rotten bark.

I have never been able to judge heights or distances, however, and the cool green light of a dense tropical forest is especially deceptive. Standing beside the trunk of the tree I didn't need to put my arms over my head to realize that the orchid was out of reach. But such a short distance out of reach! And as I looked up I saw more clearly what a really choice plant it was, and twisting my head about this way and that I could count thirteen flower spikes already pushing up through the leaves. Undoubtedly there were more which I could not see. It was a poor time to move the plant, I knew. But suppose the blossoms were pure white? Or a delicate chartreuse green with a purple polka-dotted throat? Or brown to blackness? I stood on tiptoe, stretched up my arms and measured with my eyes. If only I could find something to stand on: a rock to roll up against the roots of the tree. Or a chunk of wood.

I looked about me and there were no rocks. There was plenty of dead and fallen wood, however; small branches and one log about three feet in diameter and twenty feet long. I pulled wistful eyes away from that log, which of course would have been ideal footing if in the right place. After looking at the small sticks distastefully, I walked from side to side of the dead branch, again peering upward. Yes, it was a really superb orchid plant. Our Mrs. Dick would be delighted with it.

Like a beaver I set about gathering sticks and piling them up against the trunk of the tree. Even as I worked I knew I was doing a very foolish thing—building an exceedingly flimsy support even for my slender body. But, still like a beaver, I wedged smaller sticks between the larger ones and tested the whole by kicking it vigorously. Then clutching ridges of bark of the parent tree with my finger tips, I climbed up onto my crazy heap of rotten wood.

I reached the orchid plant easily. Then I encircled the dead limb with my hands, hoping to push the plant off its perch with one palm and into the other with as little disturbance to bulb and roots as possible. I had to lower my face, close my eyes and work blindly for I found that with the first shove a rain of fine debris showered down upon my head. Fine dust drifted into my nostrils with each breath no matter how shallowly I tried to breathe.

I pushed with my left hand and felt the dead bark under the orchid plant give and shift maybe an inch. I pushed again, harder this time, and with less thought for my feet. There was a grinding noise, and I felt a stick slip out from somewhere beneath me. I grasped a ridge of bark with my right hand again to steady myself. I would push the orchid with my left hand, push hard, I told myself; and when I felt it break away, I would put up my right hand quickly and catch it. Then I would step down quickly from my crazy beaver's platform before it could go to pieces.

I suppose I was straining harder than I knew, for when the orchid plant came loose, my body lurched sideways. I had to grab at the bark of the parent tree to keep myself from falling, and what felt like a ton of soft, crumbling earth landed—plop!—on top of my head. Festoons of dankness draped themselves about my ears. The sticks under my feet began melting away with slight cracking sounds —as though all the mischievous spirits of the jungle were snickering at my plight. Desperately and dumbly I clung to the tree, hoping no chunk of bark would come away in my hands and let me fall.

Then the rolling ceased and my feet seemed a little steadier. I opened my mouth for a big breath of relief, and promptly closed it again. There could be nothing but the shallowest, gentlest breathing for me until that disgusting thing of worm-like roots and rotten wood was off my head. Cautiously I started to let go of the bark with one hand, and most of the sticks under my feet turned to quicksand and disappeared. It was then I became aware of the presence of a second person, although I couldn't open my eyes to look at him.

"So the ladies are wearing orchids on their heads this year. How fetching! Of course it'll be prettier when the spikes bloom. And maybe a sunbird will nest among them." It was James Timothy Grove's voice, cool, impersonal, mocking.

I don't know why it should have made me so angry. Both as a child and as a young woman, I had been caught in embarrassing predicaments before. But suddenly I wanted to shout and kick and scream, and there was nothing in the world that would have given me more violent emotional satisfaction at that moment than to slap Jimmy Grove as hard as I could. Maybe I did stamp a little, for the last stick slithered away and as my body sank toward the earth my hands, which did not dare loose their hold on the bark, rose even higher above my head until I was stretched out against the trunk of the tree like a lizard. And still I dared not let go.

"Stretching exercises? Trying to lose weight? You can overdo that, you know. You're skinny enough."

Maybe that wasn't exactly what he said, but he was still making fun of me. I heard a *rrrrip!* and felt the right sleeve, the one toward him, tear almost completely out of my blouse. Then I realized that the hem of my skirt must be pulled above my knees and that inches of my feed-sacking petticoat, with its ghostly traces of red and green checker-boarding, and Mrs. Dick's delicate but violent-colored lace must be showing. Maybe my garters, too.

"Get me down out of here, you—you—you—"

I started to cry, and in a few seconds it would have been uncontrollable sobbing had not the necessary intake of breath threatened to choke me with debris. I closed my mouth, scooped around my teeth with a determined tongue, spat and sneezed. That jerked the bark above me, and I felt and heard it begin to break away. I would have fallen had not a pair of arms wound themselves around my waist and held me there in the air. My hands being free for the first time, I lifted the heavy orchid plant off my head. There was a fresh shower of dirt and again I sneezed.

"*Gesundheit,*" said Jimmy brilliantly.

I held the orchid plant out in front of me and opened one eye a tiny crack. All I could see was a mass of brown hair within two inches of my nose. I gave a wiggle and slowly began to slide downward until I could see the tip of Jimmy's nose through a screen of eyelashes, heavy with dirt. Then I felt his lips on mine, and shrank from the grit and rotten bark he pressed against my teeth. It was a brief kiss. This time Jimmy, too, swept his mouth with his tongue and spat.

When my feet landed on solid earth my arms were around his neck pointing skyward again because they rested on his shoulders and he was taller than I. I still held the orchid plant and had no intention of letting it drop.

"Stoop down," I commanded. He did and slid out of my arms like a cow out of its stanchions. He took the plant and placed it carefully in the basket on his bush-car. Then he was pushing the hair back off my forehead and wiping the dirt off my face with his handkerchief. When I could open my eyes I saw that he was almost as filthy as I.

"You should see yourself!" he mocked reprovingly.

"Well, do you think you're any picture postcard?" I demanded.

He looked surprised. Then he grinned and, still grinning, kissed me again. This time I did not shrink away.

"Did you like that?" he whispered, and he sounded almost anxious. I opened both eyes a bare fraction of an inch. His face was awfully dirty. And sweaty, too. But it didn't matter, for he was kissing me again and I liked it.

We peddled back home, Jimmy in front and me behind—where women belong according to black Africa. It was only a short ride, but I didn't see anything much during the entire trip but his back bent slightly forward and his legs pumping up and down. There was a patch on the left shoulder of his shirt. Nevertheless, just before we reached the edge of the mission compound, he stopped suddenly. I ran into him with a jolt.

"Hey!" he yelped. "Do I have to make hand signals in the middle of a jungle?"

"I'm sorry," I murmured. Only I wasn't. I think I would have felt lighthearted and gay even if I had knocked him down and broken his leg.

He didn't get off his car. He just looked back over his shoulder at me and said, "We're engaged. Aren't we?"

148 ·

My mouth fell open at his stupidity, and the best answer I could manage was a startled "Huh?" He must have taken it for "Uhhuh." Anyway, "I just wanted to be sure we understood each other," he said and looked relieved.

When we reached home Norman and his wife were sitting with my parents on their front porch. All but father got up, came to the steps and peered at us, dirty and disheveled as we were. Father laced his fingers together behind his head so that his elbows stuck out like the wings of a trussed fowl. He winked at me, and I winked back at him. Then I brushed past Jimmy, gathered up the clammy mass of orchid roots and moss and called back over my shoulder to him, "I risked my neck to get this for Mrs. Dick, and I'm going to take it over to her before it dies."

As I whisked myself off, grubby and embarrassed, I still felt a warm glow of satisfaction. It was really nice to have a man make explanations for me—if he could—and if he chose to.

CHAPTER
TWELVE

It was mother who, without putting that fact into words, called my attention to father's failing health. She began plans for Jimmy's and my wedding immediately. I wanted the date postponed until Bun returned to the field—I would not be married without my Aunt Bun, I insisted. Mother looked at father silently, and he answered her unspoken query gently, "I shall live to see our daughter married. God will give me that long, I know."

I turned amazed eyes upon my father. Strange—is it not?—how closely youth can live with a loved one and see only that which we love in his face until the loved one himself is bidding us a mortal farewell. I had forgotten once before when father seemed old and tired; now I saw him as he really was, an old man. Old and very tired. He was shrunken, too. The folds of his coat hung about his back more loosely than ever before. And although he had never been a very tall man, I remembered that one day when I was standing beside him, I had looked down into his eyes.

I ran to brother Norman the moment I left my parents. He listened to me quietly. Then, "Did you know he has given his collection of African artifacts to a museum?" Norman told rather than asked me. "He spends a little time each day packing various things for shipment to America."

Father loved his spears and shields, his little wooden gods and devil masks, his kingly stools—and all the other *"oddenda"* as he called them—which record the evolutionary history of a people more poignantly than written pages can ever do. I was certain, as was Norman, that he would never have let any of these objects go if he had not felt that his own days to possess them were numbered.

I found ways to help him in his packing. Abu Sayheed wove bamboo crates. He and father laid item after item into these with thick wads of kapok from the silk-cotton tree wedged into all the crevices. Father dictated to me the names and, as far as he could place them accurately, the geographical locations of the tribes from which each piece had come. He had been doing this himself before, briefly, on scraps of paper. He welcomed my younger fingers, for he now added bits of folklore to delight an ethnologist.

That is how I learned the story of the huge copper fan which he had shown me once before. It seemed to me that he stood a long time with the fan in his hands before packing it away, and then he hesitated again and looked into Abu Sayheed's face silently before dictating its history. The mission boy was a head taller than father, and physically there was no comparison of their strengths. Yet used to respect for father as I was, I was amazed by the homage in the face of this servant. Nor was it the respectful subservience which primitive man pays one to whom the spirits have been friendly for many years. There was in his face that reverence which a truly intelligent man accords the wisdom which comes to fruition at the end of long years of successful living.

"This fan played its part in the victory ritual of a tribe," father began. And when he finished, I had a detailed account of a nation of black cannibal warriors who raided stranger villages only in order to seize captives. They fed and cared for their prey well. When the time came for their sacrifice, the wretched creatures were tied to stakes hip-deep in the icy water of a mountain stream. A day later, the thoroughly numbed legs were severed between the knees and ankles, and the handle of a copper fan was wedged into the marrow of the larger bone of each. Then the captives were tied, back downward, on grids of green logs over deep beds of glowing coals. Their knees projected beyond the grid, their fan-adorned shanks hung free. As feeling began to return, the leg muscles twitched at first involuntarily, and finally with all the frantic strength of mortal agony, fanning the fires beneath. The better show each wretch put on, the more quickly he died.

"A brutish tale, brutishly told," father ended with a deep sigh. "But if you must judge, Laura, remember that these people were primeval pacifists of a sort; they were proud of the fact that they did not murder their victims. They merely set the stage and stood by and—and enjoyed the spectacle while their victims killed themselves."

He turned to Abu Sayheed with a look of inquiry on his face and the black boy answered gravely, "It is a quick death, bwana. Deep in the bowels of the earth where black men must grabble for jewels and gold for their white masters, death is slow. One coughs, lightly at first like a woman who wants to hide a laugh. But the mole-man continues to cough until he is like an animal with a spear through its lungs spitting up its life's blood."

I felt there was much more the two might have said had they been alone. Now they simply returned to their packing. But my record wasn't finished. "What is this tribe called," I asked father.

"Call them The People of the Fan," he answered. "That is how they used to be known."

"Where is their village?" I went on.

"Beyond the Hungry Country. I don't think it has ever been explored. It may be one of those areas on the map of the Dark Continent on which no ray of white man's light has yet been shed," he said slowly. "And we don't want a flock of sportsmen and tourists there yet, do we?" father demanded smiling grimly at the thought. "Put down that the Fan Country lies to the east and in the low foothills of a great mountain range, to the south of immense *sud* swamps, to the west of a thousand tiny tangled streams that have not yet made up their minds to become one great river. And it lies north by northeast of the Hungry Country."

That evening I told Jimmy about father and the tale of the ritual copper fan. He listened, and to my surprise with no horror. Perhaps horror was crowded out of his mind by his own obsession.

"That would be a wonderful land, untouched by other white men, for us to start an agricultural mission in, wouldn't it?" he whispered with his lips against my cheek. I don't know whether or not I answered him. It was always hard to plan or be rational with Jimmy's arms around me.

"Would you be frightened to cross the Hungry Country with me? And live among a strange people that far from everyone you know?" He cupped my chin in one palm and turned my face around so that our eyes looked straight into each other's.

"*Me?* Afraid of Africa?" I exclaimed, and laughed at him.

He kissed me lightly as a man kisses a woman when he is thinking of other things than love. I tucked my face into the niche between his shoulder and cheek and he held me tight—and kept on thinking of other things.

Then, suddenly and without reason, I was afraid. Not of Africa. Not of the Hungry Country. Nor of what might lie beyond. But I knew without thought why women down through the ages have stumbled through heaven and hell when some irrational, dreaming male has led the way.

I don't know how a wedding can be simpler than at a mission station as small and as isolated as ours. Nor how such a simple ceremony as mine could take the time and demand the attention it did.

There were no invitations or announcements to be engraved, addressed, and mailed. The reception following the ceremony could be nothing much more than one of our mission family get-together. As for flowers for decorating our small chapel, there were the common cultivated varieties by unnumbered basketfuls in our mission gardens, and a florist's paradise of exotic blooms filled the jungle just beyond. But mother, Mrs. Dick, Blanche, and Sister Hallie were all busy as a swarm of bees.

And I had two worries. "Hurry back to Africa," I wrote Aunt Bun, not knowing that mother had cabled her. "Don't let the Board send you on any more speaking trips or deputation work or anything else. And for goodness' sake, don't get sick. I wouldn't feel properly married without you."

My second worry was clothes. Oh, beautiful things were to be had in Léopoldville, but the beautiful things of your and my civilization are beyond the financial reach of missionary salaries. Many people have asked me, "What did you do with your money? There's no place in the middle of a jungle to spend it, is there?" No. But money is a curious thing. It doesn't have to be consciously spent in order to disappear. Like water, it evaporates without leaving any physical trace behind. Ask any housewife!

The other women on our staff shared this worry with me. Blanche offered me the use of her wedding dress—forgetting that she had given it to a younger sister before sailing for Africa herself.

Sister Hallie dived into the recesses of one of her trunks and came up with a silk nightgown that spoke silently but with great eloquence nevertheless of the prim days of Her Majesty, Victoria. How she had come into possession of such a thing she did not say and we did not ask. It really was a beautiful garment. Very beautiful! And she had treasured it as such.

"But I never wore it," she hastened to assure us. "It didn't seem just—right—for me." There was longing, regret, and sincere honesty in the poor woman's words.

It was beautiful, and also yellow with age, and as we handled it our fingers broke through the time-weakened cloth. Sister Hallie folded it up and tucked it away again—without tears! She was too Spartan a missionary for that!

As the days wore on Mrs. Dick looked at me often and speculatively. And inwardly I shrank lest she offer me nuptial lingerie with the legends: "Oyster Shell," "Rabbit Pellets," or even "Hog Feed" still showing ghost-like on the coarse fabric.

One morning mother came over to the hospital and said to me almost defiantly, "I've been straightening up Jimmy's cottage for you and— Esther left some very beautiful things—lots of underwear —and—evening gowns—and—"

I looked across the sterilizer at my mother and answered doggedly, "I won't wear Esther's clothes, mother. Even if I have to be married in one of my uniforms."

That afternoon Dr. Dick asked me to take a small patient back to a near-by village. Curled up cross-legged in the luggage carrier of my bush-car, the urchin looked like a piece of carved wood. His grin spread his mouth clear across his face for now he was to ride home in triumph on one of the Little-Mama's-Wonderful-Three-Wheeled-Stools.

Ordinarily the trip would have taken me about an hour but suddenly, almost with no volition of my own, I turned to Dr. Dick.

"I'll be a little longer," I told him. "I'm going to take another, longer way home."

His eyes opened in questioning surprise.

I explained frankly: "I'm coming back past—the Tree of Rags. Remember what it did for me once?"

His eyes twinkled, and I looked away in some embarrassment. But the next thing I knew he was patting my shoulder and murmuring, "Dear child, when will you women learn that if all a man wanted was a bundle of fine feathers, he'd order the things from a Sears, Roebuck catalogue."

For the first time in my life I was angry at Dr. Dick and I suppose I sniffed, for he was patting my shoulder again and adding, "But I'll admit every man wants his bride to look as pretty to others as he himself knows she is."

I had one hip on the seat of the bush-car when an awful thought struck me. Quickly I leaped off and came back to shake a finger under his nose. "Don't you dare tell Mrs. Dick. This is strictly—strictly black magic."

"Not a syllable from me," he protested. "And—may the friendly spirits keep on loving our—little white-skinned savage."

I'm not superstitious, of course. Missionaries like other intelligent people are always supposed to deny any leaning in this direction. But missionaries react just like other people when they see a four-leafed clover, or the new moon. That glow of hope and satisfaction is as common to mankind as pleasure in sunshine and laughter.

But the days wore on and more than once I told myself that if the spirits were friendly to me they were taking their own good time showing it. I tried to salve my woman's soul with Dr. Dick's kindly words that it is a wife and not a clotheshorse a man wants. But the bride within me rebelled.

Not that we did not contrive garments in which I might not suitably—for a missionary, that is!—be married. We five women, mother, Mrs. Dick, Blanche, Sister Hallie and I, had learned ways of thrift that would have put to shame the old-time housewife who took pride in the beauty of the bedclothes she had pieced together out of otherwise useless scraps of material. Three days before the wedding we had an outfit ready. There wasn't a garment which in its present form at least, had ever been worn by another woman. There was much that was *old*, a little that was *new*, plenty of the *borrowed*, and at thought of it I certainly was *blue* enough to fit the old rhyme.

I donned the outfit garment by garment before the critical eyes of my mother and the others. I viewed myself by sections in the largest mirror in the compound. Sister Hallie held the mirror, tilting it this way and that, and I had to bend at sharp angles to get a view of a hip or a knee as Sister Hallie herself attempted to see in front of and behind me at the same time. The other women made anxious dashes at me with pins in their mouths and needles in their clever fingers.

Still, the most I can say for that outfit is that it was clean and neat and white—or almost white—and that as much loving care had gone into its fashioning as one could wish. And there wasn't a ghostly trace of a flour or feed advertisement on a single inch of it. Aunt Bun would be home the next day, the jungle drums had told us. At the moment I longed for the comfort of her loving arms as I had often known it in childhood. But at the same time I cringed at the thought of the pity I knew I would see in her eyes when she helped me dress in the—to her "unmentionables" which Mrs. Dick had tried so hard to make "frilly" with her lace crocheted out of sewing thread, and Sister Hallie had "prettied up" with scalloped ruffles which bunched up under my dress to very uncertain advantage.

I awoke early the morning of the day before my wedding and began listening for the drums that some time within the next few hours would announce that Aunt Bun was coming up the river. Dr. Dick must have been very patient with me that day. He never once spoke sharply, but right in the middle of sewing up the ragged gashes torn by the limbs of a dead thorn tree through which a patient had fallen somehow, he strode to the door and bellowed in a voice of thunder for his wife to come immediately, scrub, and take my place.

I went to the dispensary and started the outpatients through the clinic. Everyone there knew I was being married on the morrow. The men looked me over curiously—to them I was only "a pair of hands." Because I was twenty-six years old, some of them questioned Jimmy's judgment at acquiring an "old woman." The women were full of the very best-intentioned and exceedingly frank advice. Verbally, they pulled no punches, barred no holds, and pretended no illusions regarding men. Believe me, please, no African girl goes to her nuptial bed ignorant.

I didn't dare dispense anything that morning but our home-made, manioc paste pills. To everyone's delight I ladled these out with a prodigal hand.

We were eating lunch when Maa Koo bounded into the dining room from the kitchen and at the same time Abu Sayheed pressed his scar-adorned face flat against a window screen. Simultaneously, but in two different dialects they informed us that The-Plump-Little-Mama-with-the-Big-Heart would be with us before the shadows lengthened.

Bun's homecoming was just like that of any other returning missionary except that she surprised Jimmy with a big hug and a smacking kiss and told him to call her "Auntie" from now on. Then, giving him no time to be embarrassed, she turned to me with a shout, "I've got something for you!" But she wouldn't say more just then than "Wait!" and when I teased her, her smile only dug deeper dimples in her plump cheeks. And wait I had to, since wedding or no wedding, the purpose of a Christian mission is to save souls, enlighten minds, and heal bodies. We carried through our duties of a full day.

After supper we gathered in father and mother's living room among various boxes which overflowed onto the porch where even bales had been piled. There was one lone missionary barrel this time, but no one even looked at it at first. The necessary things especially ordered, and the gifts sent us by friends and relatives and the good women of the missionary societies got first attention.

Aunt Bun came over and sat on one arm of my chair when I began to open my boxes. Jimmy sat on the other. Companionably, they braced their shoulders together over my head. I had to squinch forward a little to make room for them, but I wasn't conscious of any discomfort for the first box Aunt Bun laid on my knees held a wedding dress. White satin and lace!

I couldn't say a word. Aunt Bun picked up the dress by its shoulders and shook out its filmy, shimmering folds for all to see. Dr. Dick whistled softly. Mother began to sniff into her handkerchief. Mrs. Dick came over and hugged Bun so hard she almost upset all three of us. And then Sister Hallie was on her knees in front of me stroking the folds of satin as lovingly as a gentle child strokes a kitten.

There was a veil, too, and a silver filigree tiara in which freshly picked flowers could be woven. And there were all the "unmentionables" any girl could wish for, delicate, ribbon-knotted, lace-frilled. How had Bun—every bit as poor as any of us—wrought this miracle?

"I went to my own church, where I was born and confirmed. They've never dropped my name from the rolls although I belong here, too, you know," she began slowly. Then she went on with a rush, "I told them about—about a little missionary brat that I helped to bring up and who is as near a daughter as I'll ever have. I told them she was getting married now, and that of all the wonderful things I've seen come out of a missionary barrel, I've never yet seen a wedding dress or veil or— I thanked them for all the things they've done for me over the years, and then I just said, *'Forget me now!'* And didn't the old girls of my missionary society come through? Now, didn't they!"

Yes. You Christian gentlewomen, wherever you are—yes! And I still thank you from the bottom of my heart.

"But where're the shoes? I didn't see the shoes," mother exclaimed.

"Shoes? Surely there are shoes!" Bun burst out. "There must be shoes!"

As we had unpacked each box, Sister Hallie had smoothed out each sheet of tissue paper and folded it carefully along its original creases. Tissue paper is hard to come by on the mission field and it helps make a birthday party jolly and Christmas more Christmassy. Now all her precise work went for nothing. Boxes and lids were tossed about after anxious eyes had peered into each empty corner. Every sheet of tissue paper was shaken out as though shoes could have hidden between its folds. The room looked as though a few small boys and their puppies had romped through it, before we gave up and stared at each other hopelessly.

Then father rolled the one missionary barrel into the middle of the room. I think he did it at that moment because he was fearful every woman there would burst into tears if not otherwise occupied. He turned his face upward, closed his eyes, and—hammer in hand as though challenging God—gave thanks for His bounty to us. He did not say: God, please put a pair of wedding shoes in this barrel for Laura. Perhaps he felt that to voice the pathetic hope of every person in that room would be sacrilege. His "Amen" was that of an obedient servant.

But mother and Mrs. Dick—good Christians, both!—were also women. Their firm "Amens" left no doubt in anyone's mind as to what they considered divine duty at the moment.

Yes, there was a pair of white satin shoes in the barrel. Father announced their discovery with something very like a primitive warwhoop. Mother and Mrs. Dick shared open triumph with each other. Father has said frequently that when God fashioned *good women* He unwittingly created a force with which even He Himself ofttimes has to reckon.

The shoes were passed from hand to hand around the room, and although they were as beautiful as I have ever seen in my life, not a single person commented on that fact. White, satin, heels neither low nor spindly, toes neither blunt nor needle sharp, each had a shred of elastic across the instep where an ornament, a bow of ribbon, a metal clip, or a flower could be placed.

The shoes came to Sister Hallie before I knew what was wrong. She gave me an enigmatical glance, stood up, kicked off her own brogues, and pushed her feet into the slippers. But even she winced as she rested her weight on her feet once again. Then I knew!

Sister Hallie had always been too delicate, too frail physically to tramp the jungle trails. Her feet had never been broadened, calloused, or coarsened in any way by countless miles between duties. And God had favored her in the first place with Cinderella-like extremities. The shoes were beautiful, but not a single person in that room believed I could force *my feet* into them.

But I did! Sister Hallie handed them over without looking at me. I kicked off my clodhoppers, pushed my toes down the delicately arched vamp, and stood up, using my entire weight to smash my heel slowly inside the rim of stiffened cloth. I crooked my knee as though to take a step, changed my mind very quickly, and sat down. It took a good wrenching tug to get each shoe off.

"I— I wonder if—how the things Bun brought—fit," mother faltered.

Mrs. Dick drew a very deep breath and then exclaimed, "We'll find out. And we'll make them—fit."

She turned to her husband, and then to all of the men in the room, "Come on, Dick, clear out. All of you men, vamoose. Make yourselves scarce. Go somewhere else. We women have work to do."

For the next few hours I stood on the floor, on chairs, on the table, in varying stages of dress and undress while five women armed with thread, pins and needles, thimbles, scissors and tape-measures fitted cloth to my body as faultlessly as the most exclusive modiste in the world could have done. Then, because I was the bride, they sent me off to bed and to rest, and they kept on with their stitching.

I took the shoes—those beautiful shoes, shoes surely designed for a bride—with me. After I had undressed I put them on again, pushing my feet down firmly until the joints of my toes buckled. I walked across the room in them, and when I tensed the muscles in my feet hard enough, I was scarcely conscious of discomfort.

I have no idea what o'clock it was when I only half awakened to see Sister Hallie standing beside my cot. She had evidently slipped in to say goodnight, but since I lay so quietly, did not disturb me. Instead she merely looked down at me for a moment, and then leaned over and kissed me as gently as my own mother might have done.

Anyone acquainted with Africa will laugh at me for saying that my wedding day dawned bright and cloudless. We were in the middle of one of our bi-annual dry seasons. Anything but perfect weather would have called for a meteorological miracle.

Aunt Bun and Sister Hallie were up and dressed and out of the cottage when I awakened. I knew that they and the schoolchildren were gathering flowers and decorating our chapel. I knew that without money our little altar would be banked with a profusion of blossoms many of them so rare that not even the richest socialite "back home" could procure them.

I slipped out to our bath-house for my shower, and when I returned I found that someone had laid something on top of my clothes during my absence. I picked it up and laughed in spite of myself. Crudely and carelessly tied together as the bamboo, clay and bits of wool had been, there was no mistaking the phallic symbolism. I was certain, too, that the fetish could have come from no one but Maa Koo—openly rejoicing that at last I was to mate as Mu'ungu has intended from the beginning of time that woman

should—fiercely eager that I, her white childling, should be as pro-
lific as the black ideal.

I heard the latch on the front screen door click. Quickly I buried
the ridiculous charm deep in a dresser drawer where no one else
could see it. I felt no need of its good luck portent, but it warmed
my heart because of the love I bore the giver.

"Be careful, Sam, you'll spill the milk." It was father and mother
bringing me a breakfast tray. Mother made my bed and straightened up the room while I ate. When I had finished, mother took
the tray off my lap and slipped out the door. Father remained
behind.

"I've talked with each of my children the evening before they
were married, but last night was a little unusual," he began.

I waited because I knew that was what he expected of me.

"There isn't much for me to say, now, because *our* rearing is
done. We know, Laura, that you are a virtuous woman, strong
physically and spiritually, of moderate intelligence and good sense.
Mother and I welcomed you into the world. You would know
even if I didn't say it that you have our blessing as you begin this
new life. It would be foolish and wrong of me to tell you that all
will be smooth sailing and joy from now on. In many ways life
will be rougher, but it will be more rewarding. Your mother—and
Maa Koo—"

He paused to smile and I smiled back at him and nodded, knowing I would agree with whatever he said.

"These two excellent women have made a woman of you also. I
could not, and have no desire to try to emulate their—advice.
There is, however, a certain standard of wifehood set down thousands of years ago, but as true today as when first pressed into wet
clay by some scribe's stylus. You are familiar with it, I know, but
I want to read it to you again."

He picked up the Bible which lay on my bedside table and turned
the pages to *Proverbs* 31:10 and read—with his eyes always on my
face and never on the printed page. I listened quietly from "Who

can find a virtuous woman? for her price is far above rubies . . ." to the final: "and let her own works praise her in the gates."

After he had closed my Bible he clasped both of my hands in his and prayed for me as a good man prays for one he loves. Together we whispered, "Amen." When he went away I sat for a long time just looking out of the window and, now and then, in fragmentary phrases, thanking God for all His goodness to me—and for an earthly father like mine.

Then there were scuffling footsteps and some laughter and mother, Mrs. Dick, Blanche, and Aunt Bun and Sister Hallie all trooped into my room. Behind them, quiet and watchful as a mouse, was Maa Koo. I glanced meaningfully at the pile of clothing where her fetish had been placed and nodded to her. Her grin lengthened and deepened the furrows of her face, and without a word she slipped away.

Everyone was in her best clothes. With much fuss, and laughter, and simulated worry, they got me into mine. Then mother and Mrs. Dick hurried away to the chapel, and when the door banged behind them, I kicked off my uniform brogues and thrust my sturdy feet into the tiny, delicate, white satin slippers someone far away had dropped into our latest missionary barrel. Sister Hallie gasped and Aunt Bun's eyes were round, but they were women and understood and neither made a pretense of reasoning with me. Bun simply and softly yoo-hoo-ed out the window. Dr. Dick came to the door, held it open for the four of us, and offered me his arm with a storybook flourish.

It was a beautiful wedding—*so they tell me!* Mother and Mrs. Dick *together* were my mothers. Both father and brother Norman officiated. Norman's wife was my matron of honor. Aunt Bun and Sister Hallie, my bridesmaids. Dr. Dick gave me away. I have seen very few weddings in my life, but nowhere do I believe any group participates more completely in a marriage than when it takes place on the mission field. From far and near our black friends gathered, filled the chapel to bursting and an enormous overflow milled about the windows and door.

They *tell* me these things and I trust their veracity, and reason confirms my trust. Actually I remember very little of my own wedding ceremony. It was a hot day, and by the time we reached the chapel my feet in their beautiful but ridiculously tiny shoes were a welter of excruciating pain. Walking up the aisle on Dr. Dick's arm, I went even more slowly and woodenly than the usual bride, for red-hot spears of anguish were burning the strength out of my muscles and turning my knee and hip joints to jelly.

At the altar we stopped and I tried to ease the pain by shifting my weight from first one foot to the other, then from heel to toe.

"For heaven's sake, Laura, stop jiggling up and down—as though you had—ants!" Bun muttered.

I shot a quick look at Jimmy out of the corner of my eyes. He was staring at me—frowning? or worried? I tried to make my muscles rigid and thus shut out sensation of pain. I tried arching my feet, and without actually lifting my heels off the floor, putting my weight on the tips of my toes. Every toe felt like a boil, and when I tried to straighten out my arch again, it was beyond my strength to endure that new pain.

Then Aunt Bun was pinching my arm and hissing in my ear, "Say, 'I do,' Laura. Puddin', it's time now for 'I do.' "

"I do!" I squeaked, and I heard a titter run through the church.

Father leaned forward slightly and peered at me anxiously, and I stared back at him desperately, trying to push consciousness of my feet out of my mind. For an awful moment his face danced in front of me, and the light of the few candles we had been able to make ourselves from beeswax and mutton tallow danced in prismatic colors like fireflies through one's eyelashes.

Then as from a great distance I heard brother Norman's voice saying, "Repeat after me: 'With this ring I thee wed—' "

"With this ring I thee—" All of my strength went into an effort to say the words clearly and distinctly.

But Aunt Bun was shaking my elbow and hissing like an angry spur-winged goose in my ear: "No! No, puddin'. Jimmy's first, then you."

(Thereafter, as long as father lived. it was a favorite bit of teasing for him and Norman to engage in arguments as to just whom they had married to Jimmy—Bun or me. Aunt Bun had finally edged so close, they said, to catch me should I fall, and to put the right words into my mouth at the right time, that neither man could be certain to which woman he spoke much of the time.)

Sometime during that eternity of pain we knelt, Jimmy and I, and father prayed, but my thoughts very definitely were not on God. I pressed my toes hard against the floor, hoping my heels would pop out of my shoes. They didn't. My swollen feet were as firmly imprisoned in those beautiful but fiendish scraps of satin as a long cork pressed firmly down the slender neck of a bottle.

Jimmy at one elbow and brother Norman at the other lifted me upright and set me down on those red-hot, needle-sharp spears of pain again. For a few seconds I desperately considered refusing to put my feet on the floor and trying to stand on them, but rather to dangle from their hands like a child.

Then Jimmy put back my veil and kissed me and someone sat at our little chapel organ and pumped out bold if slightly wheezing chords of music. But at the mere thought that I must turn and take thirty or forty steps on those feet, tears started down my face. I couldn't do it. I simply couldn't do it.

Jimmy knew that I couldn't. And there at the altar, he bent, put an arm around my hips and lifted me off my feet, high in the air, over his shoulder like a sack of grain. Then, *so they tell me!* casually as though this were a normal wedding recessional, he stalked down the aisle. Just outside of the church he paused long enough to pull my shoes off my feet and hurl them into a near-by bush. I screamed with pain as he did so. So many pickinins dived into that bush after the treasure discarded by a white man that there was nothing left of it five minutes later but a few trampled twigs and stubby stems sticking up out of the ground. Jimmy carried me clear across the mission compound to my parents' cottage. There at my reception I did not stand to receive the "Best Wishes!" of those who loved me. I sat with my wedding dress folded back over my knees and my feet—swollen to twice their normal size—soaking in a tub of Epsom salts water.

"You silly little fool! You silly little fool!" Mrs. Dick kept reiterating while she draped a sheet around and over my footbath. "There! Now that makes it look more like a—wedding." But she laughed as she said it.

I thoroughly enjoyed my reception—although there were moments when I wondered if Jimmy were beginning to suspect that he had married into a family of lunatics. The reception finally over, I lifted my feet out of the Epsom salts water and dried them on a corner of Mrs. Dick's unconcealing sheet. I looked them over doubtfully wondering if I could get them into a pair of father's shoes temporarily. Everyone else inspected them, too.

"Now as her doctor, I advise—" Dr. Dick began pompously.

Jimmy gathered me up and heaved me over his shoulder again—to applause this time instead of wheezy music. I felt ridiculous now, and his bones cut into my stomach. I protested. I was telling him he was as big a silly fool as I, as he carried me up his steps, over his porch, and into his cottage. I know! I know you were carried over the threshold. Phutttttt! What's that to being carried home from the very altar!

At our bedroom door Jimmy and I paused, stared, and then turned surprised eyes upon each other. Across the foot of our bed lay Sister Hallie's missionary-barrel, double-wedding-ring quilt. Good Sister Hallie! It is so easy to love in an atmosphere of love.

CHAPTER
THIRTEEN

The plan had been for Jimmy and me, *my husband* and me— How nice it sounded to say that!—to leave for the land beyond the Hungry Country almost immediately after our wedding. There we were not only to pioneer a new station, but a new phase of missionary work for our denomination as well. It was more than a year before we did go, however. Much happened in that year.

In the first place, father died. He had done the work God had laid upon him, he lived through the span of years alloted him, and then he simply went to sleep.

Father's death was a grief to all who knew him. It was not overwhelming grief, however, or tragedy, and no one pretended it was. Norman and I, like any good son and daughter, tried to stay very close to mother and not to leave her alone for very long at any time.

"I have known for a long time that this was coming," she told me. "Your father prayed that he might live until you and James were married. Your father was a very wise and sensitive man, Laura. He knew, and felt, many things that the rest of us do not. Even before you and your husband were engaged, he knew what was coming, and he prayed that he might live to see it. Toward the last he lived on will power alone; there were days when he didn't eat enough to keep a cricket alive."

We buried father in the land he loved, among the friends who in his day he had helped inter. His grave is under a huge wild fig tree whose creeping branches reach out over the ground in rolling lengths as though it were attempting to gather all who come within reach to its green-gray heart. Father himself had located the mission cemetery in this beautiful spot, and laid out the lots to care for the mortal needs of a hundred years of missionary work. He had planted seeds familiar to American gardens and had transplanted the exotic blossoms of the Dark Continent in casual clumps and in formal beds according to their natures. With his own hands he had helped repair the paling fence around our cemetery when it was broken down, once by a mischievous band of marauding baboons, and another time by a rogue elephant that had kept the entire mission in terror for a few days with its blind, malignant assaults against anything that moved.

The land which my father loved, a land which he understood as well as any white man ever understands it, which he had accepted without carping criticism when intellectually and emotionally he was unable to fill in the gaps between his own and another race's emerging civilization—this land took him to its soft, warm heart in death. Many black hands turned up the earth to receive him. Many fingers plucked flowers from the branches of jungle bush and tree. Everyone—white as well as black—was glad his spirit would walk familiar paths when the body was no more. More than one voice assured us that the Spirit of Good had entered his body at birth, and that he had been blessed.

In the years that have followed, two incidents at my father's funeral have stood out in my memory. One concerns Abu Sayheed. He was very helpful to us, although the burial rites of a white man must have seemed strange to him. If he felt emotion at my father's death, he did not show it; but then, expression would have been difficult for a face so scarred as his. Brother Norman read the burial service over father; and when we left the cemetery, Jimmy stayed behind with a half-dozen black boys to close the grave. Abu Sayheed was among these. Jimmy told me that as they filled in the grave he remembered that Abu Sayheed, although not Christian, had stayed on in our mission station and had worked for father because of *an unnamed gift* he was some time to receive.

That evening Jimmy said he had turned to Abu Sayheed and remarked, curious as to what the black boy's reaction would be, "Now that the white bwana is dead, you must come to me for the gift he promised you. I will give it to you if it is possible for me."

Abu Sayheed smiled slightly and answered, "Now the white bwana himself will repay me for my labors.

Jimmy thought perhaps the black boy had not understood that he, my husband, the white bwana's son-in-law, would assume the white bwana's obligation, so he repeated, "I will give you whatever you want—if you do not ask the impossible."

Abu Sayheed, who was not demeaning himself by using a hoe but was scooping dirt into the open grave with the palms of his two hands, paused long enough to look up and answer, "I must have what I seek from the white bwana himself."

I thanked Jimmy for his kindness and forgot about the incident temporarily. But I, of all folk, should have been warned in some way, and I wasn't; and when I did find out what lay behind the fellow's words, it was too late to share my knowledge with my husband. He had then already joined my father in the spirit lanes under the great jungle trees. And I gave no further thought to Abu Sayheed himself, even when someone told me a few days later that he had disappeared from the mission compound.

Jimmy and I were awakened the next morning by Norman calling to us outside our bedroom window to unbolt the front door and let him in. Through the mosquito netting which hung over our bed, his face looked haggard, unearthly. I was still struggling with the sleeves of my robe when Norman stepped into our living room. Bluntly, without mincing his words, he blurted out, "Someone opened father's grave last night and pried the lid off the coffin and—"

"Oh, no! No!" I wailed.

Who among us at the mission did not know that the lingering traces of cannibalism, long since forbidden by strict and punitive law, found expression in the depraved appetites of ghouls!

"We closed the grave carefully and weighted down the earth with stones as you know. It couldn't have been the work of hyenas or jackals," Jimmy was beginning when Norman interrupted him.

"Since when do animals pry the lid off a coffin? Or make a crude attempt at closing a grave again?" he demanded.

"Is father—gone?" I cried out.

Jimmy put his arms around me and I clung to him, shrinking from what my brother might say.

Norman went on more slowly, although there was no softening what he had to say. "Only—just his head, Laura."

"Does Mother Woodbury know?" my husband asked at last.

Norman nodded yes. "Somehow old Maa Koo found out. She went to mother, and mother came over to our cottage. She's with Blanche now."

How long we stood and stared at each other, or what little things we said, I no longer remember. Finally Jimmy and I pulled on shoes and still in our robes followed Norman to the cemetery, but there was nothing to be seen now. Dr. Dick was there, and almost all the black folk of the mission milled about trampling over the other graves. Dr. Dick had had the grave filled in and stones again blanketed the raw earth. He spoke kind words to us, and sent us away. We knew he would appoint boys to watch and guard the grave night and day—and that these same boys would flee to the comfort and comparative security of their huts as soon as night fell.

Then we went over to Norman's house to comfort mother as best we could, but were comforted by her instead. She was surprisingly calm.

"Now! Now! Now! Where is the Christian fortitude and charity you learned from your father?" she admonished Norman and me a dozen times. "Goodness knows, I don't understand what's happened. And neither do you. But you can be sure of one thing, if anyone would ever have understood, it was your father. And what he didn't understand he was patient with—and forgiving if that were necessary. Your father isn't troubled. Never fear that. It's only—we—whose understanding is—limited."

Father had just reached the retirement age for missionaries of our denomination. Mother, who was three years his elder, had passed it. Norman and I had pitied father, knowing that he had wanted to end his days in the land he loved, feeling that a compulsory return to the land of his birth would only be exile for him. But for mother it would be—perhaps the phrase is too strong, but Norman and I had used it between ourselves—for mother it would be a social reprieve.

Now, of course, with father gone, she must return. The Governing Board cabled us to that effect. Norman was immediately appointed head of our mission as we knew he would be, and was too busy with his new responsibilities to be spared. Jimmy's and my furloughs were not due, but since we did not want my mother to travel alone at her age, I was delegated to return to the United States with her and get her settled somewhere. There was a great deal of regret expressed that I, a bride of only a few weeks, must be separated from my husband for several months, but that did not alter anyone's opinion that I was the one to go.

It was then that mother surprised us again. "I just don't see how I can break away," she would mutter. And, "Who will pick up and carry on my work with the *old* women?" she asked repeatedly. "They're going to die soon, I know—like me! But they're human beings while they live and there isn't anyone to pay any attention to them but me. Are we just going to set them adrift because—because they—because I—because we all have to grow old?" Finally she voiced a problem I had seen other elderly missionaries face and sometimes with real anguish of spirit. "How am I going to explain to these people my desertion of them and at the very end of their lives?"

But we, her children, didn't have to struggle with that unanswerable query. Only a few days before mother and I were to start down river, her old folks solved the problem for themselves. We two were sitting on her front porch sewing when she called my attention to three very old men and an equally ancient crone coming across the mission compound.

"Oh dear! Oh dear! Now that Sam is gone, I'm the only one

to whom they can come. How can I desert them!" Her voice was low, and I knew she wasn't speaking to me.

The old people seated themselves on our steps, the three old men on the top step and the woman below them as was fitting for the sexes. They passed the time of day pleasantly enough and inquired after the health of every member of mother's family and otherwise gossiped garrulously with many African circumlocutions spiced with polite and wise sayings.

Then old O'Dotgoo cleared his throat portentously and I could see mother bracing herself. With many verbal flourishes he began a long recital of mother's virtues and good deeds. Long before he reached the point where he emphasized the great love and respect everyone bore her, one felt mother must surely be some kind of paragon, ripe for beatification. There was no need trying to hurry O'Dotgoo on to the purpose of his visit. We could only wait with what patience the years among primitive peoples had schooled into us. Finally he touched upon the point that mother had been one of the missionaries who in her youth had laid great emphasis upon clothing the nakedness of the heathen.

I glanced at her quickly. She was scanning the four old people on the steps below us with some pride. Each was draped in a spotless kanzu. Then old O'Dotgoo shuffled to his feet and as he did so casually pulled the hem of his kanzu waist-high. Mother piously turned her eyes elsewhere. But I saw—as I expected to see—that while the old man wore the accepted uniform of a black soldier of Christ, he had not abandoned the simple G-strap of his more benighted brethren. From the G-strap hung the oddments necessary to the comfort of his declining days. Out of the hyrax skin purse which dangled between his knees, O'Dotgoo extracted a scrap of paper and held it out to mother. Then his old frame crumpled downward and he eased his hips carefully onto the step.

I bent forward to look at the paper with mother. It was a page torn from an American fashion magazine. Where the old people had come upon the paper I never knew, but no wonder they were amazed. It pictured a girl with two wisps of cloth around her body.

Bold lettering called these scraps of cloth a bathing suit, and readers were assured that they were the most fashionable outfit being worn by sophisticates on European and American beaches. Mother's eyes popped wide, and I'm sure mine were equally round.

Then old O'Dotgoo was speaking again to the effect that now, in her old age, God seemingly had laid a new duty upon my mother. There was, somewhere in the world if this picture were to be believed, a village of white-skinned, almost naked savages. My mother had led him and his neighbors out of savagery to Christ and the Christian blessing of a clothed body. She must now do the same thing for such unfortunate heathen as the scrap of paper showed. Did mother, to whom most scraps of paper talked, know where the kraals of these white-skinned, undraped heathen stood?

Slowly mother's white head bobbed up and down. Yes, she knew the trail that led to this pictured stranger's village.

Would mother consider going to that country now? In her old age as when she had come to them in her youth? Christ had pointed the way then, did she feel divine guidance stirring within her now also?

Mother's head kept in motion like an inverted pendulum. Through stiff lips she answered the old people who hung on her words anxiously, but she chose her words carefully lest she violate absolute truth. Yes, she would go to the kraals of the pictured woman, although to leave her African children twisted and tore her heart. And in that strange land to which she was now sent, she would end her days witnessing for her Christ as she had always done.

Our visitors assured mother that to the end of her days she would remain in their hearts and on their praying lips. Then the three old men arose and each in turn grasped mother's thumb and gave it a violent jerk. Mother arose to meet the old woman as she shuffled up the steps. Forearms clasped in each other's hands, they pressed their shoulders together for a long moment.

When we were alone again, I turned to mother with a quick jest on my lips but she silenced me with a motion of her hand.

"The constant loving prayers of three good men and one good woman to bless me throughout the rest of my life," she murmured. "What a wonderful parting gift from my people."

A month later mother and I were "home." In New York there was a luncheon in a fabulously large and luxurious hotel where mother presented father's collection of African artifacts to the museum of his choice. World-renowned men and women thanked her and said such wonderful things about father that both of us sniffed to keep back the tears—because of the sweet and simple truth of the words.

A couple of days later and a thousand miles away, we made a dutiful and formal call on Aunt Bessie. Then Aunt Elma and Uncle Ben received us into their home and hearts and we all reveled in that sort of fellowship which only love engenders.

I don't know what mother did with her days except chatter with Aunt Elma, and read and sleep and putter around the house and among the flowers. But my first morning it was not yet light outside when Uncle Ben tapped on my door and told me to "roll out of bed and come down." He was waiting at the foot of the stairs where he shoved a huge shining pail at me, ordering, "Here, grab hold. If you've married a farmer boy, you'll have to learn how to milk a cow."

So I learned to milk a cow that first morning. I also learned what pain in arm and finger muscles can be when they must keep on working hard in spite of exhaustion, for one cannot milk a cow by fits and starts. Once started one must continue as long as there is milk in the udder, else the cow is injured. I didn't understand why, since I knew that a calf sucked and a human infant nursed only until their appetites were satisfied and no injury given to either mother.

I learned other things, too: the soft music of animals munching, the beauty of warm breath steaming into frosty air, the sensual physical delight of pungent animal odors. I climbed up a narrow ladder to a loft and pushed and pulled and shoved wads of fragrant hay through a trap door in the floor. Above my head a pair of fat pigeons waddled back and forth on a dust-silvered beam and scolded down at me or gossiped together fussily.

I was pushing a small bin filled with golden corn from stall to stall, doling out exactly six ears to each horse when I was suddenly conscious that my middle had seemingly caved in.

"When do they, Aunt Elma and mother that is, call us in to breakfast?" I asked.

"They don't," Uncle Ben answered. "We eat when we go in. And we go in when we get the chores done."

Once at table I ate like a farm hand. The rest of the day I began to learn to drive a tractor, that a female hog is called a sow, that on a profitably operated farm her confinement—"farrowing" is the word I should have used—is more carefully supervised than that of most of the women of the world. At supper I fell asleep at the table.

A great many jokes were made about acquainting me, the farmer's wife, with her husband's work, but I think I learned more than anyone realized. Most important of all, I was impressed with the amount, breadth, and exactness of knowledge a farmer must have, and the executive and administrative ability that must be his if he like any good businessman is to increase the value of his acres while they earn for him. I think it was while I was riding one of the farm horses back to the house one noon that I began to understand the dreams I had seen so often behind Jimmy's eyes whenever he looked across a glade of good earth. As we drove to and from church the next Sunday morning and passed farms, good, bad, and indifferent—and on the church steps talked with the men who farmed those fields—my father's casual words rang almost continuously in my ears: "If the land is friendly to you—"

All too quickly came the day when Uncle Ben drove Aunt Elma, mother and me to a near-by small town. There he turned down a shady street and stopped before a rambling old house that was neither pretentious nor shabby. There were crisp ruffled curtains at the windows and flower pots on the window sills. Comfortable rocking chairs stood on the various porches. And about the house broad lawns and flower beds were interlaced by meandering paths. My mother's new home!

She and Aunt Elma had visited here before, but had not permitted me to accompany them. Mother made excuses at the time, but I knew she was fearful lest this Home maintained by our denomination for retired ministers and missionaries should smack of the dread "poor houses" of the novels of her youth. I also knew that Uncle Ben and Aunt Elma not only had urged her to share their home, but that they would never have permitted her to leave them had not health, physical comfort and congenial companionship been primary objectives of this establishment.

On their return that day, mother greeted me with an open smile of honest contentment. "I shall be able to grow—older—there quite gracefully, because I shall be surrounded by those—who have long been about just that," she said.

Now, as we got out of the car, friends she had made on that first visit came down the front path to greet her. Others who looked forward to the pleasure of knowing her followed behind. It was such a right place for mother to be that I caught my breath from the sheer pain of relief.

Uncle Ben's keen eyes noticed the gesture, for he laid a hand on my shoulder, drew me a step behind the others and murmured in my ear, "Your mother won't be among strangers, Laura. These are her kind of— These are her people. And she will be as free here as she would be in our house. She can come and go as she pleases. Her pension is her own. She'll discover new pleasures, and rediscover old ones. And Elma and I are always only a short drive away." It was a rehearsed speech, but an honest one.

We were all invited to lunch on a roomy, glassed-in porch flooded with sunlight, and much was made of the new "guest." When we left three ladies who had spent their lives working in three different corners of the globe were helping mother unpack—and competing with her in extolling the esteem in which their husbands had been held, the honors won in social and scientific fields as well as the spiritual.

The purpose of my trip to America accomplished, I was eager to return to my home and husband. The usual "few services" were asked of me, however, and I did my best to oblige my employers. Mother and I collaborated on a magazine article eulogizing father, the man and his works. We felt helpless before the limitation placed upon us—2,500 words—but we lopped off expressions of our love, trimmed the horizons of his accomplishments, and finally—mother called it—slashed at the soul of the man.

I met with committees and discussed with them at first-hand plans for the agricultural station Jimmy and I were to pioneer. I was so very ignorant! I had just married a farmer—I had learned only within the past few weeks how to milk a cow—and there was not a technical question they asked me which I could answer. I could, however, tell them much about a land whose own people speak of stark hunger as "always lurking just around the corner of the next season." Finally they let me go when I burst out, "Gentlemen, I hope some among you are farmers!"

I was also asked to make a brief speaking tour—which was brief in time only for I crossed the continent and back. In Missouri, partly as the result of a feeble joke about having traveled in everything but an ox-cart, and partly because of the hub-deep mud of an unpaved side road, I was perched on top of a mule for a few miles jaunt from one town to the next. At first it was fun. But before we arrived at our destination—farmer's wife or not!—I was hoping desperately that the tough hide of the mule was as pervious to our dread African tsetse fly as a horse's.

I spoke, too, at the chapel exercises of my alma mater. I remember that because I had hardly descended the sanctuary steps when the dean's secretary summoned me to his office. There the dean thanked me for the check covering my indebtedness to the school. I didn't know what he was talking about and waited stupidly while he chatted politely. Finally the secretary took a letter out of a drawer and laid it before me, and my eyes fell instantly on the words: "Yours respectfully, James T. Grove."

I read the letter backward, my mind working backward also.

Jimmy, as all missionary mates must do, had cared for my mail in my absence. Presumably he had come across one of the twice-yearly reminders of my tuition debt. He thanked the school for its kindness to me and apologized for the fact that they had had to wait so long for payment. Enclosed was a check, he said.

The dean talked on, and I nodded my head, crinkled my lips into brief smiles, and made little noises which I hoped would pass for conversation. But all the time scurrying about in my mind like a mouse in a small gourd, were the words: "Where did Jimmy get such a sum of money?" Strangely, I didn't remember that Esther had spent money freely in Léopoldville. And perhaps even more strangely, when I returned to Africa, I forgot to ask my husband for an explanation.

CHAPTER

FOURTEEN

I did not get to see Jimmy's people during that trip, but I consoled myself with the thought that it would be pleasanter for him to be with me when that visit was made. Quite by accident, however, I did make a call on a man on whom both Dr. Dick and I had often asked God's blessing—although we had long forgotten his name.

When I arrived in one of the largest cities on my "little speaking trip," among the mail which I picked up at the home of the local pastor was a note penciled on a sheet of cheap tablet paper in tremulous up-and-down letters. "I am the man who once sent you a pill-roller, and I want you to come see me," it began. He had read in a church bulletin that I was to speak on such and such an evening about our work in Africa. But he didn't get out much of evenings, and he wanted to talk to me about the use of his pill-roller. He signed himself: H. L. Wilson.

"Little old crank," I muttered. "I wonder if I should spare him a few minutes."

Then a meeting was canceled for some reason and I had several unscheduled hours on my hands. I must admit I did not say to myself immediately and eagerly: "Ooooh! How nice! Now I can go thank the kind and generous old gentleman who gave us the pill-roller and tell him—with perfect honesty—what a back-handed blessing it has been." Nothing could have looked less imposing than his note, and we are so used to the time-consuming eagerness of folk who want to know if the tin measuring cup and half-dozen spools of thread they sent in the last missionary barrel arrived safely, and did we have a use for them?

Again, I forgot about H. L. Wilson, and started out to visit a museum. I knew where I wanted to go and exactly how to get there, so many people had given me directions. "You can't miss it," they all assured me. But I did. Narrow streets, some with strange names and others without names, streets, which the directions had never mentioned, turned to right and left. Kind women and once a police officer, noticing my confusion, asked me where I wanted to go and gave instructions about turnings—all ending: "You can't miss it." I had to laugh at myself—I, who could have found my way with perfect ease through a so-called trackless jungle, could not locate a major landmark in this civilized city.

I rummaged through my purse wondering if I had taxi-fare to the museum and back to the minister's home again, and found the sheet of tablet paper signed by H. L. Wilson. My first impulse was to crumble up the scrap and drop it in the gutter, but again I read the lines: "I am the man who once sent you a pill-roller . . . do come to see me."

"Anyt'ing I kin do t' hep yuh, lady?"

I looked down into the face of a tiny messenger boy with the smile of an angel on his face and an oversized cap riding his ears. Purely on impulse I showed him the scrap of letter and asked him where and how far away that address might be.

His sole reply was to jerk a thumb over a shoulder at the building immediately behind us, while an incredulous look spread over his face. My eyes followed the direction of the pointing thumb and discovered I was literally on the doorstep of the pill-roller man.

Inside the building, it was impressed upon me immediately that I was in *an establishment*. I took a few steps and stood uncertainly in the front end of an immense but barren, uninhabited hall. Someone nudged my elbow and I looked down into the face of the tiny messenger again.

"Who'd yuh wanna see, lady?" he demanded.

"H. L. Wilson," I answered meekly.

The urchin darted across the gleaming floor to a bulletin board filled with hundreds of names. For a second he stood on tiptoe and squinted, then he beckoned me with an imperious finger. The boy struck a knob on what looked like a blank wall, cocked his head sideways listening, and then darted about twenty feet away, again beckoning me to follow. There a portion of the wall slid into itself and I looked into an elevator cage larger than most African huts.

"Take da lady up t' five. Den show 'er whur H. L. Wilson is," my tiny guide instructed the operator. We started up, but stopped between floors with a jerk. The operator turned to me and asked in carefully measured syllables, "Mr. H. L. Wilson?"

"Uhhuh." I nodded. Then I added flippantly, "He calls himself the pill-roller man."

The operator looked me over from head to toe appraisingly. Then without a word turned back to his lever and buttons. The car shot upward again. At the fifth floor he stood up, leaned out of his cage, pointed at a door, and said in a respectful tone, "In there, miss."

There was gold lettering on the opaque glass. My eyes caught the words: "The Regh Co. . . . Pharmaceuticals and Biologicals," as I pushed the door open. Inside a very suave, chic young lady was standing at a file of drawers behind a desk. She was only the first of a half-dozen women who answered my simple request with a polite but hesitating crescendo: "Not Mr. H. L. Wilson?" Each time I explained briefly, and each time I was passed on to a slightly older woman, a little stouter, a little less chic. All were gravely courteous, but my patience wore thin and asperity broke through at last. I opened my purse, fished out the now crumpled, thumb-marked sheet of tablet paper, laid it on a desk and said to whoever might wish to hear:

"I have here an invitation from H. L. Wilson urging me to come see him. I don't know who H. L. Wilson is." I must confess I mimicked their precise crescendo tones as nearly as I could. "And what's more, I'm beginning not to care. Apparently all I can do is leave and write Mr. H. L. Wilson a full explanation of why I have not accepted his invitation."

For a moment the vast room in which I then stood, a room filled with row upon row of desks and busy people, was as silent as a jungle glade after a leopard has sprung from an overhanging limb —and missed. Then a white-haired woman at a desk in a far corner arose, walked slowly up to me, held out her hand and asked quietly, "May I see this note?"

I thrust it at her. She read it calmly and without comment. Then she picked up the telephone on the desk beside which we stood and put through a call: "Miss Edwards? Mrs. Laura Grove is here to see Mr. Wilson. She has no appointment, but she has a personal note of invitation from him. What's that?"

I waited as she listened. Then she turned to me. "Where did you say you were from, Mrs. Grove?"

"I didn't say. No one asked me," I answered rudely. "But I'm from Africa. West Africa. The Congo Territory. Shall I beat a jungle drum to prove it?"

"That won't be necessary," she answered as quietly as though I were not behaving myself like an undisciplined child. "Yes. Yes. Thank you, Miss Edwards," she murmured into the phone. Then she replaced the receiver on its hook and turned toward me with a full-blown smile and the single word, "Come."

I followed her through a jungle of big, many-drawered, shiny-topped desks. It was a very quiet room now, although again there was a semblance of hustling, bustling work. I was no longer angry, but like everyone who knows he has made a fool of himself, embarrassed.

We passed through several spacious, softly carpeted halls before I was aware of the fact that there were names and impressive titles on the doors in letters of gold: "First Vice-President," "Second Vice-President," "Third Vice-President." Vice-Presidents seemingly without number. And other titles, too, I glimpsed as I trotted along behind my rescuer. There were personnel secretaries, administrative and advertising executives, merchandising heads, and what-nots.

Then my guide turned and held out a warning hand at the top of a flight of four or five steps downward. "The floor levels of the new and the old buildings are not the same," she explained as though that information were in some way important. "Mr. Wilson, Mr. H. L. Wilson, that is, never cared to move into the new building. He has spent so many years in his old office that, well, he likes it."

The hall into which we descended was narrow, the carpeting was worn, and there were only faint traces of gold lettering left on the doors. We rounded a bend and at the far end saw a very elderly man and a white-haired woman standing in a doorway waiting. The man was thin, even gaunt as only well-preserved old age is gaunt. He wore an old-fashioned green sunshade over his eyes under soft white waves of hair. His step was spry and bird-like as he came down the hall to meet us.

"Well! Well! Well! So ye came after all. I was afraid ye wouldn't have any time to give an old man like me. Dust off a chair for our company, Edwards."

We were inside his office now. It was a tiny room, and one that at first glance looked dingy; but as he dusted away himself with his own pocket handkerchief at a chair he had pulled forward for me, I saw that everything was immaculately clean. As he went to the window, opened it, and shook out his impromptu dustcloth, I swept the room with a quick measuring glance. There were two desks in it against opposite walls and flanking the sole window. Both desks were the roll-topped variety with many pigeonholes that bulged with protruding papers.

"Some old bookkeeper who is kept on beyond the normal retirement age because everyone loves him. Or maybe his daughter married the boss's son," I surmised idly.

Then we three were sitting in a close triangle, our heads and knees almost touching, and the pill-roller man was saying, "Now, young lady, tell me about Africa."

And I did. I had meant to stay only a few minutes, but for the rest of the afternoon I sat there telling him about Africa. At first I talked after the fashion of missionaries on deputation work. I outlined the present and the possible outreach of our work. I mentioned the favorable statistics, I stressed the personnel and financial needs. I tried to cover the outstanding phases: evangelistic, educational, handcraft shops, medical. And always—no matter what I sought to discuss myself—always he brought me back to the medical.

I know now that he or his elderly secretary, or both of them, was skilled at drawing others out. I talked to him that afternoon as I have never talked to another non-missionary, as I seldom talk to others of my own profession.

I told him of the speed with which the tropical mold that attacks glass, always etched our microscope lenses into opaqueness. That our medical statistics were poor, not from the lack of learning or ability of our doctors, but because few patients came to us who had not first been mauled about by their own witch doctors and given up as hopeless. I told him of men crawling miles on their hands and knees to reach us. Of women who undergo major surgery one day and return to their villages to gratify their husband's physical appetites that night, and to hoe in his garden the next day. Of the hell it is for the doctor who must amputate a crushed and mangled arm or leg without a trace of opiate or anaesthetic to administer.

I told him tale after tale of ridiculous and pathetic emergencies which had arisen. Like the time Dr. Dick, working without a nurse, was removing a stomach tumor and a sudden freak and fierce windstorm had torn our thatched roof loose and had blown it away. He had climbed onto the operating table and had stood on his hands and knees over the woman's gaping stomach, bellowing like a bull until someone had come running with an umbrella. Then with the umbrella over the woman's incision, and no light at all since none could live in that wind, Dr. Dick had clawed "the devils" in the woman away, almost literally with his bare hands, and had finally sewn her up.

"His instruments and equipment had been sterile to begin with," I tole the pill-roller man, "but he could only pray that no straw or other debris had blown or fallen into the open wound. We— We haven't any sulfa drugs, you know. Or scarcely anything else. I remember Dr. Dick's saying he rubbed the patient's incision with mentholatum before he bound it up."

"The woman, did she get well?" both my listeners asked.

"I don't know. Dr. Dick prayed—the whole mission prayed for her. That's all we can do, so very often. And sometimes I think it's just like trying to impose our will on God through the sheer volume of our importuning words.

"The woman did live for two or three days, we know. But one morning she got up and walked out of the hospital into the jungle. We found her bandage caught on a bush where she had torn it off and thrown it. She was a stranger and none of us ever saw her or heard of her again."

To what use had we put the pill-roller? I told him as frankly as if he had not been its donor. But I stressed its great value to us through the saving it effected of our small and precious stock of drugs. They laughed merrily with me at the quick and complete recoveries of the urchins and ancient crones to whom we administered our aloes and quassia-drenched pills.

Then I was suddenly conscious that the visit was over. I don't know who ended it, or how. Miss Edwards went to her telephone, called a cab company and asked for a taxi to be sent to the Regh Manufacturing Co. My pill-roller man asked me where I was staying and when I gave him the address he studied the ceiling while he did some mental arithmetic.

"Mmmmmm . . . twenty-five cents the first quarter of a mile, fifteen cents each quarter thereafter, from Maple to Radcliffe, that's . . . mmmmmm . . . I figure it comes to $2.20. How do you figure it, Edwards?"

Miss Edwards also studied the ceiling and calculated half aloud, "From Maple to Radcliffe, via Vermont . . . mmmmmm . . . I make it $2.35. They're putting in a new water main on Hancock, and that means a detour of three blocks."

H. L. Wilson plunged a hand into his pocket and drew out a neat roll of bills held together by a rubber band. Carefully, even respectfully, he unrolled two one-dollar bills. Then out of another pocket came a small bag, puckered together at the top and tied with a leather drawstring. This yielded a fifty-cent piece.

"A mite over against error, or for the driver," he explained with a sly smile. When he thanked me for coming to see him, for a moment I was bewildered.

Miss Edwards led me down the two halls, the old and the new, and through the big room with its hundred desks. Everything was quiet now, deserted, only dimly lighted. On the street she put me in the waiting taxi and paid the driver. Then she, too, thanked me. For what?

It was not until I was halfway home that I remembered a committee meeting, and a dinner party. What would I say to my host? How could I explain that I had squandered an entire afternoon—gossiping even!—with an insignificant little old man? But it had been such a pleasant afternoon. Perhaps we would be better missionaries if we had more such. That is, visits where we could talk our hearts clean and dry of worries and disappointments and frustrations. Where we could sweep our minds free of the silver dust of daydreams. Where we could share the humor of our mistakes without a blighting sense of guilt. I would be reprimanded, I knew. I deserved to be. Nevertheless, it had been a very pleasant afternoon. Very pleasant!

And then, as is the way with pleasant occasions, the memory of my visit with the pill-roller man faded into the background of my mind as I went about my work. It was only when I called at the offices of our Governing Board just before sailing for Africa that it was called into sharp focus again. A focus which I believe now will never dim.

I had scarcely sat down facing our executive secretary when he waved a letter under my nose and demanded, "What have you been doing on this trip west? How do *you* come to be playing around with multi-millionaires? And for goodness' sake, what is a pill-roller?" His words were meant to be bantering, but his eyes pressed me with eagerness.

He gave me no time to grasp the significance of his questions before he plucked a strip of yellow paper out of the envelope and held it out to me demanding, "Now what do you think of that?"

It was a check, and I recognized the writing immediately. The letters were all up and down and angular. The hand that had penned them had shaken slightly. I didn't need to look at the signature. I knew it would be: H. L. Wilson. The amount—I gasped, rubbed my eyes, and held the scrap of yellow paper at varying distances from my nose. It was always the same whether read through a nearsighted or farsighted haze: $10,000.

"Now read this," he continued, and held out two sheets of the familiar cheap tablet paper.

The note was terse and to the point. Mr. Wilson had enjoyed my visit. Edwards had enjoyed my visit. He was inclosing a check for an amount to tide the medical work of our mission station over immediate necessities. He personally wanted to underwrite a new hospital building with a substantial roof and a reliable lighting plant and care for their upkeep for an indefinite period. And then again—he had enjoyed my visit. Edwards had enjoyed my visit. If he were here when I came back to America again (I suppose he meant if he were still living) he wanted me to come to see him once more—if I were not too busy to spare an old man a little time.

I handed the note back to the secretary and stared at him completely dumbfounded. Then I heard myself stammering, "But he was—he was just a—a little—old—shabby man. Just a—a—bookkeeper, I thought. You should have seen his office. No gold letters on the door—"

"Bookkeeper my eye!" the secretary shouted. "We've looked him up. He's a multi-millionaire. One of the richest men in the United States. He started that pharmaceutical house, and it's the biggest in the world now. They say there are thousands and thousands of branches—agencies—I hardly know what—"

"If I had known— I wouldn't have— I wouldn't have dared—" I didn't interrupt. I just wasn't listening any more. Suddenly I leaned forward and picked up the note again. Hastily I re-read it and then complained vaguely.

"He keeps calling this *my* work. It isn't *my* work. It's Dr. Dick's work. And the medical staff's work. I—I just married a farmer you know, and—" I faltered into silence because the secretary was shaking his head gravely from side to side.

"No, it isn't *your* work. Nor Dick Burton's work, either. It's God's work, Mrs. Grove. We are only His servants, led— Mrs. Grove, *what is a pill-roller?*"

I saw mother again before I sailed for Africa. I had to assure myself once more that she was happy and content, but I was totally unprepared for the white-haired bundle of energy and enthusiasm who kissed me and literally brushed me aside. "Twenty-five hundred words! Twenty-five hundred words! I couldn't describe the good in your father's little finger in twenty-five hundred words," she sniffed, referring to the magazine article she and I had prepared. Now she was writing a book, a biography of my father. She had rented a typewriter, bought a ream of paper, and—

"But, mother, you don't know how to write!" I exclaimed.

Her lady-like sniff degenerated into a snort. "I learned to write a third of a century before you were born."

At first I felt inclined to argue, but finally sat and listened. Books are only words! And she would have plenty of help in stringing the words together rightly. On the tips of her fingers she totaled up for me—a constantly growing total as memory nudged her—the books which her new neighbors had written, and on a wide variety of subjects.

"And not a one of these people has greater or more sympathetic knowledge of a land than your father had of Africa," she crowed. "My trouble will not be with words, but remembering all I should—"

I needn't have ever worried in the slightest about my mother. She had come home, and was thoroughly happy to be there. And, as brother Norman said to me a few weeks later, "I think perhaps our mother has now begun *her* missionary work."

CHAPTER
FIFTEEN

Jimmy met me in Léopoldville and most of our waking hours going upriver we discussed plans for our trip across the Hungry Country. We call these missionary journeys "trips" although such a trip may last anywhere from a few days to a working lifetime. My father always declared that the term was a childish subterfuge, but the fact remains that many a missionary dream may not prove feasible, or the missionary, only a human being at best, may not be adequate to the task he sets himself. I suppose we just made psychological provision for retreat.

Missionaries on such a trip not only pick up their beds and walk. Actually they gather together everything available they consider necessary for the new work as well as the household equipment and other impedimenta dictated by the mores of a white man's land thousands of miles behind—and hundreds of years ahead—of their new home. By one device or another, this is divided or broken up and packed into bundles of not more than fifty or sixty pounds—the legal head-load of a porter.

Jimmy's and my mountain of luggage was no larger than any other missionary family carries with it on such a trip, but I wondered as I looked at it where of our slender means the money had come to pay for it. That brought to mind, too, my brief visit with the dean of my alma mater and his thanks for the debt discharged. It was then I learned that although the man I had married was not rich, neither was he quite so poor as the rest of us. He had shared with his brothers in the inheritance of his maternal grandparents' farm. His father and brothers worked the farm and sent him his portion of the profits as one sort of contribution to missionary work.

It was several months before Jimmy and I finally were ready to cross the Hungry Country. In that time we saw the kiln built to fire the bricks for Dr. Dick's new hospital, and I helped break in a new nurse who had come out from America to take my place. But at last our equipment was packed, the servants who would go with us and stay until we were settled had been hired, the porters bargained for, and our work at the central mission station terminated. There was a special chapel service for the entire mission staff and anyone from the surrounding villages who cared to come in.

There is no question that our black parishioners understood the blessing that bountiful, never-failing gardens can be to a people. So they prayed that God might strengthen the back and arms of the "hoe-bearer." As they used this term, I was suddenly struck by the fact that it had no masculine gender. I wondered as I sat with bowed head if Jimmy noticed the gender of their prayers? And if so, did he understand that it was a limitation of language? I would have to explain it to him—explain also that when they pray for a woman missionary going out to teach sewing, they pray in the masculine, sewing being *man's work*. I knew—and Jimmy, too, would understand—that our black friends' hearts and spirits transcended language, and that they sought God's blessing for both of us, and the work to which we both turned our hands.

All of the station workers saw us off. Believe me, you will never know how fond you are of the person with whom you may have bickered daily, whom you have even ridiculed and gossiped about, until you leave him or her for the uncertainties of a strange land in which you may be helpless.

When I climbed into my *tipoye* (a combination hammock and sedan chair), Maa Koo already sat in the front end, curled up like a tiny lemur in the crotch of a tree. She had not waited to be asked to go along with me, but demanded in a voice whose stridency challenged answer: What would I be in Africa without her? Or she without me now? She was old, although she denied being frail, shriveled and shrunken as an orange that dies unpicked on a tree. My carriers had laughed at the thought of her added weight being a burden when I told them she must ride with me. One of them had scooped her up on the cupped palms of his hands and tossed her into the tipoye as lightly as if she had been a puppy.

Our first day out was a pleasant one, a day that introduced Jimmy to a side of Africa he had only heard of before. It was mid-afternoon when we met a couple on the path. The man was of uncertain age—fifty, sixty, perhaps even sixty-five years. It is hard to say. His wife was young, in her late teens. The man stepped lightly and with ease. But the woman trod heavily, awkwardly as she hurried to keep up with him. It was obvious that her confinement was not far off. The man stopped to exchange the elaborate "greetings of the road" with us, and his wife squatted on her haunches and panted like a dog in the sun.

Frankly, as though we surely shared concern, the man told us of his troubles. He was penniless. He did not even possess the handful of sous for the tax collector who would be upon him in a very short time. He had heard there was a road being built somewhere ahead and he was hurrying along while there was yet time to see if the headman could use so old and stiff a back as his for a few days in return for sufficient money to pay his hut tax.

"Your wife is young. Is she not strong? Has she not made a garden and sold the vegetables in the market?" Maa Koo demanded with a sharp glance at the toad-like figure. The man ignored Maa Koo and me—mere females! *Cattle!*—and explained to Jimmy.

His wife was an excellent one. She had made a fine garden that was a credit to him. She bargained well and had received a good price for her vegetables. He had enjoyed long, delightfully titivating hours gambling with the money under the eves of the palaver hut. But, alas! the spirit of good fortune had deserted him and all the money was now gone and the tax collector was coming. Could we tell him how many hours or days traveling lay between him and the new road?

When he trotted on, the woman staggered to her feet and stumbled after him. It was no more than a few hours later when we saw the man and his wife again. Men who carry fifty to sixty pound head-loads do not step with as much sprightliness as unencumbered folk, particularly at the end of a day; so we had stopped for a brief rest.

As before, the husband walked ahead and set the pace. Even from afar it seemed to me that the woman behind him walked less awkwardly. As before, the woman immediately dropped to her haunches to rest. She did not pant this time, but her breathing was rapid, and I saw that she was very tired.

The man was grinning broadly as he plucked away the twig of thick leaves that covered something he carried on his left arm—a newborn infant. He had a daughter—a daughter to sell, he told us. Now it would not be necessary for him to find the new road and break his back over it in order to pay the hut tax.

Maa Koo snorted so violently she shook the tipoye and told him he had a thing of doubtful value in his hands. That no more than two or three infants out of every ten have the good-will of the spirits at birth—or are strong enough to combat the evil spirits through their first year of life. Maa Koo exaggerated a little of course, being jungle-born and proud of the authority old age gave her to speak positively. However the odds were very great that the child would not live through its first year.

But the old man's pride, or joy in his good fortune, equaled her scorn, and he answered Maa Koo directly. His wife bore him only daughters. The first he had sold "For nothing! *For nothing!*" And the girl had lived and was now a valuable piece of property. Her head came to here on her new owner, and he measured the child's height on his thigh. In a few years she would be ripe for marriage and since she was without blemish would bring a good price. The second daughter had brought a few more sous. She came to here, measuring, and was looked upon as a valuable piece of property. The third daughter brought a great handful of sous, and her master was satisfied with his purchase although as yet she still occasionally dropped to the earth and went about on all fours. This child—

"See! It, too, is perfect." And he jerked the tiny arms and legs out to their full length to show us. For this child he would receive a good fat price, enough to satisfy the tax-collector and something over for a few delightful hours of gambling.

Maa Koo and I turned estimating eyes upon the girl squatting on the ground a few feet away. She was resting without fuss or complaint from a labor that kept most white women in bed a week or more. She was merely *cattle*, producing *cattle*, and she had no word in the disposal of the property she had produced. Well as I knew Africa, I still wondered if she felt no love for her children, or if her apathy were merely the protection which custom and experience builds up for primitive women.

"But don't you want the child for yourself? You're not a young man, and if there should be no more—" Jimmy was arguing.

The old man interrupted him with a prideful cackle and without looking at her thrust a pointing thumb over his shoulder at his wife. "She conceives readily and calves easily," he answered.

Then he clucked to her as though she were—what she was—a domestic animal. She arose dutifully and they trotted off ahead of us.

"Well, at least *he* is carrying the baby," Jimmy said.

"That won't be for long," I assured him.

Our bearers gathered up the tipoye poles and we too started off. Jimmy did not mount his bush-car immediately but walked along beside me for a little while. I drowsed off into a light nap.

Then, "Laura," Jimmy called my attention to himself.

"Yes," I questioned with a sleepy nod of my head.

"When I was in Léopoldville I bought a supply of canned condensed milk to bring along with us just in case—in case—"

I laughed and patted his hand resting on the pole beside me. "In Africa a wife always keeps a supply of canned condensed milk around—just in case!" I told him.

He gave me a quick look, then mounted his bush-car and pushed ahead whistling.

Maa Koo and I traded chuckles. After the privilege of wives, I would tell him in my own good time, but my old black nurse and

I both had good reason to suspect that Jimmy's child already slept beneath my heart.

The questions of people who ask me about my life in Africa fall into three general categories: How many converts did you make? Is Africa developed now and a white man's country? Is game as plentiful as the travel books say?

In spite of the statistics required of him, I doubt if any missionary ever knows the extent or vitality of his influence. I'm tempted to say: God pity him if he does? I was a medical missionary, not an evangelist. Furthermore I know that I am not particularly articulate or forceful in expressing a conviction of my own—as an evangelist must be. However, I did my poor best in the presentation of my religion to a people who very definitely are not—as many individuals seem to think—empty of mind and heart and naked of soul. The Africans I have known are folk with beliefs and rituals of their own firmly imbedded by the centuries. And I must say that the general traits of humanity are not altered by pigmentation of the skin. In every mission compound, usually indistinguishably mingled with the sincere, there are always opportunists, "rice Christians." Only in Africa we say "salt Christians"—salt being the great lack there. I did my Christian duty within the limits of my understanding and my God-given abilities. On the other hand, I have never tried to count pious noses, believing rather that "by their works ye shall know them."

Now for the second question: I have actually had people rise and apologize to audiences for what I have said about Africa, explaining that I am, of course, speaking of a past era. They are wrong. I know that the maps no longer show great blank spaces, nor do they bear the quaint legends: "There are elephants here," and "There are lions here." And the white man is truly ubiquitous. He appears at infrequent intervals and for varied reasons in even the blackest corners of the Dark Continent. Nevertheless, there are great tributaries of mighty rivers whose courses have not been precisely determined by compass and sextant. There are mighty ranges of mountains known imperfectly by only a few. There are vast swamps and rain forests which only the most indomitable have penetrated. To fly over a jungle in an airplane is not to change the character of the jungle, no matter how frequent the flights. As for the roads, of which so much is said, all too many have to be hacked out of the jungle again with each dry season, for practically none of them are paved and, with the rains, lush, rampant vegetation completely nullifies man's efforts. Many an engineer instructed to continue the onward march of last season's road, has succeeded only in reopening that last season's road.

There are cities in the middle of the jungle. Cities with two- and three-storied houses, electric lights, baths, and radios, and even short lengths of paved streets. Usually they stand on a river which provides ingress and egress. I could name you a dozen such, and in each case primeval jungle literally leans over the fences which surround the gardens of the last houses.

And everywhere there is human life, not always seen, but always seeing. Human beings eyeing the strange white intruder, amused and confused by his antics—yes, only a few miles away from a modern city. A city, by the way, through whose streets hungry *simba* may stampede a herd of zebras almost any evening, and on whose telephone wires giraffes break their necks. I speak and I write of an Africa which lives on today.

Then to answer the last question: Yes, there is game in Africa, as much and more than anyone has described to you. This is due to two things. The Dark Continent is a prodigal land, and wise governments have taken the steps necessary to prevent the insane slaughter of its teeming fauna.

Not all missionaries hunt. The possession of guns requires an outlay of our scarcest commodity—money. Nor are licenses to be had for the asking. Jimmy had three guns, a light and a heavy rifle and a shotgun. At the central mission station he had been too busy to use them often, but daily on our trek across the Hungry Country he shot game for our cooking pots. It was not always what he and I would have preferred; but the porters, far from complaining, were grateful and vociferous in their thanks. Meat is meat regardless of flavor or texture and it must line the belly if legs are to trot along under a sixty-pound head-load from sunup to sundown.

And some of the meat was delicious: buffalo tongue, saddle of tommy, broiled kongoni liver or kidneys, antelope steak, breast of guinea fowl, leg and thigh of spur-winged goose, upper wing joint of greater bustard. That juicy white meat I am sure would become famous as an epicurean's delight if enough epicures encountered enough greater bustards.

Jimmy shot his first and only elephant on that trip. The animal was not noteworthy as to size of body or weight of tusks. Nor were the stalking and kill out of the ordinary. However, the adventure did introduce him to one phase of African character he had not known before. Our whole safari camped beside the elephant until there was nothing left of it but bones and hide because the porters simply refused to leave so much good meat to the vultures and jackals. Since he had provided the gargantuan feast, Jimmy was presented with one of the feet, severed at the knee joint, as a tidbit. And since it was obvious he didn't know what to do with it, the boys cooked it for us along with the other three for themselves.

First they dug a deep pit, filled it with dry wood, and kept a roaring fire going for almost a day. As this fire burned, a number of stones were thrown upon it. They sank to the bottom with the glowing embers, and when there was nothing left but white ashes, they made a red-hot lining. The four feet were set upright on these hot stones and covered over with a thick layer of green leaves. The stones were banked between and around the legs and some of the excavated dirt was shoveled back over them. Then another roaring fire was built over them and kept going all night.

Next morning ashes and dirt were scraped away, and the feet uncovered. The thick skin had burned very little, but rather had stiffened into something much like enormous cooking pots. Inside of them, around the bones, the tendons and cartilage had turned to a soft mass resembling custard, or jelly—or glue that for some reason has failed to become best quality glue.

The feet were not removed from the pit. They stayed where they were in the warm earth, and we took turns squatting around the bottom rim of the earthy cone, dipping our spoons into the gelatinous mass.

If I had not seen it, I would not have believed that anyone as old and shriveled as Maa Koo could consume such quantities of even a delicacy. More than once Jimmy put his hands under her arms and held her dangling in the air until she could straighten out her legs and stand on her feet. Her protruding stomach made her look like a child in the last swollen stages of starvation.

When the bones of the great beast were finally stripped clean, and the boys were once again willing to pick up their head-loads and move forward, they began an intermittent serenade of Jimmy which lasted for days. Their admiration and extemporaneous praise were unrestrained and their descriptions of his prowess soared into the realm of hyperbolic fantasy. I received brief mention when they petitioned the spirits of good fortune that Jimmy's wife might bear him a steady succession of sons worthy of such a mighty father. In their songs, black boys seldom mention white daughters as being desirable. Why should they wish upon the bwana they admire and respect anything which must be fed and cared for during its years of helplessness and then becomes worthless *cattle*.

But then there are many things about white men that are sources of never-failing wonder to his West African brothers. They listen with downcast eyes to tales sworn to by the most honorable bwanas that forests burst into flame and burn for days until there is nothing left but ashes and blackened stumps. These tales cannot be true, one reads in their eyes. If it were the dead grass of a plain at the end of the rainless season, yes. But everyone knows that the inside of a green tree is so wet that water drips when a tiny twig is broken, and juice runs down the trunk when the bark is smashed.

The black man also stares in disbelief of the evidence of his own eyes when a white man squats in a dugout and throws his back against the weight of water at the end of an oar all in the name of something he calls "sport," or "fun." What enjoyment can there be in *that* when it neither soothes the body, nor excites the mind, nor fills the belly?

And then, his treatment of his *cattle!* Surely there is only emptiness between white ears when a man *gives* his daughter without price to another man for that man's pleasure. Or lets her sit at home in his kraal without turning her arm muscles to good account at the end of a hoe handle.

Every safari in Africa is an excursion into a sort of never-never land for white men. I could see wonder in my husband's eyes daily as we trekked along. And although born and reared in the Dark Continent, I saw much that was new to me, too. If I had ever kept a diary it would be easier for me now to share some of the experiences which left their mark on Jimmy and me. Experiences which we enjoyed for the simple titivation of mind and spirit they gave us, and experiences which we mulled over together many times because they fortified our conviction in the value and rightness of our work and the new field we were pioneering.

For instance there was the chief we visited one afternoon and evening because the whole village was making holiday over the building of a new home. We made a point of stopping at the villages we passed, because we relied upon them for fruit and vegetables for our men—and the gossip which in primitive Africa takes the place of civilization's newspapers. These visits are usually brief, as brief as haggling over prices will permit. But this afternoon we stopped and we stayed on, and after our own restrained fashion, we helped the chief celebrate the marriage of his youngest son.

The chief had had three sons grow to manhood and he was faced with recommending to the village Council of Old Men which should inherit leadership after him. The chief had seen but few white men, and he was frank to say that he had not been particularly impressed with their characteristics or social attributes, but he was impressed with the reports which filtered in to him of their encroaching domination of this black man's land.

He believed that the calibre of a man is not measured by size of body or strength of muscles, desirable as these are. Nor is beauty

of face and figure a criterion of worth, however pleasing to look on
Size, strength, and beauty can be purchased, used, and discarded
No, these were not the secret of either a black or a white man's
success. And one must be possessed of that secret if he were to rule
over black men, and not to lose advantage to white men.

What was that secret? And how did one acquaint himself with
its mysteries? The chief did not know, and he suspected that few
men ever comprehended it fully. But he sent his three sons out, at
various times, to live for a year or a longer period if that should be
necessary, where they might discover what made the white man
powerful. By the gift which each as a dutiful son would bring him on
his return from the cities of white men, the chief would judge his
comparative fitness to rule over black men.

One son went east, where, so the chief had heard, many white
men lived in kraals that were built one on top of the other (storied
houses). Also, they dug caves like moles and bush pigs (cellars).

The second son went west where there were vast reaches of huge
trees, few white men, and many black folk as shy as their jungle-
dwelling four-footed brothers.

The third son went south where there were many white men but
still ten black men to every one of the former. And the white men,
although vastly outnumbered were overwhelmingly dominant.

Promptly at the end of a year the first son returned. He wore
strange clothing that hampered his movements and which held the
sweat and dirt of daily living close to his body and chafed his skin.
He carried his gift for his father in a sleazy bag sewn on the inside
of the nether garment (a trouser pocket). He emptied this bag,
which could not be passed from hand to hand as a proper bag should
be but was always pressed tight to his thigh, in the dust before
his father.

The gift was composed of hard, round metal disks. Some were as
big as the hollow of a man's palm, and some were no larger than
his thumbnail. Most of them were a dirty brown color, a few were
bright yellow, and some were the color of the light from a full moon
falling through the open door of a hut. These, that son assured his

father, were the secret of the white man's power. With these he acquired everything a black man did either with his spear or the strength of his *cattle's* arms.

Jimmy and I had passed beyond the limits of the tax collector's territory, even beyond the routes of most itinerant traders, and we wondered what the chief would do with copper, silver, and gold coins. He informed us immediately.

"I held the thin round bits of metal in my hand and spoke to them and they did not answer back. I bit one with my teeth and found they were not good to eat. I swallowed one and waited, but I felt no greater courage or strength of arm than I had known before. My witch doctor did not understand them, but—" The chief looked about him cautiously and then leaned forward and whispered into our ears, "I thought the witch doctor might be jealous for his own magic; so I did not pay too much attention to his words that the bits of metal might be a power for evil. However, I still have known no benefit from my first son's gift. It lies in there." And he thrust a careless thumb over his shoulder pointing toward what was obviously his treasure hut.

Then that son had purchased himself a wife and had taken his place among the men of the village. He was a good one to hunt with, for he was big and strong and dependable. Men listened when he spoke, but few asked his advice, and even fewer acted upon it when given. He was a credit to his village but not one to rule.

At the end of his year the second son returned and brought with him imprisoned in a small flat bottle a liquid magic that looked like cow's urine. His son had told him that white men sit sipping this constantly the way a black man will squat beside a pot of honey licking his fingers. Sometimes when there was very little of the magic liquid left, they fought and killed each other over its possession. The son had seen with his own eyes that it gave them great strength and courage, for after they had sat and sipped long enough they would do incredible things.

Then the chief had poured the liquid down his throat and swallowed it, although it burned like fire and choked off his breathing. For a few minutes, but only a very few minutes, it had seemed to him that magic did course through his veins. Then he went to sleep and did not awaken until the sun had risen and set twice. His wives and his people, knowing he was testing white man's magic, were afraid to touch him and had left him lie where "the little death" had overtaken him. So the sun of two mornings had cooked the meat on his bones, and the rain of two afternoons had almost leached the spirit out of his body. And when he awoke he was not wiser and stronger than he had been before. Instead he stank, for he had fouled himself many times as he lay there. And there were devils crawling through the brain inside of his head. They made him say things that even while he was speaking he knew were very foolish indeed. Foolish for a black man, anyway! And his legs when he tried to stand up and walk, shook under him like a stalk of grass when a sun bird alights upon it. And he hurt all over his body from the top of his head to the tip of his toes.

When he recovered the chief had sealed the bottle shut as tight as he could with grass and resin, so that any remnants of that kind of magic which might still be lurking in it could never get out. That, too, he had stored in his treasure hut.

That son the chief had, in the years since, given several middle-aged, strong-minded wives because, so the chief told us, if a man does not have the wit to choose between good and evil magic, neither will he be able to keep a kraal full of women in order. And the fool who is beset with domestic difficulties will not be listened to even if he does find time to babble under the eaves of the palaver hut.

The third son was a long time returning. That was because, so he told his father, the extent of white man's magic is beyond anyone's grasping completely in one lifetime. Also, he had sensed immediately upon associating himself with white men that some of their magic is not applicable to village life. So he had stayed among them, studying it. Then—unbelievable in a good son!—he had returned to his village with nothing in his hands to lay before his father.

"I was surprised, of course," the chief told us, "and the old men of the council muttered among themselves that he should be driven out of the village lest he become a bad example for other sons."

But this son had told his father that white men's magic cannot be carried in one's hands. It is only the *results* of that magic that one can pick up with his fingers. The magic itself is carried in the head, and he had been busy these years away from his village stuffing his head. Moreover there were many other sons of black Africa who were doing the same thing. They lived in groups that were called schools. This magic, like that of the black witch doctor, can be used for good or for evil, depending on the spirit of the magician.

Oh yes, there were tricks one could perform on the spur of the moment just to show that he was a magician, this son said. But the better magic was something performed day after day as need arose, something which made life better for all the village rather than for just one man.

"My youngest son's magic is curious and unpredictable," the chief said. "Sometimes it is performed quickly and when least expected that any magic is even needed. Usually in such cases the results come quickly, too. There was the time when he and I were walking along and saw that Y'llsi wished to build a kraal for a new wife where a great stone lay. Y'llsi and his sons and his brothers and his friends all put their shoulders against one side of the stone and pushed and pushed and pushed. The stone moved maybe as much as the length of one's finger. The men rested and pushed again and moved the stone another finger's length. Then my son called to them to cease their efforts, that there was a much easier way to move the stone. He said he could do it himself if only he had the help of a long strong pole and another rock much smaller than the first."

The chief paused and eyed us to see if we were impressed with his tale. Then he described how, using a pole as a lever and the smaller stone as a fulcrum, his youngest son had done the work of many men and in only a few minutes' time.

"Now that magic has become one of the chief pastimes of the young men," the chief laughed. "They spend most of their leisure moving stones until there are no big ones left within a day's walk of my village."

But that was not the extent of the white man's magic this son had learned. Suddenly the chief leaned forward and began to sniff at Jimmy and me as though he were a dog and we were a couple of bones. Then he shook out his own garment of hand-woven cloth for us to smell before he settled himself back on his stool and smiled in smug satisfaction. There was a faint odor about him which was not unpleasant but I did not at the moment recognize it.

"Yes," he was murmuring, "you too know the magic of soap."

His people had always been a clean people, the chief went on. Both the men and the women had their bathing pools in the near-by river and they had always washed themselves many times a day. But there are many kinds of dirt which do not come off in clear, cool water, and even scouring with sand and ashes will not completely remove it. As for garments, many a one became clammy and felt unpleasant against the skin long before it was worn out.

Then the youngest son had shown the women how to leach lye out of ashes, and had told them to boil the fat of animals in the lye until the fat was completely dissolved and the pot was filled with a thick yellow paste. This the son called "soap." When one applied this to the body and rubbed hard and then sluiced it away with much water, it removed everything undesirable from the skin except that evil which comes from within (ulcers and boils). The villagers soon discovered to their joy that a skin so cleaned and then annointed with fish oil did not itch, and scabies and body crabs and head lice were becoming only a memory among them.

Moving the boulder had been done quickly. It took a week at least to make soap. But some of this son's magic was even slower. It took a season to prove that it was magic to plant a fish in each hill of corn.

"Before my youngest son returned from the white man's school, our village moved after every third or fourth growing season," the chief went on. I could see as well as feel the quickening of Jimmy's interest at these words. Both of us knew that most primitive African villages are nomad, not from inclination but from necessity. The soil of the gardens becomes exhausted and unproductive and new gardens elsewhere must constantly be hacked out of the wilderness at cost of unbelievable toil and hardship.

"My son asked the men to carry their fish baskets to the river, and when many fish had tangled their gills in the wickerwork, to carry their catch to the women. He instructed the women to bury a fish in each hill of corn and beans. Then we waited, and many laughed, and some even traced in the dust with their fingers pictures of plants with fish hanging down from the stems like bean pods. There were many jokes made at his expense, but the village sat where it was for one more growing season because I commanded it. I had never before heard of fish being planted like beans, and I was curious to see what kind of crop would be grown from this strange seed."

Jimmy, the farmer, cleared his throat as though to speak. The chief very quickly hawked and spat so that whatever small spirit of evil was expelled from my husband's mouth might not enter his own. The chief went on before either of us could speak.

"There was never before such a garden in our village, although the soil had already been used too many seasons. The banana stems rustled and grew while we looked at them. We could measure the increasing heights of corn against our legs morning after morning. The manioc vines tangled with each other between the rows. The yams grew so big that some of them were pushed up out of the earth to make room for the rest. And the bean pods burst open from the number of fat beans in them. This village has never moved since. And our cooking pots have never been empty because each year now we plant fish with the seed and the gardens grow more lush with each season.

"My son says that plants eat just as human beings do and that they are particularly fond of fish. Maybe so. I do not understand it. I am content to say it is white man's magic and it is good magic."

Jimmy squeezed my hand—under a fold of my skirt, of course. It would have been a loss of caste for him as a man to have been seen caressing a mere woman. I held his fingers tight for a moment and then pushed them away. There were shouts of merry laughter down the street.

The chief smiled proudly and explained, "It was not necessary for me to buy that son a wife. Never in all my years of chieftainship have I known so many virgins to be offered one man—everyone in the village wants to be related to my youngest son. Already the number of his huts equals that of many a rich old man."

I couldn't help but smile, and wonder within myself if the young fellow had considered monogamy one custom of our civilization which he had not wished to follow. Or if he had seen beneath the sham and had sensed the polygamy of so many white men in Africa.

The chief broke into my thoughts. "The latest bride offered him is the daughter of one of our oldest witch doctors. She is a fine, fat, sturdy girl and should bear him many children. The villagers are putting up her hut for my son. Presently you will hear the song of the rooftree as the young men tie the uppermost poles together ready for the thatch. Then when the walls are plastered and the clay is dry, they will seize her in her mother's kraal and drag her off to her new home."

There was a rustle behind us and Jimmy and I turned to see who had entered. It was a man about the chief's own age and build who held in his hand a cow's tail. Our host greeted him with a sigh.

"My son will be married any day now, and I must look my best for the feasting which follows."

He got up off his stool and stretched himself prone on his back on the floor in front of us. "What a nuisance this shaving is!" he exclaimed like any man white or black, and ran a speculative hand over his jowl.

The newcomer seated himself astride the chief's chest and plucked a long strong hair from the cow's tail. Then with a deft movement he twisted it a turn about a hair on the chief's chin and gave a quick jerk. The chief flinched visibly. The primitive barber held up the first hair triumphantly for us to see, then blew it away with a little gust of breath.

Jimmy waited while a half-dozen hairs were plucked out in like manner and then exclaimed, "Good heavens! Is the man going to have his beard pulled out by the roots, hair by hair?" Then he dropped to his haunches beside our prone host and began earnestly, "Listen, there is another way of getting rid of that hair on your face, a quicker, easier way. You get yourself a raz—a very, very sharp knife, and—"

The chief waved a negligent hand from somewhere beyond the barber's buttocks. "I know all about that kind of magic, too. My son told me about that," he said. "Ouch! Wait a minute you fool! Can't you see I'm talking? My youngest son says that white men use a knife, an exceedingly sharp knife, a knife whose edge is so keen that it will sever seed-down blown against it. With this knife they cut off the face hairs of men and he supposes they use it to remove the body hairs of women—although he has never seen that done. That magic may be all right for white men, but it would be very foolish for me.

"He who sits on my chest envies me my wealth, my *cattle*, my flocks and herds, my treasure hut, my position of leadership. Would I lie helpless on my back and put such an instrument in the hands of anyone, envious or not, who sits only a hand's breath below my jugular vein? My first two sons might have found that kind of magic good. My third son shaves as I do, painful and tedious though it be."

Jimmy and I left him there, flat on his back on the ground, suffering for the sake of appearance as only a few white women ever do.

We went on the next morning, but not before a boy had come from the chief with a *presenti* for us in either hand and a message on his lips.

Here were the gifts the first two sons had brought him. They had assured their father that each meant much to white men. Would we accept them and take what pleasure from them we could? And make what use of them might be feasible for us?

The boy placed in our hands an empty whiskey bottle and a small bag of coins—$26.13 to be exact.

CHAPTER

SIXTEEN

I don't believe I ever saw Jimmy so happy as he was in the days following our visit to that last village.

"Just think," he would exclaim to me at least a hundred times a day, "a little fertilizer in the ground and they call it magic! We're on the right track, aren't we?"

Always I said, "Yes," as a wife must and smiled tenderly as at the enthusiasm of a child. I wondered many times what incidents there had been in the lives of missionary folk like my parents, and before them a paternal uncle and aunt, that had seemed magic to the primitive folk about them. The first missionary teacher, the first doctors and nurses were scarcely looked upon as men and women of God by many of their colleagues. And even today, whether or not it is recognized, a strange sort of caste system prevails in some denominations; only those ordained to the ministry are appointed to administrative or executive positions, regardless of training and inherent ability.

I remember my father's saying to my youngest brother when Charles decided to become a missionary doctor, "You have in mind, of course, that you'll always work under someone else's direction?"

"But in my own hospital—" Charles began slowly.

Father interrupted him, "In your own hospital most of all. A minister's work is limited only by his physical strength, the number of hours in the day, and his own vision. Professionally he will profit by your work, whether he recognizes and acknowledges that fact or not; and, in turn, he may even recommend that your work be terminated. He may ask your advice—it's to be hoped that he will.

And that he will give it due consideration! But it is he rather than you who will decide where you will labor. No one will ever dream of asking you for your estimate of him as a man or a Christian worker. But he—even if he knows himself a failure—will pass judgment on you, not once but almost daily."

It seems to me now, looking back to the days of my father as I do so often, searching my memory for the wisdom which he never withheld, that his best sermons dropped from his lips in broken bits of conversation. It might have been at that same time that he said: "Conversions can be counted, like the number of patients treated in a clinic and dismissed from a hospital. But conversion isn't the end. Growth in Christian character and spiritual grace is slow, as slow as that of good hardwood timber with which one must build for any kind of permanence.

"And the seed of Christianity, if it sprouts and grows, takes curious shapes and develops unpredictable fruit. Do you know what I look for when I go into a new village? Flowers! Strange mutations of the common garden varieties, and bulbs and shrubs dug up from the surrounding jungle. Why? Because if there are flowers even a few of them, a Christian—probably a missionary—once lived there.

"Given a few years, jungle growth will cover over almost anything man builds in the tropics. Primitive, animistic beliefs are almost as tenacious of life, as smothering as tropical vegetation. But something of what the resident missionary has sown always endures if it is nothing more tangible than a rosebush gone wild, or marigold and zinnia seedlings grown into flamboyant giants."

Perhaps I remember so clearly little things like that which my father said to his children, because they were always right. I, too, unconsciously looked for flowers in a new village, and I believe if Christian missionaries had ever lived among a people that fact is revealed in one way or another. I came to accept these signs as a commonplace of life, in the same way I accepted the sun and stars and the curiosity of a black sister who might hook a finger in my dress and peer down my neck, or surreptitiously lift the hem of my skirt from behind and peer upward in order to assure herself that my skin was the same revolting ashen hue all the way up and down.

There were many strange fruitings of Christian work we came upon by sheerest accident on our trip. If one could only write a history of missionary work in any primitive country! But then, to follow through, would be like unraveling the jungle vines that clamber to the tops of the tallest trees and there run rampant, forming as tangled a mass as honeysuckle on a bank.

I myself shall never forget about the book that hid in a cow. My husband and I had come to a belt of land on the edge of the Hungry Country where the tribes were herdsmen. We deliberately camped near a group of these one night so that Jimmy could examine the cattle and talk with the men about their techniques of animal husbandry. We feasted on fresh milk warm from the cow—although we sent our own containers to be milked into directly since the herdboys washed out their milking gourds with cow's urine.

As we ate our evening meal Jimmy told me that the herdsmen were also supping on milk mixed with blood. He had watched them draw the blood they wanted. First they seized a big vein in the neck of a cow and bent and twisted it in such a way that the blood banked up in a big bubble, into which a boy shot a tiny unbarbed arrow. The arrow was immediately withdrawn and a hollow reed inserted into the vein. Out of this ran a little stream of blood. When the herdboy had enough blood in his gourd, he withdrew the reed, let go of the vein, and the wound closed.

"Blood must be wonderful food," Jimmy said thoughtfully. "As wonderful as milk. And if a cow isn't tapped too often, it shouldn't hurt her particularly. It's amazing how down through the centuries people have discovered and adapted their lives to the available food supply."

After supper we went over to the nomads' camp to visit with them. I don't know, but I believe that these people must be descended from some Arab or Semitic tribe, probably driven down from the north. Certainly many of their customs and their notions of hospitality were Arabic. Before we knew what they were about, and in spite of the fact that both they and we had eaten, they drove a young bullock into the circle around the fire and killed it and made preparations for a feast. We regretted this for we knew it would be close to morning before we could make our escape and go to bed. To kill the animal to be eaten before the eyes of the guest is one of the greatest honors that can be shown him. It is incontrovertible proof that a sacrifice of value is made on his account, and that the food is not left over from a feast for another more highly regarded than he.

We had to watch each detail of the butchering—not too pleasant as entertainment. I had had this sort of thing happen to me before, but this time there was a difference. Before anything else was done, before the ox was skinned even, its stomach was laid wide open, and it was completely eviscerated. Then the oldest men, with careful, almost reverent hands, examined every inch of stomach and intestine. At last they turned the carcass over to the young men for dismembering, and settled back on their haunches about the fire, shaking their heads and murmuring to each other in tones of resigned disappointment, "Not this time. We must wait still longer."

"*Inshallah!* (It is the will of God)," others answered.

Bit by bit, as man after man felt like adding a scrap of information to the conversation, Jimmy and I learned the story behind this strange custom.

Once long ago, so it seems, there was a man of another race who lived among these people. He was a good man, strong of body and mind. His judgments were just and his magic was superior to that of the witch doctors. I asked, but I couldn't discover the nature of his magic. I doubt that anyone knew; racial memory is not prone to that kind of detail. Anyway, his magic had made such a profound impression upon the ancestors of these nomads, that they never forgot *The Man* and they spoke with the greatest respect of *The Book* from which he drew his magical powers.

Then *The Man* was gone, and I could not learn whether he died or went to another land. But in either case he left *The Book* behind him. Thereafter *The Book* was worshiped in the quiescent way fetishes are worshiped all over black Africa. It was housed in a miniature hut of its own and was brought out only when the herds, on which the well-being of the tribe depended, were being decimated by disease or animals of prey, or otherwise stood in need of powerful help.

Then one night, a neighboring people, covetous of this tribe's fat oxen and strong, beautiful women, raided the little settlement, burned their homes, seized the virgins, and drove off most of their cattle. In the morning the hut which had housed *The Book* was found burned to the ground, but there was no trace of scorched leather or charred paper in its ashes. What had become of *The Book?* The raiders had not stolen it. Of that the nomads were certain. For no one knows whether the powers of a strange fetish are for good or evil; and should it be evil, it is dangerous to have such in one's possession. But *The Book* had not burned, and for a long time no one could answer the question: What became of it?

The tribe had fled from its ruined village and had found a home on the edge of the Hungry Country. There they prospered and grew numerous again, and their herds multiplied and waxed fat. Obviously they still enjoyed the blessing of *The Book*. It was surely with them somehow, somewhere. Then one old man, who had turned his face to the wall (that is, prepared to die), opened his eyes and spoke to his people of a dream that had come to him out of that border twilight which lies between life and death. It was of a cow which looked like one he had owned in the days before his people became nomads. The cow stood in a circle of flame and munched as cows will on food which they have previously swallowed. But it was not ordinary food that the cow belched up out of her second stomach, chewed, and then re-swallowed. It was *The Book*. And as she munched and swallowed, and munched and swallowed, strange evil men with spears in their hands danced outside the circle of fire and shouted at the cow and tried to reach her, but they could not because of the heat of the flames.

The old man's neighbors accepted the dream as a message from the all-knowing spirits. A cow had swallowed *The Book* in order to keep it from the raiders, a cow which itself had escaped capture. And today, their *Book*, left them by *The Man*, was still with them. Else, how could they continue to enjoy the magic of *The Book*?

Therefore, every time a beast from the herd was killed or died of itself, the hidden recesses of the animal were searched with minute care by the old men.

It seemed to me that on this trip Jimmy began listening to the men as they talked with each other with as careful and appreciative an ear as my father had ever done. Of evenings he would retail to me the choice bits he had heard of folklore and folk wisdom: why the bat has no feathers on its wings; why the bush pig holds its ridiculous tail straight up; why the knees of an elephant's back legs bend forward like a man's and not backward like those of other animals. When the boys found that he was genuinely interested, they told him fragments of their history as a people, preserved for them not in great dusty tomes, but in the skulls of especially trained old women whose minds have amazing retentive abilities.

"But all that memorizing goes for nothing when an old woman dies," Jimmy protested to me. "You would think that just as a sheer labor-saving device they would have learned to write and set things down for themselves."

It was old Maa Koo who replied to him, surprising me not with her garrulity but her acumen: "I have seen many missionaries come and go, bwana, tall and short ones, fat and lean ones, garrulous and taciturn. In spite of all they say, a black man knows many things about them: Some of them are afraid of their God, others love Him. One thing, however, they all have in common. They all sat in schools, they say, sat for many years and had their heads stuffed by those who in a few seasons, and in spite of their own stuffed heads, must die. Then, when you missionaries come into a village you start immediately to stuff our heads, and you work hard at it because in a few seasons you, too, must die. You have many books, yes, but you do this stuffing by word of mouth, man to man and woman to child. And all your books are nothing to you and all your head-stuffing is blown away as lightly as the ashes of a dead campfire when the unseen folk [the spirits] beckon to you. You work harder than we, and you come to the same end. As for your books—poofh! You lay them on a table and the ants eat them. You hide them away in an iron box and the mold gums their pages together. Is yours a better way?"

That last was more like a snort of pitying derision than a question.

"There are times when you just can't answer them, aren't there?" Jimmy said to me. "You know you're right, and yet what can you say out of your own background and experience that fits theirs?"

Yet Jimmy, like every other white man I had ever seen come to Africa, would argue with them. And when his blunt straightforwardness was unable to follow the devious channels of their reasoning, he would wail to me, "Why do people call these folk *simple* children of nature?" Another time his words were almost a protest against intangible difficulties. "Before I came to Africa I used to think—just like a lot of other folk!—that there was nothing in these people's minds but wives and—and cannibalism."

Yet before that day was done I heard him again arguing with the cook boy that right is right and wrong is wrong, and that any man of moderate intelligence can draw a clear line of distinction between the two. The cook boy in turn protested that the keener a man's mind the more difficulty he frequently has in knowing which is right and which is wrong.

"Now if he, ignorantly or otherwise, places temptation in the way of another so that the other sins, perhaps without knowing that he is at fault—"

Supper was delayed that evening for the cook boy took time out to tell Jimmy the story of the rich man and the *sloogeh* dog. The sloogeh dog is a folk character which has wandered down from North Africa into some central territories. He is much like the Bre'r Fox of the Uncle Remus stories, but there is a difference. I suppose the moral training of white children, or that figment of white man's civilization called "poetic justice," has required that the sly cunning of Bre'r Fox be punished. His trickery usually ends in personal embarrassment or disaster. A folk tale that has not been tampered with is apt to be more realistic, truer to the day-by-day living habits of men. Anyway, the African sloogeh dog is sly, cunning, usually on the side of outwardly obvious community good, and he is admired and respected because he enjoys the love of the friendly spirits—one of the best reasons to a mind whose philosophy has been molded by the physical realities of life.

My fingers lay idle in my lap and I watched my husband's face as the cook boy talked. Jimmy's ability or failure to laugh at the right places in such a tale as this was one measure of his possible success in the work which lay ahead of him.

The rich man the cook described as wealthy almost beyond conception. The number of his wives was so great that it took him more than a day just to walk past the doors of their huts. His marriageable daughters, all of whom were strong and handsome and therefore would bring a good price, were so numerous that they were guarded by the old women in herds like cattle. The jungle surrounding his village had been stripped of young trees in order to build the granaries in which to store his beans and corn and ground nuts. The palisade around his kraal was constructed not of wood but of elephant tusks of fabulous size. And no one could describe the quantities of food placed before him daily at every meal, the number of pots, the size of the gourds or the mat platters, or the aroma which filled the air at meal time.

Now this rich man had acquired his wealth all by himself, by dint of his own strength and cunning. And the activities which brought him wealth dissolved friendships. So now, at the height of his power, no man sat and talked or dreamed with him of an afternoon. No guests dipped their fingers into his pots at meal time. None of his wives came to him when darkness had fallen except when his commands were enforced by threat of the *kiboko* (a cat-o'-nine-tails of rhinoceros hide).

One day a sloogeh dog wandered into the village and happened to pass the rich man's kraal at meal time. The fragrance of the food was so great that it knocked the sloogeh dog back onto his haunches as easily as an angry hand might have done. While the rich man gorged himself inside the ivory palisade, the sloogeh dog sat outside with his eyes closed and his nose pointed at the sun and sniffed and sniffed, deeper and deeper, until it seemed as though he would burst wide open from the quantities of the aroma with which he filled his lungs.

When the rich man could not push one more tiny morsel down past his gullet even with the most determined finger, his cook boy took the pots and gourds and woven platters away. The fragrance of food outside the palisade floated up above the trees and was gone. Then the sloogeh dog stood up and felt that his belly was as empty as ever. He trotted around to the back of the rich man's kraal expecting to feast on rich scraps, but not even so much as a scorched chicken feather was tossed over the palisade. The sloogeh dog had to go on down to the village midden and dig out a bone for himself.

Still, that food! Just to smell it was a feast. And day after day, as the rich man gorged inside his kraal the sloogeh dog sat outside and sniffed and sniffed until it looked as though he would burst himself wide open.

Then one day the rich man saw the sloogeh dog sitting outside in the shade of his ivory fence smelling the fragrance of his food. At first he laughed at the foolish mutt; but when he realized that the dog, too, was enjoying his food—and therefore his wealth—he arose in anger and shouted at the sloogeh dog to go away. But the sloogeh dog was outside the palisade where any one is free to walk and he refused to go away as long as there was such delicious food to be sniffed at. When the rich man realized that all his shouting was to no avail, he called his cook boy and had the food hurried quickly away.

And every meal, every day thereafter, was ruined for him because the sloogeh dog sat outside his gate and sniffed and sniffed and enjoyed the food as much or more than the sated man himself. Finally the rich man could stand it no longer and he went to the Council of Old Men and demanded that the sloogeh dog be arrested for theft and tried as a common criminal. The old men wanted to laugh at the rich glutton's childish reasoning but they did not dare. So the sloogeh dog was arrested and brought to trial before a certain judge appointed by the old men.

The rich man argued that the food belonged to him, every bit of it, including its aroma, and whoever took to himself any portion of the food, including its fragrance, was a thief. The sloogeh dog, for his part, pled—and even made jokes about it—that the air of heaven was free to all God's creatures from birth, and it did not matter whether that air were breathed outside a rich man's gate or elsewhere.

Subtly our cook boy implied that all men are human and are moved by human considerations—even judges. Everyone feared the power of the rich man, even the judge. No one expected any verdict but guilty for the sloogeh dog. No one was surprised when it came. But during the lengthy trial the sloogeh dog had become the friend of everyone in the village, and the judge deferred pronouncing sentence until early sunrise the next morning.

Again, everyone in the village was present to hear the sentence, curious and full of pity. Their curiosity was whetted by the fact that the judge arrived leading one of his horses, saddled and bridled. Was he making a trip later in the day? Where? What was his business elsewhere? The questions were merely friendly interest on the part of his neighbors, but the judge put them aside with evasive answers. He did not tie the horse, but merely dropped its reins to the earth and let it stand just inside the gate. Then the judge called the rich man and the sloogeh dog to come before him.

The rich man had been correct in his reasoning, the judge said. His food, all portions of it in any form, was his own private property and whoever took to himself any bit of it in any form was a thief. The fact that the sloogeh dog had come daily to the rich man's gate and partook of the aroma of the food was proof that the theft was deliberate. Theft is an exceedingly serious matter in Africa and is punished severely. If the sloogeh dog had stolen only once, his paws would have been cut off, the judge said. But the crime had become a daily habit and there was no just penalty but death. Not a quick and easy death, but a long drawn-out and pain-ful one so that he suffered according to the enormity of his crime.

The judge handed the rich man a huge, heavy kiboko. The sloogeh dog must be beaten to death and justice demanded that the sentence be carried out by the one he had wronged. The rich man seized the whip and swung the cruel lashes high over his head.

But stop! The judge held up his hand to show that he had not finished speaking. True, the sloogeh dog was guilty of theft, he went on. But since it was only the spirit, the ghost, the shadow of the rich man's food he had stolen, it was only his spirit, his ghost, or its visible form, his shadow that must be punished. The rich man must beat the sloogeh dog's shadow until it died. The shadow was a big, long, fat one now, for the sun was only peeping over the tops of the trees. But, as the sun rose in the heavens, it would shrivel the shadow until at exactly noon there would be nothing left of it and everyone could take it for granted that it had died. But until it died, the rich man must administer killing blows with the heavy cat-o'-nine-tails. And all the time he must take great care never to touch the sloogeh dog's body with one of the lashes since the animal was not being punished, only his shadow.

The rich man was dumbfounded and would have replied angrily had not the people cheered and the other old men of the council ap-plauded, and the judge himself roared out: "This sentence is just and of your seeking. You caused the arrest and the trial. Now ad-minister justice. It is your duty."

Again the cook boy went into the details of the rich man's dis-comfiture. He described minutely how the rich man had to follow the sloogeh dog around hour after hour, beating his shadow with the huge whip, his heavy labor always increased by the care he must take never to touch the sloogeh dog with one of the many lashes. When the sloogeh dog lay down for a nap, the man had to go down on his knees and hold the lashes in his hands in order to smack them against the earth accurately in the little patch of shadow. When the sloogeh dog sought a tree in order to relieve himself—well, that portion, like a good deal in African folklore, cannot be retold with propriety.

And as the sun rose in the heavens, and the shadow grew shorter and shorter, greater and greater care had to be exercised lest the rich man commit the unpardonable offense of striking another with a whip. And the whip itself grew heavier and heavier until there was scarcely strength left in the rich man's flabby arms to lift it with.

But whenever the rich man's efforts flagged, the people jeered, the old men of the council whistled insultingly between their teeth, and the judge threatened him with dire punishment if he did not fulfill his part of the justice he had sought.

At last the rich man, trembling from exhaustion, his fine garments soaked with perspiration, his eyes blinded and his nostrils choked with dust he continually stirred up with the whip, could endure his humiliation no longer. He caught sight of the judge's horse standing bridled and saddled, untied, beside the open gate. He threw down the kiboko and with a scream of despair, leaped upon the horse, dug his heels in its flanks and dashed out of the gateway. And that was the last time anyone in his village ever saw the rich man again.

Jimmy's laughter was quick and ready at the end of the tale, but the cook boy sobered him with the question: "And now, bwana, will you please tell me just where and with whom *right* lay? And who was guilty of wrong doing? I must remind you that the sloogeh dog was a condemned thief. That the sentence punished the accuser and not the accused. That the accuser himself became a thief— guilty of the crime for which he sought justice. That the judge, after careful thought, deliberately placed temptation in the way of a weak man and therefore—by the laws of my people at least—shared his guilt equally. You, who have said you always know what is right and what is wrong, and that there is never question in your mind as to one or the other, will you explain the moral of this tale to me so that I, in my poor way, may the better appreciate its wisdom?"

I had to laugh, for Jimmy's mouth actually fell open.

When he spoke it was to say, 'Back ho— Back in my village, across the big waters, they told me that I would find you a simple child of nature, hungry for my knowledge."

Our cook boy waited for Jimmy to go on, and when he did not, said simply, "I know nothing of the wisdom of your old men, bwana. I have never sat and listened to them spin tales of your people."

I was sorry I had laughed and, thinking to salve my husband's bruised ego, and to put the cook boy in his place with my superior knowledge of Africa asked, "What about the rich man's wives? You mentioned no one to inherit them, and such a large number of women—"

"Mama, do you care to eat tonight?"

The cook boy's words were slow and patient. But it was that last patience a man exercises before he calls upon Mumbo Jumbo, the vengeful spirit whose help is invoked by men when his two-legged *cattle* become obstreperous. I wrapped myself in sudden, complete silence as a wise woman will on such occasions—and finally we ate.

CHAPTER
SEVENTEEN

It was while we were on trek that the Hungry Country gave Jimmy and me the waif that, as a joke in the beginning, I called our first son. Then circumstances, as well as emotion, transmuted feeble witticism to simple fact in every way except biologically. Yet neither the wildest imagination nor the fiercest mother love could ever call Hey Boy a bundle from heaven or a blessed event.

We passed a village and as usual stopped for a visit with the chief, and to secure what we could in the way of fresh eggs and vegetables. That visit was like one of countless others, and it would be completely out of mind now were it not for the fact that as we left we heard a wail. It was a fretful cry that to my nurse's ears meant just one thing, a sick child. It came from a hut that had its matting door dropped over the low opening. I walked over to it and clapped my hands—the African equivalent of knocking. The mat was not lifted and I clapped my hands together again, louder and a little longer this time.

As I waited I happened to turn my eyes from the door and glance down the village street. Every man, woman and child in sight was staring at me. Every one of them immediately dropped his eyes or turned away. Some dived into huts, some walked away, all gave their attention to something else. And the mat over the door had not stirred. And louder and longer came that wail, more fretful, more helplessly complaining of human misery.

People speak of "thinking black." I myself have used that term. Perhaps it is language's poor best, but I do not think it is entirely descriptive of a psychological fact. The folkways of a people not only guide social behavior, but they also shape so-called instinctive reaction to a situation. I doubt if color of skin has anything to do with this. Instead, I think it depends on those associations of childhood which have to do with the basic things of life: food, clothing, shelter, deportment while at play. Whether that idea is right or wrong, I knew almost exactly what was inside of that hut, and I turned and walked back to my husband.

"Why didn't you go in?" he demanded.

"The door mat is down," I answered. "It is not meant that anyone shall go in."

"Maybe nobody's in there to lift the mat," he suggested, raising his voice slightly to cover another wail.

"There isn't," I replied. "The child has been abandoned."

My husband peered at me under frowning brows. Then he seized my shoulder with a rough hand and shook me as though I were in a trance.

"Come away," I whispered. "It is their affair and not ours."

He let go of my shoulder, and the way in which he did it was as though he had flung me aside bodily. I watched him, not with fear since I knew we were in no physical danger, but full of dread so heavy it drenched my being. I knew that by a simple act of mercy he would violate the tenets of a civilization as old, as well-fitted to bring these people through the vicissitudes they had faced in ages past, as his own.

As Jimmy pushed the door mat aside it broke in two and fell to the ground. There was no one to be seen on the street now, no one at all, yet again I knew that a hundred pair of eyes watched us both and would continue to watch every move each one of us made until we had left the village far behind us.

Jimmy had to bend his tall angular frame almost double in order to enter the hut. He crawled out on his knees and right elbow. In his left arm and hampered right hand he carried a roll of the oldest, rottenest zebra skin I have ever seen, a hide only half tanned to begin with, and now so far gone that even the oldest old woman would no longer lay it across her shoulders.

"Where shall we take him?" Jimmy demanded, rising to his feet. Then he looked around, and for the first time he, too, saw that apparently the village was suddenly deserted.

"Back to our camp," I answered. "There's no place else for him to go."

"But his father and mother? Where are they?" my husband insisted.

"He hasn't any—now. You see, Jimmy, to these people he's dead. Or ought to be."

Jimmy stood for a moment looking down the narrow space between two rows of huts. His jaw was set stubbornly and I believe if anything on two legs topped by a face had appeared, he would have forced the child into its arms. We two, however, stood alone except for the indefinable aura of our alien civilization which pervaded a seemingly empty world. He turned abruptly and strode back to camp, and I stumbled along behind trying to keep up with his long legs. And as we went I, with what little breath I could spare for words, tried to explain to my husband what had happened in the hut behind us.

We never knew the child's exact age, but because of the physical evidence of having reached puberty, we thought him probably fourteen in spite of his disease-wasted body. We did not know details of his illness until weeks had passed by. Many facts we never knew, but in essence the child told us something like this: When the devils of disease first clawed their way into his body, he was a half-grown boy and, since he was therefore nearing the time when he would be an asset to the family, a witch doctor had been hired to treat him. The black practitioner had drenched the patient with brews of leaf, bark, and poison fruits. He had rubbed his skin with salves made from fish oil and the ash of charred animal viscera. And there had been quite a hullabaloo of drums, incantations and gymnastic dancing.

But the devils were too strong and too malicious. In the midst of the drumming and dancing the boy had rolled over onto his back, his mouth had fallen wide open, and the witch doctor could tell from the choking, gasping breath that the evil spirits were ripping the boy's soul loose from its body fastenings and were preparing to flee with it. Then the gasping ceased, and the witch doctor announced to the parents and their neighbors that the soul was gone. And life must follow after the soul very quickly.

He stuffed the boy's ears with grass and wax, closed the eyes and laid weights of wet clay upon them, pinched the nostrils together with strong fingers, and bound the mouth shut with a fragment of grass cord. This was so that no other evil spirit could enter into the body of the boy and take up its abode where the soul had once dwelt. Human souls, good as well as malicious, were unpredictable enough. A human body walking among them tenanted by an alien spirit of unknown, untried evil was a horror and a risk to life, limb, and soul which no village cared to undergo.

Everything of value was removed from the hut, including the warm comfortable skins on which the child had lain and the strong, windproof matting at the doorhole, and everyone went away. When a half-day had passed during which no sound came from the hut, a torch would be thrust into its thatch and within an hour or two thereafter the only sign of the evil which had visited the village would be a heap of ashes and a few charred bones.

But just as the evil in the child had been stronger than the witch doctor's magic, his body now was stronger than the villagers, including his parents, wished. Noises began to come from the closed, deserted hut. Human noises which indicated to the horrified listening ears outside that something had scratched away the cord binding up the slack jaw. Imagination pictured flaring nostrils, and wide open eyes from which the dabs of clay had been brushed aside. When I examined my "first son" the evening of the day fate thrust him into our arms, I found that the witch doctor had done a thorough job of blocking all body orifices against an evil spirit's efforts to enter. How the child had ever cleared its nostrils to breathe or its mouth to wail I shall never know.

I could see in my mind's eye the horror spreading over the village with the first cry from the child. It meant there was now one, or even more openings into the child's body whereby malignant homeless ones who are ever seeking shelter might enter.

"What did they do then?" my husband asked. "This new emergency taxed the witch doctor's powers to their limit, I suppose?"

"They didn't do anything, Jimmy," I answered. "No one, including the witch doctor would enter the hut. For if the child had not already become a monster in human form, that calamity would overtake it within a very short time."

I spoke intensely to my husband, as one hoping he would understand and, perhaps, not condemn without pity. In any case his words surprised me, "You know better than that, Laura."

"Me? Yes, I know better. But I wasn't there. And his people—"

"What would have happened if we hadn't come along?" Jimmy demanded.

"Nothing," I said. "The human body—whether it houses a soul or an evil spirit—does not live without food. No one would have entered the hut and he would have died of starvation. Then they would have burned the hut and everything would have been the same as—"

"Suppose the child had somehow gained strength and crawled out of the door?" my husband went on obstinately.

I took a minute to catch my breath before I replied, "I don't know just how they would do it, Jimmy. But the child wouldn't have been permitted to live. To them he no longer has a human spirit, or soul, and at the very best he could never be anything but a walking, talking empty body. Death would be forced upon him one way or another."

Jimmy looked at the roll of rotten zebra hide in his arms and spoke even more slowly, "Then—when he's well—what do we do with him?"

Unaccountably I felt like laughing. "He's yours from now on," I told my husband, and added whimsically, "Jimmy, you've got a son."

He didn't give a sign that my words had stirred him in any way. But after a moment of silent contemplation of the bundle of filth in his arms, he turned and started off again with the quiet words, "Well, let's get the tyke back to camp—and wash what's left of him."

The child was awake and conscious when we entered our tent. Hastily I set up a folding table and spread a towel over it.

"Hey, boy, don't be frightened. We're your friends. We're going to feed you and make you feel good all over again," Jimmy assured the child several times as he unrolled that morsel of humanity from the zebra skin.

Then it was, "Hey, boy, swallow the food the bwana mama gives you. It'll make you strong and well."

And, "Hey, boy, now don't cry. This will take all the hurt out of you," as I rubbed away what filth I could and soaked the scabrous portions with oil so that they would be softened and removable in the morning.

Before we learned the name his mother had given him, Jimmy's soothing "Hey Boy," had become attached to the child, and he was never called anything else. I suppose the black folk about us took it for granted that the syllables were freighted with white man's wisdom, since all tribal names have a meaning and are usually descriptive of the individual who bears them.

I'm not possessed of enough medical knowledge to be able to tell just what was the nature of Hey Boy's illness. Gray suppurating ulcers of varying degress of repulsiveness had perforated his skin. But ulcers are indigenous to primitive Africa and unless a muscle is eaten away or an expanse of bone exposed, they are scarcely considered incapacitating. There is no way of telling how long he had lain without food and his body was so thin and his skin laid so close to the bones that it looked as though someone had stretched a black rubber balloon over a skeleton in a fit of impishness.

But whatever the nature of Hey Boy's illness, it had run its course, and the will to live and the phenomenal vitality of youth were asserting themselves. About all I did for the child was to cleanse his body, dress his ulcers, and feed him. I sacrificed a few cans of condensed milk to him until we came to the next village. There we bought a nanny goat whose milk Jimmy and I shared with Hey Boy and whose kid shared the fore end of my tipoye with Maa Koo, and our human bag of bones.

Tipoye beaters are always stalwart fellows proud of their stamina and the evenness of their stride over any kind of terrain. They can swing along mile after mile, singing and changing places with fresh bearers without a break in pace or the gentle sway of the hammock chair. Their position in a safari is always different from that of the other porters, special and important.

Now, when I asked solemnly if their manhood was equal to the burden of Hey Boy—if my old nurse and I took turns walking occasionally—a pretense of the greatest consternation spread over one face. That boy picked up a leaf and laid it on the seat of my chair. Then he grasped his end of the tipoye pole and struggled with it as though it were close to impossible for him to seat it on his shoulder. And with the pole finally adjusted his knees began to buckle as though a giant weight pressed him inexorably earthward. His fellows immediately followed his example and I suppose it was a good five minutes before we three strangely assorted passengers were finally loaded onto our African palanquin and under way. Even then, one among them made up a song about the enormity of the burden put upon them; and all joined in the lugubrious chorus:

> "Throw out the leaf.
> Throw out the leaf, mama,
> Before our backs are curled into
> an old man's bow
> And our feet sink into the earth
> like tembo's pads."

It seemed to me that ever since I had first met Jimmy on the boat out of New York he had been teaching me. Soil and fertility, animal husbandry, the relationship between these two and the dependence of a higher civilization—with all of man's devious social complications—upon their development and continued progress. I had never thought much about agriculture before I met him. A farmer plowed and planted, had a strong back and got his hands dirty, by popular conception which I accepted without question was "independent" and not too amenable to formal social usage. Appreciation of the fact that the successful farmer is a combination of intelligent executive, capable administrator and indefatigable laborer all bound together in a person of unsentimental, far-sighted social consciousness came through association with my husband. Every woman who loves and respects her husband—although she may never put it in these words—believes he was sent to her by God. Looking backward over my life, I know this was true of Jimmy and me. He was more than fulfillment of heart and body. I am putting it poorly for many to understand, I know; but women—good women!—will appreciate fully what I mean when I say that he took his turn at "bringing me up" just as Maa Koo and my father had done in their turns before him.

But somewhere, sometime during that trek across the Hungry Country, our places changed, spiritually at least. I was teaching Jimmy although the forthright textbook type of instruction remained his prerogative. Jimmy was a good teacher, and I'm afraid I was not because I "felt" so much of my knowledge instead of having it stored away in more or less readily articulate form.

The acquisition of Hey Boy was something of a starting point in this new relationship. I tried, but still I don't think I ever made Jimmy quite understand that no primitive African would ever have felt that the child had been murdered if he had died in his hut. In the native mind, the spirit, the essence of being human, had gone out of him, and one cannot kill what is already dead although neglect may quiet the impatient shell's whimperings.

Also, Jimmy could never accept the fact that mental and physical filth are comparative matters. To me, a nurse, my husband after his evening tub, was dirty compared with a patient prepared for surgery. More than once I saw him shudder involuntarily in villages where I knew the skins were cleanest. Not only had the inhabitants bathed a mere once a day. Some of them scrubbed away the dust and sweat of their exertions a half-dozen times a day. And after each scrubbing—sometimes with sand, sometimes with a handful of dried grass, always with running water—they had anointed themselves with fish oil or castor oil, or some other unguent whose origin might be a primeval mystery of the witch doctor. The castor beans could be crushed and left to drip through a bamboo tray. The fish oil could be obtained only by allowing the flesh to rot and the oil to rise to the top where it could be skimmed off. Neither unguent could be mistaken for a product of the French perfumers' art. Both prevent sunburn—and contrary to popular conception, black skins do sunburn. They prevent chafing. I believe they heal incipient ulcers without number. They keep down lice and scabies, and therefore are disease preventatives. But my husband—long inured to white man's smells—judged cleanliness like a white man, more often by his nose than by reason.

Only once did I ever try to explain to him about food, that what is at hand and most readily obtainable with the weapons and other instruments which have evolved through the years, determine what a man shall eat. He replied with the brilliant argument of a facial grimace, a disgusting noise from his throat, and the three words, "Grubs! Snakes! Rats!" And again that noise.

"What is so different between a grub and an oyster?" I demanded hotly, since I knew my argument was lost before it had begun—that it had been lost centuries back as the two civilizations developed in their different locales and on their divergent planes.

"Just what makes the great difference between a rat and a squirrel or a rabbit?" My foregone failure urged me on. "All three are rodents. All three are dainty feeders. And birds and snakes? Both are descended from the same ancestors. The snake is far the cleaner of the two. Yet breast of guinea fowl is a delicacy. Yes! But python steak—"

The words were choked back into my throat by the smothering fingers of a big hand. Why is it that men think rough arms about one's shoulders, still rougher lips on one's mouth, should answer all arguments? We women, too. We try so hard to be rational, coldly reasoning creatures, and yet who among us does not rate a caress above flawless logic?

Yes, more and more as we trekked across the Hungry Country, it was I who became the teacher, but not according to any of the accepted rules of pedagogy. These, however excellent, are not workable marital techniques as any wife can tell you. We must be far more subtle—or crudely blunt. There was, for instance, the time I kicked Jimmy's shins so hard I had to put compresses on his swollen ankles an hour later.

Jimmy had just seen a flock of sheep. They were sorry-looking animals, skinny and covered with open sores that fouled their scant wool with pus and blood serum. They were feeding on a type of wire grass that even to my unpracticed eyes seemed devoid of any nutrition. The grass sprang up among a sparse shrub growth which had just gone to seed. And these seeds, everyone of them, were miniature, many-barbed, shaftless arrowheads. It was impossible to pull these seeds backward out of our own clothing. They had to be pushed on through, even if that meant stripping off the most intimate garment on the spot. An animal which brushed ever so lightly against one of these bushes in seed time must have had its skin punctured in a hundred places by these living barbs which could only work forward. They must have suffered horribly.

The sheep we saw were under the care of several abnormally tall, thin, yet remarkably healthy-looking men. They stood at ease to talk with us, swaying slightly on one leg, the foot of the second leg propped against the inner thigh of the first.

"Dinkas—from the north—slaves," I whispered to Jimmy as we came up.

One word glanced adversely across my husband's mind. "Slaves? Nonsense! Slavery's prohibited by international law now. You know that," he answered.

"Yes, I know it. But *they* don't," I replied.

He brushed my feminine logic aside with a masculine snort, and began to discuss the condition of the sheep with the men. For a moment I debated in my mind whether or not I should remind Jimmy of the old man we had passed on the road a fortnight back —the old man whose human brood mare had conveniently borne him a slaveling which at the last hour obviated the necessity of his earning his own hut tax himself.

I decided against that. Instead, while Jimmy talked with one fellow I drew out of the other—with what I hoped was adroit questioning—a tale which is an all too common African Odyssey. A stripling is given to a chief in an effort to curry favor. He is then traded for an ancient and contraband rifle—which probably exploded and crippled its owner the first time it was fired. Southward the boy comes with his masters, ever southward, passing from this hand to that when financial necessity demands or a profitable bargain can be struck. The slave to whom I talked had been in this village six seasons and hoped that his present master would generously give him a wife. Not a young wife for his pleasure, or even one on whom he might possibly father her last child, but a woman who would at least cook his mealies and keep his back warm on chilly nights.

Jimmy gave no sign of overhearing us. I broke off my conversation abruptly, however, for I heard him beginning to ask the number of flocks, and the number of animals in each flock. As surreptitiously as I could, I kicked his ankle. He gave me a surprised look and put out a hand to steady me, thinking perhaps that I had taken a step and stumbled. Again that forbidden question, and again I kicked, harder. This time the look he shot at me was stern, and he moved out of range. Again, "How many sheep would you say—" Swiftly I moved into position and kicked. He winced openly and turned an angry face toward me.

"For heaven's sake, Laura, what's the matter with you?" he demanded.

The slaves snickered. My husband had not changed language, and they understood his question. Understood, too, that here was a husband having to deal with an irrational, irritating female. They watched, and listened, avidly curious. Another man's techniques for dealing with his *cattle* are always interesting, always entertaining—and then a man may learn something which will be useful to himself upon the right occasion.

Rapidly, and in English, I explained to Jimmy that it is an unforgivable insult, an injury even demanding redress, to ask a man to number his possessions. The jealous, malicious spirits are always listening, and the man will tell any lie to escape arousing their envy and greed and spite. Also, the generous, friendly spirits are disgusted with and flee from a man who boasts, taking their favors with them.

"Even the government census-taker only estimates," I ended.

Again the slaves snickered, staring down at Jimmy with half-pitying, half-contemptuous eyes. And he was surprised at their amusement, for how was he to know that they had expected him to subdue this garrulous creature with one word?

I was contrite and humble, of course, as a wife must be when I rubbed Jimmy's ankle with oil and put a compress over the blue and swollen knots. But I was not prepared for his simple question apparently apropos of nothing.

"Just how prevalent is slavery, Laura? Here in Africa, I mean."

I hesitated for a moment. Words can be so broad and nebulous in their meaning. And who can plumb the inherited mores back of the ears into which words fall? Mores which tinge and shade every syllable beyond the conception of the speaker.

"Slavery—is everywhere—about us," I said finally and let it go at that.

CHAPTER
EIGHTEEN

If this were a certain kind of novel adhering to the rules fiction writers have permitted others to impose upon them, it would have ended when, punk in my hair, and orchid roots in my ears, Jimmy kissed me. But no one brought up as I was can believe that pre-marital sex dalliance is the sole end of human existence. And every woman who has stood before an altar with a man and answered, "I do"—even when she has had to be nudged in the ribs in order to get the promise out at the right time—knows that human problems are not forever dissolved by the magic of this holy ritual.

And I suppose I should add that if this were a travel book it would be full of the many wonders that make up this ancient, mysterious land that tolerates white men in its darkest recesses, but covers up his footsteps and forgets him almost as soon as he is gone. There would be chapters picturing the rugged snow-capped mountains on the equator, the chains of dead craters each holding within its precipice-walled heart what might be a forgotten Garden of Eden, the great escarpments and the sunken rift valleys within laced with long shimmering lakes of unbelievable depth, rivers as mighty as ocean currents, flights of birds that blot out the sun and paint a noonday sky with sunset colors, migrations of animals so numberless that the progress of a caravan is halted as effectively as though a flood of molten lava pushed its way across the plain.

As Jimmy and I trekked through deep jungle and across sun-baked plain, like others before us we were awed by the cathedral-like solemnity and splendor of the magnificent trees—and irritated by the heat and sweat and flies and human frailties of our porters.

The time came when we had to measure our day's trek from water hole to water hole, be it ten miles or forty. Always we knew there was water ahead. My father had said so. Always within sight were at least a few animals cropping assiduously where it was difficult for human eyes to see herbage. And always, at first only a pinpoint on the horizon, there was a clump of deeper, truer green—plants growing with water at their feet.

Once we had to camp a half-mile back from a dry water course and send a boy ahead to hide in the bushes and watch where the zebras would dig in the sand with their hooves. When these small circus horses had located the course of the sub-surface stream for us, we drove them away, dug a half-dozen shallow wells and filled our canteens and water skins.

Once we came upon a pocket of absolutely arid sand on which a score of round-bottomed clay jars stood scattered here and there in haphazard fashion. "Abandoned cooking pots," Jimmy remarked. "And big ones, too."

But they were *hods,* clay watering-troughs. There was water here? But exactly where? And how to get it? Scanning the plain all around us we finally located a herdboy with a small group of emaciated cows. He may have been two—or ten—miles away. One cannot judge of distances seen through heat devils that make objects shimmer crazily as though shaken by a perpetual ague. Inevitably, as the sun sank, he and his cows would amble back to us and his hidden store of water. And since we were men and women of peace, he would share with us.

That day had been a difficult one. I had said or done something that irritated Maa Koo and she had lunged forward onto her knees in the tipoye and slapped me as though I were still a child.

"You are a woman now, with a husband and a child in your belly," she shrieked. "Don't try to plague me like an untrained girl."

Jimmy did not want to wait beside the silent empty hods for the shivering herds, and when the headman of our safari insisted and I agreed with him, my husband turned on me angrily. We said

234 •

things to each other that were not meant and are best forgotten. Contrary to popular expectation in such circumstances, my husband had the last word.

"Sometimes I wonder what it is you believe in—God or—or your father or—or just—these people."

Not only did the cowherd we had seen come in well before sundown and the tropical darkness which immediately follows it. Seven or eight others, pasturing too far away for even the keenest eyes among us to see, also came up. Each traveled in a straight line although the hods which marked the site could not have been visible above the floor of the arid plain more than a quarter of a mile away.

The cows milled around the dry hods mooing softly on an anxiously complaining note, while the herdsmen consulted among themselves concerning us. We sat waiting with what patience we could. Then one came over to settle the price of the water: so many gourdsful tonight per man for drinking; so many gourdsful in the morning for drinking; so many gourdsful in our water skins to carry with us. Apparently he thought he drove a stiff bargain; but it cost us less than five pounds of trade salt.

Payment was made in advance and it was then we discovered that the fellow could not count and had no idea of numbers or their addition, but it would have been difficult for anyone to have cheated him. We had to line up and one by one walk past a certain spot. As each one of us reached this point, one of the cowherds made a long mark in the sand with a nimble toe. Jimmy carried Hey Boy in his arms and called the talesman's attention to him. The head cowherd gave the child a cursory glance and answered, "We do not charge for sick calves."

Then Jimmy doled out the amount of salt agreed upon for each one of us, one measure at a time. As each individual measure was completed to the chief cowherd's satisfaction, and it was poured into a gourd, the fellow who had made the parallel marks in the sand erased one with a swipe of his foot.

This completed, one of the cowherds began what looked like a shuffling dance where he stood. Sand flew in all directions, and in a few seconds he had swept four or five square feet of flat limestone clean. Then he grasped at a huge iron ring imbedded somehow in the rock—a ring which hundreds of years ago might have been removed from some Crusader's castle far to the north, or from some Moslem potentate's palace far to the east. We saw a segment of rock move. Another cowherd bent over to help the first, and together they lifted and moved to one side a round tapering plug of stone.

Immediately the lowing among the cows increased, for they smelled the water. Jimmy and I looked down into the small opening and we could see the water throwing back the last rays of daylight like polished black glass. The gleaming surface undulated gently; it was a flowing stream. We waited until the cows had drunk their fill because, the chief herdsman explained to us solemnly, no one has learned as yet to speak cow language, so no one can explain to the brutes that he who pays should eat and drink first.

When everyone's needs had been cared for, the stone plug was inserted in its hole, and a layer of sand kicked back over it. Five minutes later, not a one in our party could have located that well except by accident, or by sweeping the entire sanded area clean.

Some time during that trek across the Hungry Country, a change took place in my husband. I don't know how to explain it or to what it was due. Perhaps the psychologists of my own race understand and have scientific terms for what happened; these changes are fairly common to both white and black people—and people of any other color, I suppose. Primitive Africans are very sensitive to the first subtle signs of this metamorphosis of personality and sometimes even of character. They do not struggle against it, but merely sigh and shake their heads and murmur to each other that the individual has been deserted by the friendly spirits.

The first indication I had of this change was when Jimmy indulged in a fit of sulking. I am told by other wives that this is a relatively common masculine state, and I have heard techniques for dealing with it discussed that range all the way from the craven to the ridiculous, even sadistic. Believe me, every wife encountering it for the first time is bewildered. But I was then too young in wifehood to know that these phases of masculinity are "dealt with."

I simply lived through a day in which my husband looked through me not at me, over my head and past my shoulder as though I were not there to be seen. All of his remarks were addressed to others as though I had no ears. At supper when he lunged across the table to help himself to dishes that sat within six inches of my plate, I told him that if we had not found Hey Boy, and if by some miracle the child had lived on in his village, that was exactly the same way his "savage" people would have treated him.

My husband looked at me then and replied with none of that tenderness with which the writers of romantic fiction usually dress up such scenes. But bluntly, apparently unemotionally, "Are you pregnant?"

"Yes."

"Then why didn't you say so a long time before this? Why didn't you say so before we started out. Now all this time—and effort—and money have been spent for nothing. I suppose I'll have to tell the headman to turn around and head back over that damned desert tomorrow morning," he exclaimed pettishly.

"For heaven's sake, why?" I demanded in amazement.

"Well, you can't have a baby away off up here a thousand miles from nowhere," he muttered.

"This isn't nowhere," I answered. "It's the home of people. And babies are born here all the time, every year. Every day in some village. Women have been having babies where we're going for thousands of years past."

"But white women—" he began.

"I was born under a trailside bush," I reminded him.

"Don't tell me that story—again," was his logical rejoinder.

Maa Koo came over and stood beside my chair and Jimmy turned belligerent eyes on her.

"I have borne many children," she told him in a softly reassuring voice as though he were a child. "No one can say which spirits will be present at a birth, the friendly or the evil ones. But when the little mama calves, I will be with her."

"How can you put up with that?" my husband fairly snarled. "Her speaking of you as though you were a cow?"

"Haven't you already learned, Jimmy, that in this country women are—*cattle?*" I rebuked.

"When the time for the little mama to drop her calf—" Maa Koo began with gentle insistence.

"Oh shut up!" Jimmy interrupted rudely.

It was the first time I had ever heard my husband speak to anyone in such a tone. I started to get up, but a camp chair is not conducive to quick and dignified risings. Moreover my heels slipped in the sand underneath them, my feet flew forward, and I kicked both of Jimmy's knees. Intent to quick and sincere apology surged through me, but I heard myself saying instead, "Don't you dare speak to Maa Koo like that!"

For a moment I thought he was going to slap me. Then both of us turned to Maa Koo in amazement. The old woman was African before she was Christian, a primitive tribeswoman before she was a mission girl. She loosed a flood of words on Jimmy's head, a torrent that grew in volume and invective. I should have stopped her, but I could only sit quietly trying to find a firm place in the sand for my heels so I could ease myself up out of my chair and beat a retreat.

Jimmy glared, but my old nurse was unafraid of any man's frown. I wonder now if she were not enjoying herself as she had not done for many years. Jimmy's heels did not betray him, but then his feet were twice the size of mine. He arose so suddenly his chair tumbled over behind him.

With Jimmy's going, Maa Koo stopped as abruptly as a phonograph record when one lifts the needle. We looked at each other, and being women, we smiled. She did not offer advice or crow in triumph; she merely pointed at Jimmy's plate still heaped with good food. I nodded and with one swing of her arm she scooped the plate off the table and onto the ground. There, squatting above it, she devoured every crumb and swiped up the juices with a forefinger which she sucked noisily. I waited until the plate looked as clean as if it had been washed. Then the two of us each bent nearly double, my old nurse with the weight of her many years, and I with the strength and vigor of my child which I had begun to feel when there was any change in posture, hobbled into my tent. I undressed and went to bed while Maa Koo kept herself exceedingly busy doing nothing. Strange when I think of it now, but I was as comfortably calm and as much at peace with the world as in the days when my life was man-less.

However, once in bed I remembered that my husband had been rude, rough, and on the verge of the physically abusive. Almost dutifully I began to sniffle. Out of the corner of one eye I glanced at Maa Koo to see what her reaction might be. She smiled and nodded and slipped out of the tent to the tiny one the safari boys had put up for her alongside us. It was as though the old woman had said to me out of her ageless wisdom: In the heart of the Dark Continent, there, too, women must weep. When I had really warmed up to the business of tears, I was sorry my husband was not there to witness the fine performance.

When I awoke, it was sometime in the middle of the night. I tried to turn over and was helpless. Jimmy was in my bed with me, his arms locked about me suffocatingly tight. One skinny shank was sprawled heavily across my knees. I tried to lie as slender as I could and turn a trifle. It only wedged me more firmly against his chest. My child was cramped, too, and kicked unmercifully.

"All I need to be perfectly comfortable now is Hey Boy sitting on my head," I muttered. Then with as wide a yawn as I could manage, I went back to sleep a perfectly contented woman.

But when I awoke early the next morning, Jimmy had not

shifted his position, and he was wet with sweat. So was I—with his sweat. That day was the most frantic one in my existence. Not that I had never seen or cared for malaria patients before. Nor was it because I had the entire oversight of our safari on my hands. We went on, as we had to. The chair portion of my tipoye was slung to one side and the hammock end was extended by a blanket pinned over and around the poles by long thorns. For the most part, I walked beside the hammock, and when I was resting I peddled along on Jimmy's bush-car. The carrier on the front of that was partially emptied of Jimmy's effects, and Maa Koo perched on top of what was left as though it were a tall stool. Porters took turns carrying Hey Boy on their shoulders, his legs dangling around their necks.

Many folk on trek complain of their porters' grumbling when anything beyond the bare tasks bargained for at the beginning of a journey is asked of them. Mine did not, although even the slightest extra duty adds materially to the fatigue of a day's work. Even the weight of the emaciated body of a sick child can double a man's burden, and when borne for no more than an hour at a time multiplies the day's weariness.

Jimmy lay in the tipoye for three days, and the morning of the fourth was back on his feet again. He was no longer delirious, but he stumbled occasionally when he walked, and now and then I saw him seize a boy's arm in order to steady himself. Still, being a man, he was irritated, and then furious with me when at first I refused to ride the tipoye in his place. But I had to give in before he would even get onto his bush-car. He quickly fell behind me, but not before I saw that his shirt was completely wet with the sweat of exhaustion.

It was not until several days later when he was much stronger and, therefore, more like himself, that I had time and opportunity to indulge myself in the self-pity which attacks every woman during pregnancy. My thoughts were a chaotic mixture of the rational and the ridiculous. Jimmy wanted a child, I was very certain of that. But in that case, why had he broached the matter of my pregnancy as though it were a deliberate check on his personal ambitions? I know now, and I should have acknowledged that fact then, that Jimmy's brusqueness was rooted in his oncoming bout with malaria, but it was a fairly enjoyable experience to feel that I had been abused. From that it was an easy next step to imagine that when my time came, there would be "complications." Suppose I, too, like Esther should die in childbirth. I woke Maa Koo up out of a sound snooze to ask her if, in case I should die, she would take my child back to Blanche, brother Norman's wife; and if, as she had done with my mother, and me, she would help my sister-in-law to rear—

Maa Koo stretched out on her back, put her hands up over her head, and began to sing a silly song in a quavering and cracked falsetto. Her theme was: Which is the bigger fool—an adolescent boy, or an adolescent girl? The answer: Neither! But the same boy and the same girl given a few more years of life and inches of stature. I leaned forward, although I had to hold my breath because of my uncomfortably full stomach, seized her by a heel and shook her leg in order to call her attention.

Maa Koo only raised her head to look along the length of her prone body at me and to murmur scornfully, "Silly-Child-in-a-Woman's-Body, my voice is not sweet in my own ears, therefore, I cannot expect you to enjoy my tune. But it is pleasanter by far to listen to than your querulous whining." She crooked her scrawny neck sidewise so she could see past me and I knew she was looking at Jimmy. Then, "Who do you imagine that you are?" she said to me in substance. "Mu'ungu? Do you think you can flee men when —when they are being male animals? And turn a listening ear only when they please you?" Her head fell back on her crossed arms once again, and she lapsed into her ridiculous ditty. I was debating within myself as to whether or not I should weep again when Jimmy came peddling up abreast of us.

"What's that?" he demanded pointing at Maa Koo. "A broken-down calliope?"

We looked at each other and laughed. And then looked at each other again. And looked. And looked. It was as though each were seeing the other after a long absence. And each of us knew without words that both of us were on the road to marital health once more.

Many people have said something like this to me: When you missionaries start off somewhere into the trackless wilderness, how do you know when you've got where you're going?

We know. In the first place where people live there are no trackless wildernesses, and we do not go into unpopulated areas. We go to a definite village or a people because the work of missionaries is in villages and with people. If the site has not already been decided upon for us by others who have visited the new territory and sometimes know it very well, the pioneer missionary must settle temporarily in some likely spot and let the experiences of the days and years to come help him locate a permanent station.

We knew we were beyond the Hungry Country at last when we came to the first small village surrounded by a *boma,* a crude fence of thorns only a trifle higher than the old men said a lion could jump. There was no attempt at a gate. A hole was torn in the wall by those inside each morning, and the breach in the thorny barricade was repaired each night.

Jimmy took time to try to explain to them that two posts in the ground and a swinging wall of solid wood would save them immense labor—and countless scratches. They answered that there were no trees in the territory which grew thin and flat as he described the wood to be used. They had no saws or adzes and listened to my husband's descriptions of these wonders as a child does to the marvels of fairyland. Too, they wondered if such a thing as a gate might not so arouse simba's curiosity that the king of the beasts would never cease admiring it and so would never again go off to his grass-grown *dongas* and leave them in some small peace. But these were not my father's People of the Fan and we went on.

I cannot rightly say that we found the village of Fusora. It was the other way around, Fusora found us and a delegation came to stop us, turn us around, and lead us *home*. We were a couple of hour's walking to the west of it, and an African woodsman's eyes would have read immediately that we were near a large, long-established, fairly populous village. We were passing through a wooded area of immense old mahogany trees, an area that was so free of wind-pruned dead wood underneath the forest giants that it looked park-like.

In a primeval forest that clean-swept look can mean only one thing. The women of some village, who do not cut wood for their cooking fires, had broken up all the branches the wind had torn loose and carried them away. It is always amazing to me that one can live in a country so long and yet not see one of its commonest sights. Jimmy had never seen a woman gathering wood or carrying home the load she had assembled. We came upon one now, bent double so that the huge bundle of sticks seemingly rested evenly on her head, back, and hips almost parallel with the ground.

When I came up, Jimmy and the woman were standing still, staring at each other. Her head was turned sidewise as much as the burden on it would permit. The back of one of her hands rested on the ground to help balance her overburdened body.

"Look at that!" my husband gasped pointing. "I wouldn't load a horse like that!"

"May your back grow ever stronger and your load lighter, old mother," I called to her in formal greeting.

She did not reply in kind. Instead she gave me a searching look. Then she straightened up, letting her immense burden tumble to one side, turned, and sped away.

"Scared to death," I heard Jimmy mutter. But instinctively I knew that the woman was not frightened. There had been surprise but no fear in her staring eyes.

Jimmy motioned for us to go on. It was early afternoon and there were still several hours of trekking time left in the day. But I did not want to go on. I felt—I knew instinctively—that this was the country we had come so far seeking.

The wood-gatherer was back before our boys came up to us.

There were two other women with her. One of them bore what looked like a child on her shoulders, its legs astride her neck. But no! It was not a child she bore, but a woman older even than Maa Koo. Incredibly old, incredibly shrunken. The skin on her face looked like wet black cloth draped across a fleshless skull. Africa is cruel to those who have passed the years of their communal usefulness, but even in its cruelty it is respectful of great age as an achievement. Wordlessly my old nurse arose to her feet, clapped her hands together softly before her nose, spread her palms narrowly apart and spat very neatly between them. It was homage.

The three strapping younger women stopped about ten feet from us, but I saw only the burning eyes in the shrunken poll above one of them. Time and physical necessities had seemingly passed the ancient crone by. She didn't blink her eyelids even once as she stared at me. I felt naked of soul and waited as though for judgment.

Then the ancient one held up a claw-like hand and crooked a finger at me. The three younger women turned and trotted off in the direction from which they had come. The pig-a-back crone twisted her scrawny neck until she faced directly backward. She fixed me with those burning, unblinking eyes and I arose and hurried after her.

"Hey! Where the dickens do you think you're going?" I heard Jimmy shout, doubt, wonder, bewilderment in his voice.

I hurried on, a little awkwardly perhaps because of my pregnancy. Even if my husband had commanded me to stop and turn back, I could not have done so. In the language of my father, it was as though the hand of God were on my shoulder pushing me forward gently, insistently. I heard the skitter of Maa Koo's light footsteps behind me in the leaf mold underfoot and I was dumbly glad. But I felt rather than heard Jimmy's heavier tread and my heart leaped and I could have broken out into song.

I don't know how long we hurried through the forest like that, but finally we came to an open glade where a village stood among the few scattered trees. Many men, women and children stood chattering in groups between the two rows of huts. They fell silent and backed out of our way as we passed. Then, still silent, they fell in behind and followed us.

We passed through the village and beyond it, perhaps three hundred feet, to where a lone hut stood on a small knoll. To casual eyes the hut would have looked new, for the outside was freshly plastered with clay and the thatch had been renewed within the past year. But I felt, even before I saw, that it was very, very old. There was moss on some of the posts supporting the overhanging roof that formed a low, cool porch around the entire building. To one side of the hut stood the now barkless skeleton of a small dead tree killed by the weight and smothering embrace of an immense bignonia vine. Looking closely I could see that only a confusion of propping poles kept the dead tree standing. Beside the entrance a giant, densely leaved shrub towered higher than the peak of the conical roof. Because of its size I did not recognize it until I brushed against it and was enveloped in a pungent perfume. I hesitated momentarily to peer into the branches which were as large as my arm. The main stem was as big around as my body. I pinched a leaf and sniffed at my fingers—old-fashioned rose geranium. All around the hut, even under the thick foliage of the geranium, the ground was swept clean of all debris.

At the door of the hut the younger woman picked the crone off her shoulders with one hand and put her down. The old woman bent forward, rested the knuckles of her hands on the ground, and with surprising agility ran into the hut on all fours like an animal. In the cool dim light inside I could see that everything was as spotlessly clean as on the outside. And it had been a white man's—or woman's—hut, for placed against the wall stood a chair, a table, and a metal-bound black chest. The chair and table, the glue of their joints long gone, were held together with thongs of rawhide. On the table were three objects: a paper-thin porcelain saucer, and lying in it the three pieces of a matching cup. I picked up the three fragments of fine china and fitted them together as a woman will, and for some reason—balance perhaps, the gum of years, I don't know what—they stuck. Carefully I set the fragile vessel back in its saucer.

The old woman ran to the table, pulled herself up with one hand, peered at the cup with her abnormally bright, unblinking eyes, touched it delicately with a finger as sere and angular as a crushed reed at the end of the dry season. The pieces of cup still held together.

The crone dropped on all fours again, ran to the door and shouted to those outside in a thin, eerie voice, *"That One's* strange drinking gourd leaped together in *This One's* hands and now it is as it was in years past."

I picked up the second object on the table—a small bundle. The oiled silk in which it had been wrapped shattered to bits as I pulled it off two books. The top one was a Book of Common Prayer, and I think the bottom one was a Bible. I can't be sure, however, for its pages were so brown and gummed together and ravaged by mites that all lettering was illegible.

The Prayer Book was in scarcely better condition, but there was an inscription in faint brown letters that I could decipher in part:

"To our beloved daughter, Jo Ellen,
Xmas, ... 9 May God bless you
and keep . . ."

That was all I could make out.

Again the old woman hurried to the door and screeched in her weird treble, "The bundle on the high-legged stool speaks to her as it did to *That One.*"

Then the crone ambled back and stood in front of me. She expected something. But what? I felt like one trying to understand sudden unexpected pleading in a dog's eyes. I looked about me and my eyes fell on the chest. It was padlocked, and my heart sank. Idly I picked up the lock and although I was not conscious of tugging at it, it slipped out of the rotten wood almost as easily as though its staples had only been pushed into butter. A little stream of rust followed the prongs out of their holes and sifted onto the floor.

I lifted the lid carefully. Even so, one of the hinges broke. I held the lid straight until I could lean it against the wall. The trunk was absolutely empty except for one object at which I stared with unbelieving eyes. A teapot, around which cloth had once been wrapped, lay there. A silver teapot so thickly tarnished that it iridesced blues like a scrap of mica. The old woman rested her chin on the edge of the trunk as a puppy might have done and peered down at the teapot with me. As softly as her thin voice would permit she murmured, "Her other gear was buried with her so that she would be comfortable after her own fashion in the spirit world. This she asked that we leave for one who would come after her, saying that such a one would understand its magic."

The old woman twisted her head around on her snake-like neck and I could see the bones sliding under the skin as she did so. But again as always her eyes seized mine and held them as she asked, "Do you understand that magic?" The words were simple enough, but I understood that this was the supreme test.

I nodded yes and bent over and picked up the teapot. I was surprised at its weight. It was heavy as only sterling is heavy. It was beautiful, too, its feet, fat middle and hinged lid were a confusion of inter-twining vines, overlapping leaves, and heaped-up bunches of grapes. I took hold of the knob on top, but the tarnish of uncounted years was so heavy that it seemed cemented shut. I took a clip out of my hair and ran its sharpest edge between the lid and the teapot, then, with some wrenching, I got the pot open. The sides and bottom inside gleamed faintly, softly blue. It seemed —but it could have been only imagination after so long a time and so much tarnish—still its inside seemed delicately fragrant, as a gentlewoman's teapot should be.

The crone had once again pulled herself up to her full, pathetically shrunken height. If possible her eyes were rounder and brighter than ever with question. She pointed a finger whose joints wobbled unjoint-like even while she tried to point, and asked in a whisper that cut through the silence like the point of a sharp knife, *"That one* said that she who would come after her would understand what she left for her." One horny fingernail at least three-quarters of an inch long, tinged lightly on the bottom of the teapot. "Do you know the magic of that, too?"

I heard myself saying to her, "First I take a cloth and a heap of the cleanest of ashes. With the cloth and ashes I rub this—this strange pot. I rub and rub and rub it until all of the inside and outside of it are the color of—of—of the cutting edge of an iron spearhead that has just been sharpened on a stone."

The old woman's eyes were as keen and alert as a terrier's watching a hoped-for tidbit, but she gave no sign to help me as I searched for words.

"Then I open it—this way—and inside I drop a pinch of dried leaves that I have brought with me from my kraal far, far away. On the leaves I pour boiling water—*mah sukani kateer!* Not just hot water, but water that bubbles and hisses as I pour it. Then I wait until the room is fragrant before I pour some of the water into this—" pointing at the cup on the table "—and drink it. By then the water is a golden brown and it is good to taste and refreshing to a tired body. I may drink several cups of it, and however tired I have been, it rests me and I am ready to go about my woman's work again."

I remember that I felt anxious as I ended and wondered if there was anything more I could say about the teapot. Should I try to explain to her that the possession of such a household utensil was a source of the same sort of pride to the women of my race as the lengths of copper wire wound around their arms and legs are to the women of her own?

But the old, old woman had fallen on all fours again and ambled to the door. At the entrance she looked back again and crooked her finger at me as she had done in the woods. I followed her outside into the sunshine Jimmy stood beside the rose geranium tree, Maa Koo clutching his pants leg on one side, and Hey Boy on the other. Behind him the villagers had drawn into close ranks and stood waiting with an air of tense expectancy. Then suddenly the men before me looked familiar, tantalizingly familiar. I wrinkled my forehead with the intensity of my effort to pin down that haunting sense of having seen these faces before.

Then I knew. And it was almost as though I should shout out, "Abu Sayheed? Where are you, Abu Sayheed? Come forward, young man, so that we who have known your loyal service may give you greetings." The tribal cicatrices on the faces of the men were exactly the same as those which had scarred the forehead and cheeks of the boy who had served my father for an unknown gift of great value to him, a gift which he was to have after my father's death. And there had been one other whose face bore these same tribal markings—a musician, a convicted thief, a jungle phantom whom I had never seen but once, and whose name I did not know.

But the old crone's voice brought me back to those about me. "This is the one who was to come," I heard her say.

I looked at Jimmy and smiled, but he was staring at me with a perplexed frown on his face. "What's that?" he asked with a quick look and short nod at the blackened teapot I still held in my arms.

But the old, old woman was speaking again to a tall, powerfully built man, "I have done the work which *That One* and your father laid upon me, and now I feel the weariness of my years."

Again maybe it was only my imagination, but it seemed to me that her voice grew thinner, more ghost-like as she spoke. Certainly the pleading note in her eerie tones could not be mistaken. And her body seemed to shrink visibly as she stood there, to grow even frailer, more child-like in stature.

"Abu Sayheed twenty years from now," raced through my mind as I looked at the big man to whom the crone had spoken.

"You have done your work well, old mother," he answered her gravely. "Seek your release when you will."

The old woman darted away so quickly that the men and women scarcely had time to step aside to let her pass.

I turned back to my husband, but he did not demand an explanation. Perhaps he understood as little of what was going on about us as I did. He just said, and it was statement of fact we both recognized, "This is trek's end for us, Laura?"

"Yes." How true he was, neither of us at the moment could possibly know.

Then the big, powerfully built man, who was Chief Mu'muou, was greeting us, inviting us to take up residence in his village, to move into the well-preserved, immaculately clean hut, promising us vegetables and fruit from the women's gardens. I don't think it occurred to any villager there that we could refuse. It certainly didn't to us. I believe that if we had wished to leave, we would have been prevented from doing so. Jimmy and I both wondered at first silently and then openly to each other as we made preparations for the evening meal and the night to follow, if two missionaries had ever entered a village under similar circumstances before.

And the wonder of it had not ceased with our reception. We were getting ready to sit down to supper under the overhanging thatch of our new home when Maa Koo came to tell us what she had just heard from the village women. The ancient crone who had greeted us in the forest and led us to the village, was dead. With Chief Mu'muou's permission she had fled to her hut, dropped upon her pallet of skins, turned her face to the wall, and had given up her spirit to that shadowy world it had long wished her to enter. The next morning Jimmy and I, with the whole village watching us, gave the old women Christian burial. We placed a wooden cross above her head, but we had no lettering to burn into the wood. The old woman had lived so long that everyone about her had forgotten her name.

"That old woman lived just long enough to meet us," Jimmy remarked as he smoothed the small mound of earth above her. "Laura, if we'd been another five or ten years coming, I think she would have been here waiting."

"I know it," I answered him.

"Do you really think so?" He didn't mean to question me. His words were merely relief that I shared a conviction based on nothing more tangible than one of the still unfathomed mysteries of the Dark Continent. "How do you explain a thing like that?"

Neither was that a question, only an expression of wonder. Still I blundered an answer, "I don't explain it. It is simply Africa. One has to accept much without reason here because—well, because our civilization is different, and primitive folkways—"

CHAPTER
NINETEEN

Each time I have told others of my life, I have wished at this point
that I could report a great new field of work opened to Christian
missionaries, and a strong and growing station established. It may
be that these will come in the future, and that I shall thank God
for the part I have been permitted to play in developing them. If
they do, they will be a monument to my husband, for his was the
vision. But there is little—very little—accomplished yet. It is still
a vision.

Our welcome to the village of Fusora and the beginning of our
life there was most unusual for a missionary couple pioneering work
in a new community. We did not have to make our way in any
sense of that phrase. The-One-Who-Had-Been-There-Before-Us, the
"beloved daughter, Jo Ellen—" of the Prayer Book flyleaf, must
have been an exceedingly remarkable woman. I learned that the
ancient crone who had ridden pig-a-back to greet us in the forest,
and who had tested me with the ritual of the teapot, was the last
human being who had ever seen her. But Jo Ellen's memory was
a green and decidedly growing thing in the minds of others. At least
a hundred men and women described her to me as their parents had
described her to them.

And the descriptions differed so greatly that about all they had in
common was that the nebulous Jo Ellen was tall, gaunt, white haired
and white faced, hooved like myself (that is, she wore shoes on her
feet), and every day of her life she talked often and long with
Mu'ungu. Mu'ungu answered her questions, and she passed this
divine wisdom on to the people of Fusora. Then Jo Ellen had died

and the jungle mold had claimed her body and the vagrant winds of heaven had blown the memory of her words of wisdom out of the minds of her people. And Mu'ungu, no longer finding congenial companionship in the village of Fusora, had gone away. But she had impressed upon these people before she died that *One* would come after her who would also talk much with Mu'ungu and would pass His wisdom on to them. *This One* they must welcome and love and respect regardless of whether she loved them in return or censured them like an old woman whose mind is full of days gone by when the world was peopled with better folk.

Respect and love are human growths which must be cultivated, but there is no question that at the very first I was welcomed and with some awe. Let me stress, *I* was welcomed. Jimmy was merely accepted, as Maa Koo and Hey Boy were accepted. They were all three appurtenances of mine. This in itself was most unusual, for in primitive Africa it is the man who is important, who is a personality. The situation was reversed with Jimmy and me. The "beloved . . . Jo Ellen" must indeed have been an exceedingly remarkable woman.

At first neither my husband nor I was conscious of this curious reversal of standing. We moved into the house left by our predecessor, built a hut near by for Maa Koo and Hey Boy, paid off our porters and sent them back across the Hungry Country—not, however, before we had written numerous letters for them to carry along. I covered pages telling what little I had found out about the shadowy Jo Ellen, her cup, her Testament, Prayer Book, and teapot. Could and would my Governing Board find out who she had been, where she had come from, her denomination and country; even to whom I should send the heirloom teapot?

The evening before the porters left we were introduced to a delicacy which Jimmy simply could not swallow and even I found difficulty in getting more than a few morsels past my lips. About mid-afternoon Chief Mu'muou, a score of councilors, and a half-dozen or so of his wives came to call. These latter included the latest acquisition, an abnormally fat dumpling of a child who could hardly move because of her weight, and old Tuou. Tuou, like Maa Koo, was of indefinite age, but they were like-minded women in many ways and became fast friends almost immediately. Chief Mu'muou, who was obviously half of wife Tuou's age, assured me casually—as though that were a simple matter for social discussion—that he had never lain with Tuou. He had inherited her from his father and the number of wives had been so great and the children had been so numerous in his father's kraal that neither he nor she could remember whether or not she was his mother. He had not sold her to some other man as he could easily have done because as head wife she had kept his other *cattle* in line and had ruled his household with the merciless efficiency of a labor recruiter.

I knew something was expected of me in the way of hospitality and I decided upon the ritual of the teapot. Gourd cups appeared as if by magic and we kept Maa Koo busy for the next hour heating pots of water. Since my supply of tea was limited we steeped each pinch of leaves until there was little of tea flavor left in them. Toward the end I took to adding a teaspoonful of epsom salts to each potful of water, since I knew the brew would be expected to have some magical effect.

Then a half-dozen fat-tailed sheep were driven before us and slaughtered. My hosts and hostesses were childishly eager to learn if I knew this was an honor being done me. As casually as I could I remarked to Jimmy and Maa Koo at least a half-dozen times how wonderful it was to see the animals killed because now we knew that the meat was fresh and the beasts had been healthy, that they had not died by accident or from some disease and so were simply being devoured to keep the meat from being wasted.

The tails of the sheep were enormous. Two of them had dragged on the ground as the animals walked. The smallest, I estimated, must have weighed at least twenty-five pounds. A fire was kindled and the unbelievably fat tails were cut off and roasted on the spot for us and the chief and his entourage. The rest of the animals—heads, eyes, lungs, and entrails as well as flesh—were divided up and carried away by villagers who gnawed at the dripping fragments as they went. Melted tallow ran down our fingers and splotched soggily in the dust at our feet as we tried to hold the sizzling tidbits of pure fat handed us—tidbits weighing three or four pounds. Then, when the first pangs of greed had been satisfied with gulping mouthfuls of the half-raw tail, pots of wild honey were passed from hand to hand. What portions were left of the fat were dipped repeatedly in the honey and licked with gusto and loud smacking of lips. By dint of some sleight of hand and Maa Koo's and Hey Boy's enjoyment of the feast, I was able to get through it with proper circumspection. But Jimmy—helplessly and most discourteously—dropped his chunk of tail in the dust and fled. He got no further than the back of the hut where all of us could hear him retching, but I couldn't see that it spoiled anyone's appetite. By Chief Mu'muou's order, the portion Jimmy had dropped was retrieved, given a little shake and laid in a crotch of the rose geranium tree against his return.

Jimmy and I set about our work in the village of Fusora immediately, and since the duties of each of us were so different in nature I don't suppose either of us had too clear an idea what the other was doing. I know that being a woman I talked enough of my hopes and plans, but Jimmy was never garrulous, and I probably listened with only a wifely half-ear to the little he did have to say. My excuse, if such is acceptable, is that my pregnancy was plumply obvious now, and I thoroughly enjoyed being of interest to my black sisters.

I had no difficulty at all setting up clinical work. Chief Mu'muou was suffering from a boil the size of an egg on his left shoulder when we arrived in the village. He described the swelling as the kraal which devils had built for themselves under his skin. He really knew something about boils and how to express the pus when one came to a head. This one, however, was so located that he had to push his shoulder forward and twist his fat neck in order to look at it—both painful processes. He could reach only one side of it with his pudgy fingers, and stabbing pressure from one side occasioned only still greater pain. He told me plaintively that the devils were thumbing their noses at him.

I asked him why none of his wives had opened and cleansed the boil for him. He answered me, logically enough for a black chief regardless of how it may appeal to you, that he administered corporal punishment whenever he thought any of his wives needed it, that he had to lay the whip on heavily since *cattle* are relatively immune to pain—and he did not trust any of them with his shoulder.

The handkerchief I was carrying at the time was a very old one with several small holes in it. I placed one of the tiny holes over the head of the boil and pulled all four corners as tight and flat against the flesh as I could. The gentle pressure, equalized over a large area, scarcely aggravated the pain he was already suffering, and the head of the boil was out before he knew what was happening.

It was a miracle. A small one, but nevertheless a miracle, and Mu'muou demanded of me that, as a very great favor, I give him the worn-out and now fouled handkerchief. With such a magical aid, he assured me, he would never again let a boil get beyond its initial stages. I assured him with equal solemnity and great earnestness that the magic of my profession demanded that I burn the handkerchief immediately lest the devils now wrapped up in it escape to plague others in the village. I thrust it under a cooking pot before he could suggest that the local witch doctor exercise the current devils out of it.

By way of thanks for my simple surgery, Chief Mu'muou ordered his wives to line up for my first clinic. Furthermore he assured me that if I were curious I might cut open any but a few of the very youngest and newest among them and peer at their insides to my heart's content. He had heard that white witch doctors sometimes did this.

Following a brief talk with the women in which I explained the purpose of a clinic and invited the wives to come to my hut the next day, Chief Mu'muou and his mother-wife Tuou, took me on a tour of his kraal. This was a huge affair covering several acres entirely surrounded by walls of woven bamboo. The entrance, leading up to the chief's hut which stood in the exact center of the enclosure, was roofed over with bamboo. The earth underfoot was meticulously clean. Not a weed or spear of grass or dead leaf from the small clumps of mango trees showed anywhere. Loads of firewood leaned against this or that hut, but there were no splinters or fragments of bark scattered about. Every hut was a semi-circular dome covered with squares of woven matting held in place by bamboo poles laid across them and tied to the framework underneath.

I wandered at the time if these roofs shed rain, and I learned later that they did. I also wondered why the hut Jo Ellen had left for us was thatched. I could only guess that she had lived elsewhere in Africa before coming to Fusora. In any case, I was grateful to her, for under a noonday sun our dwelling was the coolest in the village.

Each of Mu'muou's wives had a hut of her own, where she and her children dwelt in moderate privacy. The chief's hut was three or four times larger than any one of theirs. His windowless interior was divided into two sections by a curtain of tanned hides. In the smaller section he slept on a pile of skins. The larger was apparently his audience room. Both were so completely bare of furnishings that I wondered if the man's wealth consisted solely of *cattle*.

As soon as we had finished inspection of his dwelling, he led me into a hut which stood immediately to the right of it. This was his treasure hut. I had never been in a native treasure hut before and I looked about for the odds and ends of white men's trash with which white men's gossip fill such rooms. There was some of this, of course—four china doorknobs for instance, laid out in a neat little row on a mat. On a swinging shelf there was a collection of pickle, vinegar, catsup and liquor bottles.

But the first thing of importance which caught my eye was a geometrical pattern of elephant tusks completely covering the wall of the hut. The pattern was crowded, and I asked Mu'muou what he would do when he had too many tusks to fit into it any longer. He sighed heavily as though wealth weighed upon him and answered that every now and then he had to take a number into the jungle and bury them.

"Have you done this often?" I asked in astonishment. "How many mounds of buried ivory do you have?"

His face became an amusing study. Like many another man he longed to boast of his wealth but innate cupidity and fear of the reaction of the spirits to boasting restrained him.

"If you forget where some of your heaps of ivory are, they could be carried away and you wouldn't know you had been robbed," I twitted him lightly.

He smiled, but something about the lines of his face assured me that Mu'muou was not one to forget. "Forgotten wealth cannot be stolen, for what is out of mind is no longer a possession." I use the word "possession" quite loosely here, for it might with equal truth have been "care" or "burden."

I wanted to ponder his words, but with casual pride he pointed out other treasures. There were piles of skins, some of them rotting. A half-dozen old slave sticks. Many weapons—spears, knives and crude battle-axes of untempered, hand-forged iron, knobkerries with iron-like root nodules weighting one end, shields of bullhide stretched over wicker framework, and something that must surely once have been a Crusader's mail shirt for there was an iron Maltese cross welded to the front of it. It was much rusted and so frail now that I was afraid the links would fall apart as Mu'muou stirred it with his fingers.

"They say that men long dead treasured this," he remarked. "Maybe some day I will understand its value."

That seemed to arouse a train of thought, for he turned and stared for a few seconds at a small gourd resting on a drum. Then he picked it up, shook it gently close to his ear and then close to mine.

"My father's father's father bought this before my father was born because he was told that it was the most powerful medicine in the jungle," he began slowly. "Since then it has lain in the treasure huts of my ancestors, and now it lies in mine. But none of us has ever known how to invoke its magic."

He pushed the gourd into my hands and asked hopefully, "Do you understand it, white woman? Examine it carefully. Perhaps

258 ·

you can tell me its uses. Shake it by your ear, perhaps it will whisper in a language you understand."

I turned the gourd this way and that, and discovered that a small section had once been sliced off and then very carefully stuck back on again. That would account for a faint slithering sound when shaken. The seeds—which would have rattled loudly, anyway—had been removed, and something else had once been placed inside. What that might be, however, I had no way of knowing. I handed the inherited treasure back to its owner. He weighed it in his hand, still thinking deeply.

Again he spoke slowly, "My youngest and most beautiful wife has a hard round knob on the top of one of her ears. I do not like to look at that knob, it reminds me of the horns of animals. There are times when I have wondered if the spirit of an antelope might not have entered into her mother's womb. It is cold and unpleasant to touch. Our witch doctor is afraid of the ear because it no longer feels like human flesh. They say that *That One,* who was here before you, never knew fear of anything. Are you also ignorant of fear? If so, will you cut the evil off my wife's ear so that I may handle her with complete enjoyment? If so, I will give you this immensely powerful charm."

"I will cure your wife's ear if I can," I answered him. I hoped that the knob might be nothing more than a simple cyst. Still I paved the way for other difficulties: "It is possible that I shall have to cut away a portion of the ear so that the evil may be entirely removed from her and—"

"Are you skilled in this cutting?" he interrupted quickly.

I confessed that I was not—but I did not tell him that the medicine men of my own race would have been up in arms had they seen me pick up a scalpel.

"Then I shall send some of my older *cattle* to you to practice on," he answered calmly. "You can cut off as many ears as you need to improve your skill. It is possible that it will amuse me to watch you."

Quickly I shook my head. "I—I—am not so unskillful that I need that kind of practice," I assured him. "But I must study the evil in the ear and see if it lies within my power to drive it away."

He shrugged his shoulders, laid down the gourd and remarked casually, "Just so long as you remember that she is my youngest and most delectable wife and that I do not want her mutilated for at least a few years yet."

We passed on to the other treasures, some of them too strange to describe adequately. Two among them stand out in my memory. One was a small clay pot full of the quill ends of large feathers. Each quill was stoppered with a plug of down from some sort of grass seed. Those I picked up were abnormally heavy for their sizes. Mu'muou pulled out one of the plugs and poured what must have been a spoonful of tiny yellow flakes into the palm of his hand. Gold!

"Those among my young men who have visited the cities of your people tell me that white men kill each other for the possession of this yellow dust." He poured the gold back into its quill, dusted his palm off on his thigh, and inserted the wad of down firmly, and tossed the quill into the pot carelessly. "It must be of some value," he remarked, and started on to show me other treasures, but I pulled him back.

"Where did you get this?" I asked and then wondered if my hasty question would give offense. It did not.

"A little to the north of here, where legend says a river once flowed, is a patch of white sand with a few of these yellow grains lost in it. One finds the yellow grains by lying on his stomach with his face on the sand and blowing gently." He whooshed a little breath by way of illustration. "The white sand is without much weight and it flows away, but the yellow sand is heavy and it stays behind. Then one flicks out his tongue like a toad or a viper—" another illustration—"and picks up the grain of yellow sand on its wet tip and stores it in his cheek. When he feels the weight of the yellow sand in his mouth, he spits it into a gourd."

"How long does it take to gather a quillful?" I asked.

"That depends on where and how diligently one blows," he answered me. "Sometimes an hour. Sometimes a day. And sometimes longer."

I looked at the pot wondering how many thousands or even tens of thousands of dollars lay there with the spiders spinning webs over their quill containers. "You must have lain many hours blowing into the sand," I remarked lightly.

He smiled indulgently and explained, "When the boys return from their initiation into manhood, none of them goes into the House of Bachelors until he has brought me a quillful of the yellow sand."

I suppose that in a fleeting way, that was the first time I gave thought to Hey Boy's upbringing. Should he be trained after the fashion of a white child, here in the middle of the Dark Continent? If with Maa Koo as nurse that were possible! Or if his upbringing should be after the fashion of the people among whom he must live, his own race? If with Jimmy and me trying to guide that training it could be black.

The thought was born at that moment, but I had no time to dwell on it. Chief Mu'muou had lifted back a curtain of zebra skins sewn together by huge stitches of rawhide. Against the wall hung a row of thirteen huge fans. The leaves of the fans were semi-circular. Of pure copper they had been beaten into shape by some long-dead craftsman. I touched one of the leaves, it was paper thin. It could only be swung back and forth when suspended downward. The handles were from six to eight inches long, roughly square, and tapered to a blunt point.

I turned and looked at Mu'muou a moment, scanning his face carefully. For the second time in this village I remembered the strange mission boy Abu Sayheed. Again, I was struck by the fact that line for line, the cicatrices on Mu'muou's face were the same as those on Abu Sayheed's forehead and cheeks.

"You are the People of the Fan," I said slowly.

"That is what we have been called," he answered. Then, "I understand there are some who call us Fang Men."

His words startled me and I wondered how much he knew of

my civilization and—remembering the cooking pot full of gold dust—how little or how well he understood it.

"Do you—use the fans—often?" I asked even more slowly as though the thought itself protested being spoken.

Mu'muou leaned forward slightly and peered into my face, his eyes darting from one to the other of mine. His lips moved once as though to ask a question, but it did not come. Instead he suddenly threw the zebra hide curtain over his elbow and pointed at a spider that was busily spinning a web between two of the fans. He tapped the handle above her with the tip of his finger and a thin silver dust slid from the enormous fan and slowly drifted downward through the gloom of the windowless hut. Very old cobwebs broke loose and floated in mid-air as though their own weight were enough to pull them earthward.

"I have often wondered why The Little Many-Footed-Black-Wife builds her kraal among so much debris," Mu'muou was saying again, pointing at the spider. "When we build a new village, we leave the outworn old one behind and seek a spot where man has not built before. There we push back the jungle with fire and everything is clean for our new homes."

Suddenly I remembered *That One's* hut, kept in perfect repair for an uncounted span of years. "How long has it been since your village was moved and new homes built?" I asked.

He sighed as though reminded of a grave problem. "We have sat here for a long time now. My father built this village, but—" and there was real pride mixed with some vexation in his voice—"although the site is old our huts are new. A long time ago, it seems, our women learned that the dried poles and matting of an old hut crackle more merrily under a cooking pot than a moss-grown, water-logged limb fresh from some tree. They are always yapping at their masters for the poles with which to build new homes."

I laughed heartily with him. Fusora was a clean village, as I have said, even remarkably clean, gratifyingly clean and I knew he was proud of it. And I wondered if *That One,* now so long dead, had started the women "yapping" at their husbands. I wished I might have known that intrepid and "beloved daughter, Jo Ellen" who had left me her teapot and her village as a spiritual inheritance.

Then, without my quite knowing how we got there, we were outside of the treasure hut. I looked at the smaller hut on the other side of the chief's dwelling, but Mu'muou made no move in its direction. When I looked up at him, his eyes fled elsewhere but not quickly enough to hide that he had been watching me narrowly.

Old Tuou, head-wife and perhaps mother, was squatting at our feet, obviously waiting for us. She was eating green lentils fresh from the pod like nuts and she offered me a vine. They were good, like green peas only sweeter.

"She is one of my treasures, too," Chief Mu'muou remarked lightly. He stirred her to her feet with a firm but not ungentle big toe. "She is wise beyond most old women," he went on. "Even now, with her years numbered, I could sell her for more than most young women bring. But—" with a great sigh that sounded decidedly artificial—and perhaps it was meant to sound artificial!— "custom forbids that one sell one's mother, and how am I to remember, after so long a time whether or not it was she who suckled me?"

Carefully old Tuou bent over and picked up every leaf and lentil pod and clutched them tightly in her hand. There would be no trash left behind to clutter up the dooryard of her lord and master —and son. Then, with her eyes fixed on mine, she jerked her head in the direction of the women's quarters—an invitation to join her in a tour of inspection there.

CHAPTER
TWENTY

I cannot tell you how many wives Chief Mu'muou had because in the few seasons I have known him the number has constantly fluctuated. Men seeking to curry favor with him have given him virgins much more honestly than the men of my own race usually tender their bribes. Too, Mu'muou is a canny businessman. He gives a new wife from eighteen months to two years in which to produce a child. And if she fails in this paramount duty of wifehood he sells her elsewhere, culling her from his harem as an American farmer culls pullets from his flock which fail to lay eggs, or heifers from his herd which do not produce calves.

I asked him once, point-blank, when an argument between us concerning the evils of polygamy had resulted in something closely akin to a verbal brawl, if he was certain he had slept with all of these girls. He shrugged me off with a gesture that was a combination of boredom and scorn and the statement that it was not fitting he should take account of such details.

"Old Mother Tuou brings the wife of the night to me," he added and refused to discuss the matter further.

"The one who is to be wife for the night prepares the evening meal for Mu'muou," Tuou told me now, as we walked from hut to hut and came upon one woman cooking a much larger potful of mush and greens than she and her two children alone could possibly have eaten.

"Do any of the wives ever feel that they are being neglected by their husband?" I asked.

Tuou hesitated for a moment. The idea that a mere chattel possession could consider herself neglected seemed novel and decidedly amusing to the old woman. I tried to explain something of a white woman's sense of uxorial rights. When the mother-wife realized that I was speaking seriously, she frowned deeply with the effort of shaping new concepts.

"No woman complains to Mu'muou," she said slowly. "And if she chattered such empty-headed nonsense to me, I would see to it that she carried much wood and hoed long hours in her garden— and I would also see to it that she had the opportunity to conceive. Yes, that is a woman's right."

Some of the huts we peered into were empty. The women were working in their gardens, or gathering firewood in the forest. All who were at home were busy, cooking over a tiny fire in the middle of their huts, weaving mats of shredded bamboo leaf, patching the dome-shaped roofs, scraping hide preparatory to a sort of tanning, or meticulously cleaning up debris from chores just finished.

"*That One! That One!* She would have nothing lying underfoot," old Tuou sighed as she pushed her handful of lentil vines and empty pods under a cooking pot. By now I knew that *That One,* always spoken of in a tone of respect and some awe, meant the white woman who had once lived among them. "There must be nothing to walk on but clean white sand carried up from the river on our heads," Tuou went on.

There was a double semi-circle of wives' huts; and since to have neglected any one would have been to give offense, we inspected each. The interview with Mu'muou and the inspection of his treasure hut, and then the tour of his wives' residences had taken the greater part of a day. And since Tuou and I ended near the mat-walled corridor which led to the gate, I supposed I would now be ushered out. But that was not the end of the chief's possessions which I must see and appreciate. My guide turned and scuttled toward the middle and back of this primitive walled compound. We passed between several huts and entered the dense shade of a grove of huge mango trees. Passing out of the bright sunshine I was blinded for a moment, but my feet walked on a deeply sanded stretch of earth and a stench of urine assailed my nostrils. Such a smell in this otherwise surprisingly clean and tidy kraal was amazing and I stretched and blinked my eyes in an effort to adjust them to the semi-gloom.

When I could see clearly I was dumbfounded. I turned to Tuou but my attempt to question her only ended in inarticulate gasps of amazement. The old wife was watching me with such a smile of triumph on her face as I have never seen on another human countenance.

She pointed and then she counted on her fingers, naming the girls who swung in huge wicker cages, suspended from limbs of the mango trees, like so many monstrous exotic birds: "Gansa—one, N'tiere—two, Edd—three, Falettun— Affaloon— Cachee— Hata— Kumpa— Mummalee—nine!"

I cannot express for you the pride with which the mother-wife told me that these caged girls were Chief Mu'muou's daughters. They had been through "bush school," which is where native virgins immediately upon the advent of puberty are trained for wifehood and marriage. By restraint of all physical activity and forced feeding they were being brought to what is considered by the men of Fusora, the peak of physical beauty, that is extreme obesity. When a girl had become so heavy she could only walk with difficulty, she would be ready to be sold as a wife. As a chief's daughter, each would naturally command a fancy price. Forcibly fattened to beauty almost beyond a man's dreams, their price must have seemed astronomical to many a black swain.

"Only the oldest and therefore the richest men can buy wives from Mu'muou," Tuou told me proudly.

I looked at the girls in the cages. Not a one was over twelve or thirteen years of age. Yet the old woman of Mu'muou's household considered their bodies "ripe." And their husbands—their first husbands anyway—would be fifty-, sixty-, possibly even seventy-year-old men.

As we walked past the cages, Tuou smiled, called advice to the girls, and peered into the gourds sitting on the floor of the cages.

She looked all of the girls over critically and advised this or that one to eat more. Dutifully they dipped their hands into the mush swimming with peanut oil. One gourd was empty and old Tuou set up such a screaming as only a flock of angry parrots could have equaled. A woman came scurrying past me and ladled more mush into the bowl. Lackadaisically the girl began to eat, peering back at us from eyes whose lids were lost in bulges of fat.

"That Kumpa will bring a nice price—possibly as much as three tusks of ivory," Tuou remarked, and reached through the bars of the cage to pat Kumpa on her shaven poll.

The child was too lethargic to smile either at the compliment or the motherly caress. She would remember, though, with pride in the years to come when the many pregnancies and heavy labor required of her had melted away her unhealthy and fortunately temporary beauty. And she would twit her half-sisters who had commanded a smaller price.

"How often does Mu'muou have a crop of daughters like this to sell?" I asked my guide.

"After every bush school," she answered. "Once a year the virgins who have ripened are trained, and he always has daughters among them."

"No wonder he has to clear the ivory out of his treasure hut and bury it every now and then," I laughed. But Tuou had not heard me.

"None of us now living remembers *That One* who taught us cleanliness, but the mothers of us older women, who knew her, they beat her loaned wisdom into our thick skulls with many hard blows," she said with evident pride at having learned a difficult lesson well.

When I started back to my own hut I was elated because old Tuou had just invited me to attend the next bush school. Every missionary has heard tales without end of these hidden sessions where the adolescent girls are trained for the duties of wifehood which lie ahead of them at such an early age. I know that the invitation came to me because I followed *That One* who must have been one of the unacclaimed geniuses of the human race. She had made a powerful impact upon the lives of these, her people. I wondered, had she, in preaching the religion of her Lord associated faith, worship, and the Golden Rule with the social customs of that small portion of her own race with which she had grown up? Or had she, too, attended bush school and—as my father would have done—tried to understand from the experience what it was that had preserved these people and brought them more or less triumphantly through untold millennia of hunger and disease and black magic?

My mind was full of these thoughts, pleasant pride and vague attempts at profundity, when something stopped me in the middle of a stride. Was it my name I had heard? Was someone calling to me? I was passing the palaver hut, that combination of council chamber and male sanctuary common to most African villages. I listened, but there was no hum of voices as there should have been. Whoever sat inside to smoke and gossip or deal with the current communal problems had broken off speech as abruptly as I had stopped striding along. I walked over under the overhanging eaves of the palaver hut and peered across the low wall.

A half-dozen old men squatted on their haunches around a clay pot full of coals and hot ashes on which little red yams were roasting. One of the men was carving a huge-breasted monstrous-bellied figurine that was both male and female. He was working on a fragment of rootwood with branches that formed uplifted arms. He was using broken shell to scrape and smoothe the belly and balloon-like hips. When a bit of shell dulled, he cracked off a new edge between his teeth. And very carefully he deposited all debris of shell and shavings on a mat between his feet after the fastidious neatness undoubtedly taught his parents by *That One*. He did not look up and I would have turned away disconcerted had not the wood carver, without raising his face from his work, begun to speak in an impersonal but still conversational tone. "Brother greybeards, have I ever shared with you the story my father once told me? It

268 ·

explains why black women must cultivate their gardens with a short-handled hoe."

"Share your wisdom with us, ancient one, that we may in turn share it with our sons," five voices chanted in unison. And now five pairs of eyes were staring at me as piercingly as hawks.

From the tone, the formal phraseology, and the careful, staring attention paid me by the five, and the equally careful attention paid his work by the sixth man, I knew his tale was for my ears. The wood carver cracked another edge on his shell and began, "In the beginning after Mu'ungu had created the earth and all the creatures in it, he also created a man to enjoy His handiwork. Before lying down to sleep in the shade of some sweet-scented tree, He took a look about Him to assure Himself that everything was as it should be. It was then that He noticed that all creatures which fly in the air, swim in the water, creep and crawl and walk on the earth and below its crust, had mates—except man. So he created woman. And everything in the world belonged to the man and the woman, but the woman grew greedy and wanted still more."

It was the old Adam and Eve story but more involved, as the old man told it. The point of the whole thing was that the woman used her ears where it had not been intended that she should. She had eavesdropped as the moles and shrews and lizards and wart hogs and other ground-burrowing animals gossiped among themselves. They had spoken of the treasures buried in the bowels of the earth and she had started digging for them. As a result, the free bounty of the earth had been taken away from her and she had been condemned to dig in the soil for the rest of her life—and the handle of her hoe must ever be short as had been the handle of the spade with which she first dug. In this way, her toil would be the greater and no generation of women would forget the transgression of that first mother.

The story ended and the wood carver held up his pot-bellied hermaphrodite for his companions to admire. They turned their eyes away from me and, thereafter, ignored me as completely as though I were no more than a green and gold spider spinning a web in the roof. I walked on to my hut.

My husband was waiting for me, a laughing husband with a rueful, puzzled expression on his face. Beside his chair lay an armful of garden tools which he was wiping clean with a greasy rag. Against the back of his chair leaned a hoe, a hoe with a keen-edged head weighing next to nothing, a hoe with a slender handle twice the length of an ordinary African hoe handle. With such an implement in her hands, what strapping wench would consider her garden a perpetual punishment for the sin of that First Mother?

Suddenly I was shocked at my own stupidity. "Oh, Jimmy, you didn't!" I burst out, as though it were he who should have known instead of me who should have warned him. His shoes were covered with dust, the sleeves of his shirt were wet with sweat, and there was a streak of grime across his forehead and one cheek.

"Apparently I did! But what it is I did I'm blessed if I know," he answered. Greasy rag in one hand, spade across his knees, he stared up at me all questioning.

"Digging in the earth—making a garden—it's woman's work. Men never do it. It—it's a loss of caste. It's woman's punishment—for being a woman. They have a tale, something like Adam and Eve and the Garden of Eden, only she, the woman, is called The First Mother—"

Quickly, in a tumbled confusion of words I told him the story I had just heard under the eaves of the palaver hut. I understood now the reason why that tale had been told for my ears. Woman does not have many privileges in an African village, but among them are gossip and subsequently keeping her husband informed of current happenings. I had before me the embarrassing task of telling my husband, the embryo agricultural missionary, that he could not make a garden or dig in the earth. That by so doing he offended age-old tradition, and violated social mores as ancient as the Dark Continent itself.

When I had finished, we sat and looked at each other helplessly, and then Jimmy asked slowly, "Isn't medicine—witch doctoring—man's work in Africa?"

"Yes," I answered. Then anticipating the question I knew he was going to ask, I went on, "But there always has been an occasional woman witch doctor, or a woman warrior, or even a woman chief. Father knew one once, a woman chief, that is. She lived just like a man, and bought and sold 'wives.' She wasn't a Lesbian. Since she had taken a man's place in the world, 'wives' were simply prestige and wealth to her as they would have been to a male ruler. She treated the girls she bought just like daughters and got them all real male husbands eventually. But while they were her 'wives,' they made her gardens and—"

But Jimmy interrupted to call me back to the subject of women witch doctors and male gardeners, and I couldn't tell him if they had had a rough time in the beginning.

"How about those big plantations to the south and east? Male labor does the farming there, I know," Jimmy murmured.

"Yes, they do," I answered. "But that's—that's where white civilization is coming in. That's becoming white man's country."

"White!" my husband burst out. "Statistics say there are at least ten blacks to every white man in even the oldest colonized area in Africa. What do you mean calling any part of Africa a white man's land?"

"I'm just calling it what other people do," I said defensively. "In South Africa, and East Africa, white men own so much of the land— Oh, Jimmy, I'm not trying to argue about Africa the country. It's just that— Well, where white men dominate, black men work for them at whatever tasks are put before them. A primitive African from a jungle village doesn't make any pretense of understanding a white man's way of life. He just serves the term the labor recruiter lays on him, earns his hut tax, and then returns to the bush to be a man once more—after the fashion of his ancestors. And here, in any native village not dominated by white men, the women—"

"*The women do the farming!*" Jimmy finished for me.

"Yes," I answered. Then hastened to add, "But the men care for the herds—*that's man's work*."

Jimmy smiled ruefully at me—the sort of smile a child too old to have a broken heart mended with a worthless trifle will smile at a well-meaning but stupid adult.

"Then—I've got to do in my way what those first women missionary doctors and nurses did," he said thoughtfully.

My heart quailed for him. "Oh Jimmy, dear, you don't know what you're up against. You don't know Africa! This country—these people—they can be so slow, so stubborn, even so—cruel without thinking of it as cruelty."

"Does a missionary ask for, or expect easy work? And quick results?" he chided.

Supper time came and went and we could hear Maa Koo and Hey Boy smacking their lips over a pot of mealies not far away, but neither Jimmy or I ate. We took stock of our work that evening as neither of us had done before. I think it was then that I stopped living, in a spiritual sense anyway, under my father's domination, trying to remember always what he would have thought and said and done, and accepted the guidance of my husband. And never will I forget my first sight of the Dark Continent through Jimmy's eyes.

I remember his saying to me, in tones that fell on my soul like a gentle palm on my head, "Laura, honey, I don't mind telling you there were times when I, like a lot of people, have wondered why missionaries meddled with the lives of primitive peoples. I've heard natives—yes, yes, I know. 'Nationals' is the missionary term I should use!—I've heard them called 'simple, healthy, happy children of nature,' and I, too, thought it a poor thing that the complications and problems of our civilization should—should have to go along with our religion.

"But the lives of these people aren't happy ones. Their civilization—social order, whatever you want to call it—isn't simple. It's as complicated as our own. And they aren't at peace with the world just because—because they don't owe any mortgages at the bank.

Their lives are mortgaged to fear of one kind or another from the time they are born until they die. And the women—*cattle. Cattle!*

"And no one who ever lived in Africa could call these jungle natives a healthy people. They're disease-ridden from head to foot. Six to eight out of every ten of the children born die in their first year without medical care. And when they aren't actually hungry, they're fearful of being hungry. They eat like pigs when there's anything in front of them they can push into their mouths—snails, mice, grubs—you've seen them in the woods tearing off rotten bark looking for—for whatever may be there. And there's no reason for their hunger here. The earth is unbelievably fertile, but they don't know how to farm it. They exhaust it, and then they hack and burn out a new little patch of jungle for another garden. This village has stood here for fifty, seventy-five years at least; and as the ground was exhausted, the women have had to make their gardens further and further away. Do you know how far they walk to their gardens now?"

I didn't, but he went on without giving me time for more than a negative shake of my head.

"I'd say between two and three miles. And do you have any idea of the value of some of the trees they've destroyed in pushing out their gardens? And they've no idea how to deal with vermin. Maa Koo told me once that sometimes mice come out of the jungle by the millions. She said she saw such a drove of mice once and that it looked like a gray skin being spread over everything. She said that not only do they denude the earth on top like a swarm of locusts, but they even burrow into the earth and eat the roots."

There was more, much more to the grim picture; and all of it true. It struck me that in many ways my husband was seeing Africa more clearly and understanding it better than I ever had. His point was this:

"Mission boards now pretty generally accept the fact that a sound mind and sound body go together and make the most fertile ground for the seeds of Christianity. So missionary doctors and nurses are sent to almost every field. I believe we've got to have the farmer here, too, teaching improved agricultural methods, for a well-fed body makes the doctors' and teachers' work easier. The first doctors, even the men doctors to say nothing of the women, didn't have it easy. We've got a long and hard stretch ahead of us to travel, Laura, but maybe not any worse than any missionary faces—"

"Jimmy, you said we!" I burst out. "We?"

He had not finished his discourse, and he looked at me in mild, husbandly disapproval, but I rushed on unheeding.

"I'll go with you and help you make your garden. It's women's work, tilling the soil. You can teach me, as you have been doing for so long. The women will listen to me, and the men to you!"

Slowly, as though struggling for birth, a smile broke across Jimmy's face and widened until even his ears and eyebrows seemed happy, even merry.

"Do you know what?" he demanded. "I was invited to attend the village sewing circle today."

"Sewing! Man's work!" burst from me. Women's hands, calloused and work stiffened, are much too awkward to handle a needle as many an African tribesman, male or female, will assure you. "What will *you* sew? I—" Words failed me.

"I'm going to learn how to weave," he answered. "A lot of men weave—in America."

"What does America have to do with it?" I demanded abruptly.

He didn't answer for a moment, and then again his words were slow and thoughtful. "I've thought a lot about that, especially of late. We—I mean missionaries as a whole—are here to preach our religion, but sometimes the social customs we're used to seem to grow in importance until we begin to mistake them for Christianity. If our religion isn't more than a bag of social tricks, a veneer, if it can't strike down deep roots into any civilization, then our work is like—like breeding a jackass and a mare. You may get something strong for a little while, but it will also be stubborn, opinionated, not very adaptable, and completely sterile. It will last for one generation only, and with each new crop of human beings, that work will have to be done all over again."

The cook boy and Maa Koo insistently put supper before Jimmy and me, and stood over us while we ate. It was not a satisfactory performance, however, and Maa Koo made grumbling noises, frankly intended for our ears, for some time after the dishes were removed. But Jimmy and I sat on into the night, talking, talking. Sweeping our hearts clean with many searching words.

We decided that in so far as was possible, we would adapt our lives to the customs of the people with whom we worked. I would learn from him, not just in theory from farm journals, but by actual practice, how to plant and cultivate, to conserve the soil and produce bigger and better crops. I assured him over and over again that it would call for no more physical strength or effort than many a safari I had been on. If by so doing I could make an impact upon the fundamental thinking of these people, it would be worth a sweat-grimed brow and sometimes aching muscles.

Jimmy could help me with my medical work. And there was the whole vast field of animal husbandry for him to explore. He who had once grimaced at the thought of teaching, proposed that he start a school, not just for tots, but for men and boys of any age. I would help him make his primers, and there would be no inanities in them. The facts of scientific breeding, the feeding and development of productive flocks and herds can be put in very simple words. We would do that. Later there would be primers on the fertilization of soils and the preservation of food stuffs—then I would have a school, too.

As I have said, we talked until late into the night. Each of us felt that this was a critical turning-point in our lives and together we prayed earnestly for guidance. Still, serious as we were, I laughed a little at Jimmy's invitation to the "sewing circle."

"It's a good idea," I teased him. "I'll be relieved of the family mending from now on."

Then I remembered the invitation I had received from old Tuou to attend the bush school where the girls are prepared for marriage.

"'Bush schools' have always been considered pretty wicked, indecent places, haven't they?" he asked. "Very few white people know what goes on there and, being fearful of the unknown, we condemn them. But I'd go if I were you, Laura. Then, if you don't like what you see there, you can lay intelligent long-range plans for changing it, putting something better in its place. You're not helping any one if your best effort is merely to say: 'I don't know what you're doing, so it must be wrong.'"

Before Jimmy and I went to bed that night a messenger stood outside our door and coughed and clapped his hands to attract our attention. He spat on the ground at our feet when we stepped outside to talk with him, thus showing that he cleansed his tongue of all evil before speaking to us. Then he held a small, well-dried gourd out toward me.

I was surprised that a gift should be proffered me at this time of night—and a gift of so little apparent value. As I held it in my hands and Jimmy talked with the messenger, I noticed a scar on the smooth surface of the gourd. A portion of the shell had once been sliced away and then neatly stuck back on again. Then I remembered. This was one of the treasures Chief Mu'muou had inherited, a treasure of surely great but unknown magic. The chief had promised it to me if I could cure his young wife's ear without mutilating her.

The messenger was explaining that a hole had appeared in the ear of the young wife and the evil had started to sneak away unseen. But Mu'muou had seized the ear tightly in his big fist and the evil had leaped out in a spurt of fright and buried itself in the hairs of the skin on which the wife's head lay. Surely my magic was great if the mere thought of me scared body-dwelling devils and I cured at a distance without ever having seen the patient.

I tried to give the gourd back, explaining that I had had nothing to do with the cure. The messenger shook his head, and exclaimed in wonder that never before had he known a witch doctor who was modest. But, he added, it was said that *That One* before me had worked wonders and disclaimed credit for them also. I felt like laughing, but was glad I did not when he explained further that it was not well to return or refuse the gift of a chief, even if mistakenly tendered.

The messenger gone and our door closed, Jimmy and I carried the gourd over to our lamp. He drew out his pocket knife, opened the blade, and carefully inserted the point in the seam circling the gourd and then paused.

"As your father would have said," he began looking at me quizzically, "if I were a betting man, I'd lay you odds that it isn't even monkey bones we find. Peanuts. Pebbles. At best, jackal claws."

"No," I answered. "It doesn't ping! like anything hard. It must be a strip of bark, or grass."

A turn of Jimmy's wrist and the gourd parted in halves. Inside was a scrap of paper. It had evidently been folded when inserted, now it was spread loosely open, lining the bottom and sides. Jimmy started to pick it out, but I stopped him.

"Don't," I cried out. "It's so old and brittle it will break into pieces if you pull or bend it at all."

We held the gourd under the flame of the lamp and bent our heads over it together. The paper was covered with fading Arabic script which Jimmy could not read at all and of which I knew only a very few words. Up in the top left-hand corner where our eyes naturally went first was some English script.

"D. L-i-v- Livingston," we read. Then our eyes met in amazement. "David Livingstone!" we exclaimed in unison.

Once again, eagerly, we scanned the scrap of paper imbedded in the gourd. At the bottom right-hand side we read: "To Mutesa," then a blurr, and ". . . nth copy."

"Who was Mutesa?" my husband asked.

"Just about the biggest, cruelest, blackest-hearted scoundrel Africa has ever produced," I answered.

"What could he have been writing to David Livingstone?" Jimmy went on.

I wished desperately that I could read the Arabic, but there was only one tantalizing curleycue: *"Abou*—Father."

"Mutesa was not writing to Livingstone. Livingstone was writing to Mutesa," I explained. "Arabic script is the opposite from ours. It begins at the bottom and comes up the page, and runs from the left-hand side to the right."

"Livingstone must have known him. Could he be friends with a scoundrel like this Mutesa?" my husband pressed me.

"They knew each other well," I answered. "Livingstone struggled for friendship. And Mutesa often pretended it—but he was always the kind of friend you do not dare let stand behind your back with a spear in his hands."

Again we scanned the scrap of yellowed paper nested in the gourd for other familiar words, but there was only that one: "*Abou*— Father."

"I guess we'd better preserve this, hadn't we?" Jimmy murmured, and I nodded.

Carefully he glued the two pieces of gourd together again and tied them with a string until the seal should be hardened and permanent. And as he worked I repeated over and over to myself like one hypnotized: "*Abou*—Father."

The words were in my mind when I went to bed. English and Arabic, they floated before my eyes in that gray nether world which is neither slumber nor waking. Then perhaps I was dreaming for I was wandering about alone, covering vast distances on the edge of the Hungry Country crying aloud, wailing: "Father! *Abou!* Father!" Sometimes it was a frightened child's scream for the strong arms and sturdy shoulder of a parent. Sometimes it was a bewildered woman's prayer to her God for peace and guidance.

CHAPTER
TWENTY-ONE

As I grow older, I can't help being amused whenever I read or hear sage and learned dissertations about the computation of time and calendars. Once as a child—already a big girl in Maa Koo's estimation—I asked my nurse how long it would take to perform some duty laid upon me. The old woman, shredding palm fiber for mats with busy fingers and teeth, did not even look up as she replied with a question: "How do I know, Little Worm? Is there a smile or a pout on your lips?"

There was a smile in my husband's heart and almost constant song in my soul for the next few weeks. Or was it months? Yes, surely it was months, for Jimmy's child grew big within me and kicked this way and that unmercifully whenever I lay down to rest. Often I laid my palms on what Maa Koo called my "toad's stomach" just for the exquisite pleasure of feeling and estimating the vigorous energy of my child. The pleasure and the pain that was no pain.

"Sometimes I think I must be a mass of bruises inside," I told Maa Koo once when she saw me wince.

A few hours later she told Jimmy with all solemnity that she did not think it was going to be necessary for me to divorce him. For a second he was startled, and then that slightly foolish look spread over his face—the look men are unable to avoid when they know they must take instruction from women. Together Maa Koo and I, with some ribaldry on the old woman's part, again told Jimmy what he had already heard so many times: Woman does not have many rights in Africa, but she does have one, however, which she guards so jealously that real social pressure is brought to bear upon an individual in many communities if she does not avail herself of it. A woman who has done her duty for nine long months not only can, but is expected to divorce a man who takes his pleasure of her body but fails to bestow upon the infant he fathers the gift of life. It does not matter that from six to eight out of ten children born in the primeval jungle or bush or upon desert and veld die within the first year of their lives. That is always due to the jealousy of the envious spirits or the malice of the unseen evil folk. The important thing is that a child must come gasping and squalling from its mother's bowels. Maa Koo insisted to Jimmy that she had already heard the child cry out, and that he, my husband, could hold up his head among the men.

Many women have told me that as the time for their confinement nears they have been, at least for a short period anyway, obsessed with the notion that they will not come through the ordeal successfully, that they will die. Nothing could be further from my experience. Perhaps that was because I had been born and had grown up in black Africa where the processes of procreation are not cloaked with prudery and a black man's two-legged *cattle* are expected to calve as naturally as the antelopes of the veld drop their young.

By the above statement I do not mean to imply that the bearing of children in primitive Africa is simple, painless and knows no complications. Those who would have us believe so speak out of wishful thinking and in complete ignorance of the facts. But neither is life—in primitive Africa as elsewhere—simple, painless, and without bewildering complications. Sex, procreation and birth simply take their places as duties as well as pleasures and without undue emphasis among the other burdens and complications of the seen, tangible and, therefore, fairly understandable things of this world.

These things I had known in a vague way because I had absorbed them unconsciously under Maa Koo's direct, progressive, and completely unembellished tutelege. They were drawn into the open, as conscious facts of my thinking as I attended bush school with

Tuou. Since my latest return to America I have visited several "marriage clinics," and my amazement at the vapid, emasculated, embarrassed hedgings called "instruction" and "advice" only grows with each experience. Apparently we white people have striven to strip life of its crudities, but in sober fact the crudities remain and all we have succeeded in achieving is a sort of pathetic game of make-believe—social if not spiritual dishonesty. We are members of an "advanced" civilization; but it is my belief that our black sisters of primitive Africa—crude, blunt, even brutal though they often are—have outstripped us where preparation of their daughters for wifehood and motherhood is concerned.

The bush school that I attended for at least a small portion of each day, lasted about two weeks. In it there was no theorizing, no vague philosophizing, no time squandered by the instructresses. Woman's duties in life are those of a brood and draft animal, many pregnancies and unremitting toil lie ahead of her. She is valuable to her owner in direct proportion as she is obedient, submissive to his desires, and adaptable to the restraints of a polygamous household. She is never ignorant of these facts, but in bush school she is trained to these duties quickly, in much the same way a colt is broken to harness and the plow on a farm. And at the same time all the sheer brutalities, which pass for "masculinity" in a more effete world, were expounded, illustrated where possible, even lampooned mercilessly for these girls, every one of whom would be a bride in less than a season thereafter. I could not help laughing at the old women's mimicry. Although I had lived in Fusora only a very short period, it was easy to recognize the village men. And I could not help admiring the vitality and toughness of spirit that had brought these women through unspeakable cruelties with laughter on their lips for the foibles of their masters.

The school itself was supposedly hidden in the jungle, but the trail leading to it was well worn. No masculine feet trod that pathway, however, for charms and fetishes in gourds and small animal skins hung from various branches overhead. Old Tuou opened one of these to show me its contents. There were no feathers, fangs or claws, only very small soft bones. Human bones. I was holding a tiny skull in my hands, a broken hollow sphere of bone no bigger than a small orange when Tuou told me that these were the bones of the infants that were a lasting shame to their fathers. They had never breathed. Their fathers had been divorced. No man would willingly walk under these fetishes.

The path ended before what looked like an ordinary *zeriba,* or thorn-fenced shelter for animals. The mother-wife, Tuou, did not bother to pull back the vine-laced poles forming a gate, but clambered over them. I followed her, snagging a half-yard of Mrs. Dick's hand-crocheted lace off my petticoat as I did so. Inside were little huts here and there, exact replicas of those the girls would occupy as wives. Their first night "in school" the girls had spent on the bare ground under the open sky seemingly alone. But old women had watched and those girls who had whimpered, or had wrested a cowhide cape from another as protection against the night wind and cold were noted. Then the next day Mumbo Jumbo— who is really primitive Africa's god of marital discord—had burst into the compound. He was a fearful sight in grass flounces, woven bamboo splint mask, and a heavy, many-lashed whip. Unerringly he had picked out the cowards and selfish thieves of the night before and, shouting a magnified recital of their misdeeds in a thin, high-pitched voice, had pursued them about the enclosure and beaten them one by one, until no strength was left in their legs and they had sunk cowering to the ground.

Then Mumbo Jumbo had disappeared and the old women teachers entered. They herded the girls into the forest where each must gather the materials for a hut. That afternoon each girl either built her hut or slept in the open on the bare ground if she were clumsy or lazy.

The first time I entered this human zeriba it was empty. The old women had said to the girls something like this: Today a famine is upon us. There are no beans or ground nuts in the storage pots. There is no corn in the granaries. Tembo has uprooted the plantain trees, and field mice have devoured the seed in the ground before it could sprout into gardens. Into the jungle now, every one of you, and bring back all the food you can find. It may be that you will have two or four or even six children in your hut when the hungry days fall upon you. Bring all the food you can find, *but do not return without stuffing for at least two bellies.* It is *you and your husband* who must remain alive until rains fall and seeds sprout again—he to father children and you to bear them. Let the little ones whom the spirits have already given you die if they must—and let them die quickly! If you keep them alive for a few days beyond your own death, you have labored and died like a fool, to no purpose. But you, no matter how low the sun sinks, do not return without food for two. And if the friendly spirits are with you and you find more than your two hands can carry, eat all your belly will hold where you stand—a hungrier one can never take that away from you!

I saw the girls straggle in one by one. One girl carried a nest of carterpillars and a handful of wild spinach—a good supper anytime! Another had the tender shoots and heart leaves of wild celery. Still another carried a young python about her neck. Everyone, including the old instructresses, stared at her enviously for the meat of python is tender and sweet and juicy and good to the tongue as well as nourishing to the muscles. One girl's head was covered with swollen lumps from bee stings, but she carried triumphantly in her hands a lump of bee-bread and a white soggy mass of still wingless young bees. Her stomach was round and tight and there were dribbles of wild honey on her chin and between her two breasts. The friendly spirits had indeed been with this class of virgins.

The girls already knew African cookery. As tiny tots they had played at "helping mother" as little ones do the world over. Each prepared the food she had brought in and set it beside the fire without touching it. Then she squatted back of her fire and food, waiting for the old woman who would pretend to be her husband. As I watched these old women go from fire to fire pretending to be all kinds of men except pleased and satisfied ones, I too had the honor to be *a husband,* choosing the cooking fire beside which I wished to eat. I dined on steamed bamboo hearts and broiled fish filet. Both were excellent, but my young hostess squatted on her heels across the fire from me, not even smacking her lips once until I had completely finished. When I started to wash my fingers— nature's way!—by sucking them clean, she gave me a tuft of some saponaceous weed to crush between my palms and brought a gourd- ful of water to pour in a twisting silver stream over my hands and wrists.

Then she herself ate. Tired and hungry though she was, she dipped her finger tips into her own cooking pot as daintily as Chaucer's nun at the tavern board. And she carried her food to her lips far more gracefully and with infinitely less dribbling than I who by reason of my greater age had undoubtedly eaten "native fashion" more often than she.

It was not so pleasant beside some of the cooking fires that evening. More than one girl had her cooking pot kicked over by the foot of a mimicked angry, contemptuous male. If such a girl could salvage anything from the dirt and ashes for her own food, she was fortunate. Otherwise she went to bed hungry in spite of the length and labor of this her first day out of childhood.

I know that many women, privileged as I was to witness the training of these girls, would have found the process brutal and disgusting. I, too, African bred as I was, shrank from much that I saw. Nevertheless, there is sincere admiration in my memory for the old women who knew from experience the hard life that lay ahead of these girls and trained them for it. Complete obedience even to the most unreasonable demands was beaten—literally if necessary—into the girls. And none of the instructresses turned coy, or strangely ignorant after a half-century of wifehood, or resorted to euphonious, less than half-honest phraseology in describing any phase of cohabitation. There is no so-called "rape of the first night" in primitive Africa. If I had tried to explain such an expression to these old women, I am sure they would have been filled with amazement and contempt for any group of women who ignore in their daughter's training the functions for which nature patterned women.

I remember, too, the pleasurable hours when we all sat about a central fire listening to the old women, one after another, recite the legendary history of their tribe. More than once it seemed to me that with the exception of surnames and geography some tale had been lifted bodily from the Old Testament.

I would not give up the experience of that bush school for a very great deal. Many a scientist has visited Africa at great expense, with tons of equipment, and has worked zealously. When he left he has carried away with him reams of notes and measurements and tons of artifacts and countless cylinders recording strange customs. Yet not only has this phase of a culture remained an unopened book to him—he has not even suspected the existence of the curious volume.

But Africa is like that. I remember a traveler who once stopped overnight in my father's home. He complained that much of his journey was monotonous and dull. Yet he had without knowing it just passed through a section of country that we called The Kingdom of Snakes, where the python was worshipped with intricate ritual and the adder, the viper, the mamba and the cobra were all lesser gods.

I tried to drink in as much knowledge as I could of my people during my visits to the bush school. I remembered my father's oft-repeated statement that no missionary can serve to his fullest ability until he understands and appreciates the culture of the people among whom he works. I twitted and teased my husband with the fact that I, a mere woman, was privileged above him in this one experience. I suppose I should have been, but I was not prepared for his blank question one evening:

"What about Hey Boy?"

"Hey Boy? What's the matter with Hey Boy? Isn't he all right?" I asked in turn.

"Old N'ragde—you know him. He's the old fellow who's always squatting in the palaver hut carving monstrosities," Jimmy began.

"Well, N'ragde stopped me the other day and asked me if we were sending Hey Boy into the jungle with the next crop of 'budding men.'"

Unconsciously an emphatic "No!" sprang to my lips but died without being born before Jimmy's smile. Just as I had heard tales without end of the atrocities and obscene practices of the bush schools for young girls, I had heard fulsome gossip of the initiation rites for boys. I had accepted the invitation to visit the girls' training school because I was the daughter of a man as much scientist as he was preacher, a man whose intellectual outreach and humanitarianism transcended race. In that school I had found rigor which in another civilization would have been cruelty. I had found what a more effete social order would have called obscenity. But I had also found a system of training for life exactly as the trainees must live it. The wrong is in the way of life, and not in the preparation to meet it.

Why then should I believe only in the evil report of the initiation school for boys? If the invitation had come from old N'ragde for Jimmy to visit the rites and ceremonies, I would have said without hesitation: "Go, by all means."

"Hey Boy is such a little fellow," I began, forgetting that I had seen even smaller girls beaten and others alternately doused with cold water and then water hot to steaming to teach them obedience to even the most ridiculous male demands.

"Little fellow! Do you remember what happened the last time you thought he needed a spanking?" my husband exclaimed.

I had to laugh. Hey Boy had thrown his arms around my neck, and his weight on his arms and easily pulled my head over to where he could kiss me on the cheek. That was almost all the punishment the scamp had received, for when Jimmy had arisen and started forward, my heart had pushed me between my husband and the child. Then my old nurse had darted at him with what she herself would have described as "a baby-sized switch" in her hand and had cut him smartly across the calves with it. For a second he had curled up his lips in scorn of any thought of pain.

Then, while she thrashed away, being taller than the old woman, Hey Boy had taken her topknot of gray wool in one fist, bent her neck back and rubbed his impudent nose all over her wrinkled face.

When he released her he had said quite solemnly, "I shall not be able to do this to you many times more, Mother Maa Koo, for soon I shall be a man." He stooped, picked up the baby-sized switch she had dropped and tossed it into her own cooking fire. Then he had swaggered away with his shoulders exaggeratedly erect and one hand thrusting up and down at shoulder height as though he were a young warrior testing the balance of a new spear.

"Hey Boy is a good kid and we'll do the best for him we can, you and I," Jimmy was saying, watching me quizzically. "But he's just an ordinary kid, neither dull nor awfully smart. He's not outstanding in spite of the fact that we love him. There are many others here in the village who should be sent to mission schools before him."

I knew all the points Jimmy was trying to make, but still, emotionally, I rebelled. Initiation school for my Hey Boy? The obscenity? The cruelty? Never!

"Hey Boy can never be half white, half black. He isn't smart enough for that. He's got to be all black—and *all man* here among his own people," my husband argued.

Perhaps for the first time in my life I felt virtuously like my mother as I shook my head and pled quickly, "What would people say? And we Christian missionaries! Let me think about it for a while. Yes, I must think about it."

So I thought and I thought. Day and night I racked my brain searching for the right answer and I reached no decision. But the evening before the "budding men" disappeared into the jungle I walked down the street with a procession of other mothers. The hair on their usually beautifully combed heads was deliberately tousled. Their neat, one-piece wrap-around garments were gone and I could scarcely believe the tatters in which they were now clothed. Each carried in her hand a gourd filled with palm wine, or banana beer, or strips of celery hearts, or roasted ground nuts, or some other delicacy.

When old mother-wife Tuou had sent to ask me if I would dance with the women that night, I had answered yes. Usually such an invitation simply meant that I should be present at some village celebration—in this case it was what, I learned later, was called "The Death of the Striplings." As I left our hut Maa Koo pressed into my hands the neck of a gourd dipper. I peered into the bowl end and saw she had filled it with roasted locusts. I was not twenty feet from my door when a line of the other mothers appeared out of the darkness before me. Each held her gourdful of delicacies out for whoever might wish to sip of it or dip his fingers into it. Her left hand was on the right shoulder of the woman in front of her. The line parted and old Tuou and Maa Koo—and I think Jimmy, too!—pushed me forward. Then, like a college boys' snake dance we wound around every hut in the village.

"I feel like a fool," I yelled to Jimmy every time I passed him. He only grinned and applauded and otherwise enjoyed my embarrassment.

"I wish I had a piece of tattered gunny sacking to throw around you," he yelled once. Another time it was, "Howl like the other women and you'll be perfect."

And periodically the other women would break out into the most exaggerated pretenses of grief. I turned my head to look over my shoulder at the woman behind me and bellowed to make myself heard, "Why are you wailing?"

Her pretended grief broke off instantly and there was only pride in her voice as she answered, "This is the night of the death of the striplings. We mothers are losing our little boys tonight. We will never cuddle and caress or punish them again. When they return to us—if—if—" She faltered and something akin to terror spread over her face, and I could see in her eyes the resolute will with which she put it out of mind before she went on. "When they return to us, they will be men, and arrogant, and our masters."

Shortly thereafter, because I was heavy and awkward from my

pregnancy, the line passed around my hut and let me out of it. But the other mothers of the village kept on celebrating the loss of their little boys until far into the night. Hours later I awakened and could hear the wailing from afar.

Then an absurd thought entered my mind— Ridiculous! but I couldn't put it away from me and go back to sleep again. I slid my feet over the edge of my bed and into my slippers. Then I tiptoed out of our hut and past the beloved Jo Ellen's geranium tree to the shelter Maa Koo and Hey Boy shared. I believe my footsteps awakened the old woman, and that she watched me surreptitiously—her snoring was too perfect to be real. She was alone. I turned away without speaking.

Jimmy was standing in the door of our hut when I returned. It was such a sweet comfort to have his arms around me there in the darkness. Still, "Suppose Hey Boy doesn't come back?" I couldn't help asking. It might have been my father speaking from my husband's lips as he answered, "Hey Boy's where he wanted to be, Laura. And, darling—one has to trust God more completely when he doesn't understand than when he thinks he does." Then he kissed me and tousled my hair with a big hand, and told me to go to sleep.

But I did not fall asleep immediately. Hey Boy was too much in my thoughts. This African waif who had stubbornly refused to die as any right-minded black boy should when the spirits had stolen his soul was suddenly more important to me than he had been at any time since my husband had violated the closed door of his death hut. Perhaps it was a psychological after-effect of having celebrated "the death of the striplings" with the village women, but I felt very certain that Hey Boy was not coming back to me. Lying there with my husband comfortably snoring only a few feet away, I was very certain of that as only a pregnant woman swinging dizzily at the end of her own emotions in the night can be certain of anything.

The next few weeks—or was it days?—were the busiest of my life. Perhaps that is why the broken pot over which I stumbled one morning on stepping outside my door meant nothing more to me than a moment's irritation. Jimmy and I were full of plans and duties, and I merely kicked the shards aside and called to a group of women who were watching me intently, "I believe I get more awkward every day—but it will soon be over now." I shouted for Maa Koo to come and pick up the fragments and throw them on the village midden.

The watching women smiled and seemed strangely relieved as they turned and walked away. Maa Koo, too, smiled at me and her voice was full of pride as she said, "I have told them that you are a greater one, my little frog belly, than *That One* before you."

I knew she referred to the beloved Jo Ellen of the teapot, but I did not catch the fact that her prideful words were weighted with a double meaning. Nor was there anything unusual in the women's watching me. Yet I was to learn that unconsciously I had behaved with becoming decorum for a village woman. I had done what properly trained *cattle* should do when the malicious spirits have shown them unkindness.

CHAPTER
TWENTY-TWO

As I have said, the next weeks were busy ones. Jimmy and I began the construction of a church. It is seldom, I think, that missionaries begin a church structure so soon after coming into virgin territory. And in spite of *That One* now embedded in the people's memory and rapidly becoming folk legend, this really was virgin territory. Like my father, I invited whoever wished to do so to join in family prayers with us; and the old women, avid for entertainment and hanging onto the fringes of only second-hand accounts of *That One,* whose prayers had also evidently been shared by her neighbors, came in flocks. We were compelled to have our family worship under the eaves of our hut with this attentive if not reverent audience spread out before us. Chief Mu'muou informed us that the crone who had held on doggedly to the burden of life until I had arrived and had been tested by the ritual of the teapot had often said that *That One* had had a separate hut in which to recite her incantations and perform her ritual.

(Those of you who read these lines, please understand. I do not intend any sacrilege by my phraseology, but only to translate faithfully, not word for word, but meaning for meaning and spirit for spirit. It is only in this way that I can pass on to you the reactions of a primitive people who have been given but the barest taste of our religion, who know nothing of denominationalism, and even less of the impact our creed has made on your civilization.)

Our church was started and finished as I am told many a small community church in rural America is built—by the physical hands of those who will worship under its roof. Jimmy was so outwardly happy when plans for the church sprang up, grew and came to fruition spontaneously that I questioned him about his enthusiasm which seemed to me a bit overdone, even for a missionary. He confessed a little shamefacedly that he found it difficult to keep his mind on God and the things of the spirit when some old woman redolent of fish oil—although scrupulously clean under this odoriferous ointment!—rubbed shoulders with him.

"And sitting in a sanctuary, perhaps I'll be far enough away so that I won't hear them crunching roasted nuts and—and—and grubs and slugs," he ended.

Old N'ragde, the wood carver coughed and clapped his hands to attract my attention one day as I was passing the palaver hut. I stepped under the eaves and leaned over the low wall in some surprise, for he had never before spoken to me directly. He told me now that for a long time after the soul of *That One* had joined The Unseen Folk of the jungle glades, her fetish hut (church) had stood untouched except by the spiders, and cockroaches and mice. He and a group of the "unripe men" had been fascinated by the empty hut and had often peeked through the gaping door hole.

Then one night their courage screwed to deeds of bravery, these small fry had entered the dead white woman's fetish hut and each had seized whatever he could lay his hands on and fled to the warmth and security of his mother's kraal. Each boy, fearful of punishment, had hidden what he had seized. Old N'ragde did not know what had become of the other boys' prizes. All of those boys, long since grown to manhood, had themselves entered the world of the spirits.

N'ragde stuck his hand into a skin bag that lay beside him on the floor, drew it out, and held a beautifully carved rosewood cross up before me. This was what he had taken, he said. At first it had been plain and ugly, but when no one was looking, he had cut into its beautiful grain replicas of the jungle leaves and vines and flowers his mother had told him *That One* had loved. Would I like to have it for my fetish hut?

My hand trembled with eagerness, but I hesitated to hold it out for the cross when I saw the old man caress it as though it were something living.

"Take it! Take it!" he urged me. "It is right that it should go back into a proper fetish hut—for soon I, too, shall wander under the trees unburdened by this old body."

I tried to thank him, but he brushed my words aside with the question of whether there was anything else he could carve for my fetish hut in the days left to him by Mu'ungu. I racked my mind trying to think of something. Pews were too much for the old man, I told myself, and then added silently that pews were silly when intended for a people who rested most comfortably squatting on their haunches.

Then old N'ragde was telling me that legend said *That One* performed her ritual before two stools. When before one 'stool,' she told them what men long dead had said. Before the other 'stool' she shared with them what Mu'ungu had whispered into her ear.

I smiled at the old wood carver again, and nodded understanding. No wonder that he called the beloved Jo Ellen's altar and lectern "stools." The cooking pot, the gourd dipper, a stool for the husband, if he were of sufficient age, and sometimes a low framework for the bedding mats and skins are all the manufactured household implements a primitive African home knows. What else could N'ragde call an altar or a lectern?

I described these two pieces of church furniture to the old man in some detail, mostly because it was pleasant to talk with him, and his questions for the most part were discerning. Also, it was pleasant to gather what vague bits of information I could concerning the white woman who had once lived in this village.

I leaned across the low wall of the palaver hut and chatted with N'ragde for an indefinite period as though the two of us, he a man and I a woman, were equals. With my hands I measured for him the breadth and depth of an altar and lectern. I showed their height against that portion of my body which showed over the wall. He watched every movement, his eyes bright with the glaze of years and the eagerness of one whose pleasure it is to perform a service.

And as we worked on our church we also started the construction of a school building. This was a simple affair, a small copy of the palaver hut. There was a matting roof, conical in shape, with supporting posts that could be walled with bamboo mats against driving rain and the occasional chill winds that blow down from the hills during the wet season. A small depression in the center of the floor would hold a nest of coals when weather demanded the warmth of fire.

What I would teach the girls was simple enough: personal hygiene, prenatal and baby care, simple first aid, and the tenets of my religion. I had no way of knowing the creed of the first missionary to Fusora, but it seems to me now that always as I prayed God for guidance, I petitioned also for something of her skill, her devotion, her unerring sense of direction, her genius. I brewed tea from native herbs in her heirloom teapot every day and refreshed my body. And my spirit was equally refreshed by the thought of *That One* who had made such an impact on these people that she had become one of their most precious legends.

Jimmy's problems as a teacher were more complicated. In a man's world, he was a man's man; but when he attempted to cultivate, to plant, to grow vegetables and grain— "The men sneer, and the women snigger," he muttered one day. "I don't know whether this land is topsy-turvy, or whether we came to it with topsy-turvy notions of what we can do here."

Animal husbandry, however, is man's work in Fusora. But even here Jimmy was faced with social custom as impregnable as our own inherited notion that soap and sin are mortal enemies. It appears as stupid to the African tribesman to kill a bullock, or cow that has passed her calving days, as the burning of money because it is old, dirty and frayed does to any white man. Nearly all bargaining is done on the "sight-unseen" basis; and if a cow drops dead after it has passed into a stranger's hands, an African is sorry as you or any American is mildly regretful when an acquaintance loses a wallet. Consequently, Jimmy was regarded as slightly insane when he suggested that certain old and sick animals be destroyed. Amusement and pity turned to anger when he tried to count one herd. He was told vehemently that a man never arouses the cupidity of the greedy spirits or disgusts the benevolent ones by detailing the extent of his wealth.

Very decidedly Jimmy's educational and practical work among our People of the Fan was beset with many and unpredictable difficulties. But we kept going, he and I, each of us laboriously printing primers by hand from which we hoped to teach the small fry and a selected number of their elders to read. We had a little blank paper with us, a pitifully inadequate amount. We also had a very small library, perhaps a half-dozen books. We stripped each volume of every blank flyleaf, and then of the pages clean on one side and with only a very small amount of printing on the other.

Our labor was broken into one day by an exciting message. Don't ask me who received the news first—everyone except Jimmy and me. Also, please don't press me for an explanation of how it was understood. I know as much as any white ever knows about the telepathic drums of this country.

But Jimmy and I were told that a native letter carrier was on his way toward our village with a missive tied securely in the cleft of a stick he clutched in his hand day and night. The message was addressed to a white man who for some strange reason was trying to do a woman's work under the direction of the greatest of the gods. While the letter carrier was still in white man's country, he had stopped every white man he met and asked him to look at the envelope and to claim the letter if it was meant for him. These white men in the colonized areas, and later missionaries and hunters and traders on the plains and in the jungles, where white men had not yet established farms, had all read the address and replied, "No," that the message was for none of them. Then they had bade the letter carrier continue in the direction of a rigidly pointing arm and hand. A few of the white men explained that they had heard that somewhere in Fang (Fan) Country there was a Man-Who-Talked-

Much-with-God who had set himself the impossible task of bettering the physical existences of his converts by showing them how to grow more and better food and to develop fatter, healthier flocks. That letter could be for no one but Jimmy, and all we could do was wait with our best patience often strained to the breaking point.

We knew it was coming almost a week before the messenger arrived. When he asked my husband to look at the envelope, dew, sweat, sun and grime from much handling had completely obliterated name and address. I stood on tiptoe to peer over Jimmy's shoulder when he pulled three sheets of impressive letterhead out of their ragged covering. We both grabbed at the third sheet and then gasped at the titles typed beneath the signature. It was from the District Commissioner of a large and prosperous area—colonially one of the most progressive in all East Africa.

It was a kindly, courteous, generously encouraging letter from a fine gentleman who was also a man of vision and a sincere Christian, unashamed of his religion. He wrote Jimmy that he had heard with the greatest interest of the work we were attempting. When he had come to Africa, a much younger man, he, too, had dreamed of some such work. But everywhere he had met a blank, unscalable wall of primitive customs and beliefs many of which he still did not understand although he was approaching the end of his professional career. True, during his administration black men had come to work by the tens of thousands on white men's plantations, but they did not carry the agricultural techniques they learned home with them. Apparently they sloughed off such knowledge as easily as they shed the G-strap which the white man's virtuous concern for the delicate sensibilities of his womenfolk compelled the native to wear in towns and on plantations. The handful of farthings, the few pence, the chance shilling the black man carried back home with him did nothing to eliminate periodic starvation in the thousands of tiny villages hidden in the jungle, or the diseases of malnutrition from which nearly all "bush natives" suffer constantly.

It was a fine letter from a fine man who had given a lifetime of as hard, devoted work to the people over whom he held political domination as any missionary who strives to sow the seeds of his religion. It ended with an invitation for Jimmy to visit him if that should be convenient so that the two could talk over their endeavors and the techniques each had tried or was trying.

"We can ponder together over why some of the best laid plans have failed and marvel over the sheer accidents that have succeeded," he wrote. He ended on this note, "We call our black people here 'children,' yet I often think it is we who are naïve, for you missionaries and we civil officers seek to implant in their lives in one generation what it has taken our own race many centuries to absorb and with indifferent success."

There are few if any secrets in a native village, and our People of the Fan, who had waited with as much eagerness as ourselves for the arrival of the letter, now pressed forward in a body to share it with us.

"Cannot your talking paper be made to speak aloud like a man?" Chief Mu'muou demanded.

"It only whispers and so silently that one hears it inside of his head rather than with his ears," Jimmy answered him.

"Is it the words of a malicious woman that it should be so secretive?" Mu'muou went on.

Jimmy assured him that that was not so, that the message was born of the wisdom of a very big and fine man. A man who was a chief among his people with power greater than Mu'muou's, I added quickly, in order to impress the villagers with the importance of the folk who sent messages to my husband.

"The message speaks the language of—of my tribe of people," Jimmy put in. "I shall have to translate for you."

"Wrap it up in our words then, so that it will enter our ears as a welcome guest and not as a stranger who must be watched because his intentions are unknown," the chief commanded.

"The great man has sent this talking paper on a many days' journey over mountains and deserts, through swamps and jungles

• 297

in order to ask me to visit him. He wants to—talk with me about my work here in your village," Jimmy explained at last.

"Then you must go," Chief Mu'muou announced without a moment's hesitation. "It is an honor which cannot be ignored when a great man beckons to a lesser."

"Perhaps I shall go in a few months," Jimmy started to reply. "But as you see, my wife is now great with child—"

Chief Mu'muou snorted so violently that it was as moist as a sneeze. "White man, when will you learn what is woman's work and what is man's work?" he demanded. "You cannot, even by the strongest exertion of muscle or will, rip infants from *your* bowels. Shoulder to shoulder you are as great in stature as I, but are you big enough for the life of a man inside?"

Jimmy and I stood rigidly like two children before the chief. Every muscle, every nerve in our bodies was tense. Maa Koo had often castigated me with her tongue, but I had never heard a black man talk in this fashion to a white man. I stirred uneasily and slid the fingers of one hand against Jimmy's palm. He squeezed them lightly and whispered, "Be quiet. We are beyond the domination of white men. Our color is without prestige here. And we can learn from him. We can learn much from him."

I twisted my neck to stare up into my husband's face. For one awful second I thought he was afraid. Then what I saw in my husband's face satisfied me. He was wiser, more understanding than I. He was as much bigger than I as my father had been bigger than my mother.

"Must you continually behave like an unripe man? Must I talk to you like a boy not yet initiated into manhood?" Mu'muou stormed.

Jimmy did so look like a little boy as he took Mu'muou's tongue-lashing that I felt like laughing one minute and, like a mother, stepping between him and the storms of this world the next. I don't quite know how it was done, but it was decided then and there that Jimmy should answer this "beckon" from a great man "on nimble feet," as Mu'muou put it. He must leave with the next sunrise.

That night, when Jimmy was inclined to waver, I upheld Mu'muou's decision. The birth of my baby was still almost two months off, I told my husband. He would be back long before that time. And if he weren't—I tried to make a joke of it—if he weren't, I would not be the first missionary wife to bear a child in white solitude. Even if it came to that, I was a nurse, I knew what to do in any contingency. I had supplies. I had Maa Koo who was a competent midwife. I argued all these points vehemently and added that we needed supplies—paper for the primers we were busy printing, tea for the beloved Jo Ellen's teapot, and many other things.

The next morning Jimmy and a half-dozen boys left while the dew was still on the gigantic rose geranium which *That One* had planted beside the door of the hut that was—that *is* my home. I walked to the edge of the village with him and then far beyond to where jungle gave way to veld and watched him until he was out of sight. He turned to look back many times, and although it was uncomfortable to do so, I always threw my arm high above my head and waved vigorously to him.

He did not have to cross the Hungry Country, but only skirted the edge of it for a short distance. Still, the dry, quivering desert air danced about him, and one minute he looked as though he were swimming, floating above the earth. The next instant, points and needles of light from a dew-shot mimosa tree wrapped him in a prismatic aura so that he looked like an old saint ascending to heaven. He seemed to hang thus for a short minute above earth although his feet swung back and forth and I knew he was walking on good hard soil. Then he was gone.

He was gone and I turned to Maa Koo who had snickered every time I had waved to him. For, although she had lived among white people long enough to be familiar with the gesture, it still seemed a silly contortion to her. Then, something in her face held me. Her eyes were old, but I think she, too, had seen the strange trick the sun, the dry air, and the scintillating dewdrops had played on us, for her lids were wide apart and unwinking.

A strange feeling of half-prescience flooded through me. "Suppose—" I said to my old nurse. "Just suppose—that I—that I never see him again. That my last sight of him—was—thus—between heaven and earth."

Maa Koo took her time about answering. When she did she was her dry self again for she merely muttered, "Why must pregnant women always talk like fools!" But she did not glance in my direction as she turned about and stalked back to the village many steps ahead of me.

CHAPTER
TWENTY-THREE

While Jimmy was gone we completed our church. Roughly it was about twenty or twenty-five feet wide and forty long. Its walls were woven of wattle to within about three feet of the roof and then daubed with a mixture of clay, straw chopped very fine, and cow's dung. We thatched the roof, which overhung the walls about four feet. There was a door at each end, and a bean-shaped slightly raised platform of puncheoned logs against one side. It was a light, well-ventilated, cool building for the hot days; and two fire holes in the floor made provision against the chill of the rainy seasons.

The last bit of thatch had not yet been tied in place along the ridgepole when N'ragde, the wood carver, called on me. I saw him coming and would have gone to greet him had I not noticed the positive swagger with which his gnarled old legs swung his age-twisted body along. I waited inside my door watching as he walked back and forth outside coughing to attract my attention. Waited while he plucked a leaf of the rose geranium and rubbed it between his palms and then sniffed the fragrance almost greedily. At last, when he had half the village peeking or staring openly at him, he stopped immediately in front of my door and clapped his hands.

I stepped outside and by way of greeting inquired solicitously after his health, the health of all his wives, and then the health of all his children. He did me like courtesy, including in his concern my unborn child. I could see he was enjoying the occasion immensely and would welcome any prolongment; so I began asking about the well-being of his in-laws, taking great care, of course, not to mention any of his mothers-in-law. For in the interests of marital accord, most African tribesmen never look their mothers-in-law in the face.

Finally, however, there was nothing left with which we might consume time if the visit had any point at all, so N'ragde informed me that "the fetish hut stools" were finished. He himself had placed them in the sanctuary. Would it be too great an irritation for me to come and pass judgment on his poor handiwork? The lilt in his cracked old voice, the swing in his twisted shoulders, the pride on his face contrasted ludicrously with the humility of his words.

I was curious and eager and I almost ran to the church, half the village following. Inside the door I stopped short, but those who crowded in behind pushed me stumblingly forward. Then I gasped, for on our bean-shaped platform rested two stools only a little taller than sitting-height stools. I was conscious of a breathless silence in the church and N'ragde anxiously peering up at me almost from under my elbow.

"They are—to your—liking—?" he began. I think the old man was as near to tears as one ever comes when the weight of years has pressed his tear ducts dry.

"They are beautiful. Beautiful! I—I never expected anything like these!" burst from me and the crowd behind applauded my complete honesty with much noisy inward sucking of breath. N'ragde stood almost erect, almost as tall as I in his pride.

It is true: they were beautiful, but I have never seen lectern or pulpit like them before. Old N'ragde had carved scenes from our village life around the roughly square sides of each piece and had scraped the rounded surfaces smooth with broken shell and then had rubbed them with his palms wet with sweat and spit and fish oil until they glowed as though alive. There were women bent almost double under their enormous loads of wood; women bending over to shape wet clay into pots; women, with babies astride one hip, roasting meat over a fire; women grasping their short-handled hoes in both hands and widely straddling the row of vegetables they cultivated.

The activities of the men were depicted, too. Herdboys with their cows and sheep; young warriors with their spears; old men with their spindles, spinning as they walked about; men bent over their narrow looms weaving, with the warp looped over the big toe of one rigidly extended foot in order to keep the thread taut; men carrying home the game they had killed on the veld.

Across the top of the altar there was a narrow row of figures above the smooth surface I had told the old wood carver we should have there. My first reaction was to the beauty of the figures, the wonderful proportions, the delicacy and wealth of detail. Then I stared again, scanning each carving carefully. Jimmy had said much to both men and women about burying fish in the soil of the gardens and, thereby, keeping it always fertile. There, on the altar, N'ragde had pictured the labors of native fishermen, working with spear, with seine knotted from green bark, with trap and weir woven from reeds and wattle. On the smooth surface, so lightly carved, intaglio fashion, that it gave the impression of being etched, was a fat fish. I looked at N'ragde quickly, and his eyes stared back into mine, as brightly pleading as a child's begging for approbation. I wondered what inspiration had led him to beautify our altar with the sign of the ancient Christians. I wanted to ask him if the legends of his people, so many of which parallel the stories of the Old Testament, also borrowed from the history of the early martyrs. Then I could only repeat, "Beautiful! Beautiful!"

"No fetish hut of my people ever had a more beautiful altar or lectern," I told N'ragde. "You are an artist." And then it took a half-hour to explain to him something of what it is that lifts the artist above the mere good workman.

As I have said so many times before, perhaps it was because I was born in Africa and had had as nurse a woman not even one generation removed from savagery, that I instinctively sank to my haunches before the lectern—as a normal position for resting—the pose which puts both host and guest at ease in an African village. And yet, today, there are no ministerial chairs in our pulpit. N'ragde had measured the churchly stools to come exactly to the height I had indicated on my bosom as I leaned across the wall of the palaver hut—to exactly that height when I squatted on my haunches as he had been at the time, as he probably supposed I would be had it not been necessary for me to stand in order to peer over the wall.

One midnight shortly thereafter I was awakened by the acrid smell of smoke. I leaped out of bed so quickly I felt the child within me almost swing and bounce as though my now pendulous stomach were something apart from the rest of my body. Quite slowly and sedately I walked to the door and stepped outside. All down the street I could see dimly that men and women were standing outside their doors, with the arms and heads of children seemingly tangled around and about their bare legs. To the east and south—the direction Jimmy had traveled—the night sky was shot with the rosy streaks of a dreaming painter's dawn. Many miles away, out on the veld beyond the jungle, a spark from some careless one's campfire, or the deliberate torch of a herdsman, had fired the dead and tinder dry grass which smothered the plains.

We watched for a minute, then many soft voices called kindly advice to me that I dive back into my kraal and pull the door to quickly before unseen malicious ones who love the darkness could enter and take possession of my dwelling. I called back my thanks and wishes that the rest of the night might be blessed with sweet sleep, and went back to bed. I did not worry about Jimmy. By now he was surely under the roof of the great one who had beckoned to him.

The next morning the sky was dull and gray with smoke. Overhead many birds circled, confused and frightened by the acrid pall. When one stepped beyond the village huts into the jungle keen eyes saw many animals which either roam by night or flee from the smell of men. They, too, were filled with strange fears, and so were unbelievably incautious. I think I could have put my hand on the back of a tiny duiker which stood and trembled without seeing me as I walked past it.

But the fire was not burning near us or traveling in our direction, so we witnessed no hegira of plains' animals or massed flight of birds. After a day or two, it had either burned itself out or the rim of flame had moved so far off that it made no difference in our night sky and the pall of smoke soon blew away. No one remarked the fire as a disaster or gave it much thought. I least of all. The grass grows tall and thick on the plains of Africa, in some places the elephant grass reaches a height of ten to fifteen feet. When it dies during the dry season it must be burned away—as it always is by accident if not design—before the wild and domestic browsing animals can reach the new grass which springs up within hours after the first rain. The young warriors exchanged a few wishes that the rains would not be delayed for, until it fell, there would be so little game on the plains that it would not be worth their while to soil their feet with the soot and ashes in search of food.

"There may be a few nights when we shall have to dig our fists into our bellies when we lie down to sleep," Chief Mu'muou said to me.

That was a custom new to me and I asked him its purpose.

He smiled at my ignorance and explained as though to a child that when there is no food to be put into the stomach that organ must be fooled, else it will growl like a beast and gnaw at itself. "The children? The women feed them sips of mud when there are no beans or mealies or flesh for the cooking pots. But those of us who are grown have no taste for river slime. We press our fists into our bellies so hard that the stomach must be still long enough for us to slip into the state of half-life. We sleep long hours during the hungry days," he ended.

I wished Jimmy were there to explain about fertile land which raised enough food to store against such hungry days. That evening I heard drums in the jungle and I supposed that Mu'muou and the other men were performing the dances and reciting the proper incantations to curry favor with the spirits which persuade the heavens to weep upon the bosom of long-suffering Mother Earth. Whether I was right or wrong I do not know. The next evening drumbeats throbbed through the jungle again, but this time before the evening meals were finished. Those men who had dallied over their food hastily gobbled their full, and many among the women went without their suppers so they might line up along the street in a grinning expectant row.

Two women stood stiffly, shoulder to shoulder, in back of the others. I was struck by that fact, for there is no human being so gregarious as the African. I also noted that they were not grinning like their sisters in front of them. Nor were they frowning nor weeping. Rather, their mobile features, usually reflecting the vivacious spirits within, were as blank and devoid of all expression as though they had suddenly been paralyzed beyond all movement. I had no way of knowing what troubled these two or set them apart from the others, but quick warm sympathy surged within me, and I walked over and stood beside them. Maa Koo joined the general mob of women and children that laughed and tittered with that barely suppressed excitement that always seems on the point of boiling over into bedlam. I glanced at her questioningly and she was watching me, perhaps in order to catch my eye, for she smiled and nodded at me with such an air of satisfied approval that I knew that somehow, ignorantly, I had done a right thing. We three lone women, standing behind all others, clasped hands, and the next day there were bruises where my neighbor had pressed her strong fingers cruelly into my flesh.

We did not wait long for whatever was to happen. Suddenly a veritable thunder of drums enveloped us. Even I noticed that they were all the heavy-timbred, deep-throated male drums. There were no thin-voiced, high-pitched female instruments in that cacophony.

Then I understood, for the boys who in such an exceedingly short time had become men, danced down the street, whooping and yelling like witch doctors at their busiest professional moments. And they looked like witch doctors, too, every one of them. Each wore a grass skirt which swirled about him as he pranced. Some had breastplates of woven bamboo. All were topped by fantastic masks of carved wood, coconut fiber, fur, feather, claw and every other oddment of the jungle designed to make the wearer a fearsome object. Every mask made the boy wearing it, however young and slight of frame, seemingly of man's stature.

I leaned forward, eagerly peering at the boys, hoping I might recognize Hey Boy in spite of the costuming. The woman beside me didn't move a muscle. It isn't possible that above that din I could have heard Maa Koo's hiss, but I must have felt or sensed it, for I glanced at her. She was frowning and shaking her head *"NO!"* Then she hunched her old shoulders crookedly erect as command that I should do the same. I obeyed as though under compulsion and the woman beside me sighed heavily. It was the only sign either of my companions gave that she was under emotional stress.

Then I noticed that the women in the line in front of us three were calling out to this or that masked dancing figure, trying to recognize their sons, trying to tempt the maskers into betraying their identities. There was one little fellow who I was sure was Hey Boy and I, too, leaned forward and shouted.

Until the day of my death I shall never forget the moment of stunned silence, paralysis of all movement that fell on that carnival crowd in the firelight. Men, women, children, and masked dancers all turned toward me and stared.

The woman beside me hissed faintly under her breath and I knew without looking that her lips scarcely moved with the words, "That was not fitting, sister. You have not yet borne a man. The pot you shaped was too frail for the fire." By the force of her will alone she pulled me erect once more and I stood thus, like a woman of stone for the rest of the evening. My body was cold, but my thoughts raced about here and there within my skull like little wild things in a trap. I knew what the woman's words meant. I saw once again, as though every detail were etched on metal, the pottery shards beside my door over which I had stumbled one morning. Symbolic of my Hey Boy who had cracked and failed in the fiery tests of his manhood and his fitness to take his place in the tribe. I knew, but helplessly, hopelessly I tried to escape that meaning.

Finally there was a last parade of the masked boys through the village, a pause before all but three huts which had had sons in this initiation class, much stamping and swirling of skirts and the shouting mob disappeared into the jungle again. In the morning the boys would be back in the village we knew, not in their mother's huts, but in the huge kraal at the end of the street where the barely ripened men not yet old enough or rich enough to possess wives led a community life. They had all fished, hunted, herded the cattle, spun thread and woven cloth, but mostly as boys at play, aping their elders. Now overnight they had become men, and these pleasures had become responsibilities which they must shoulder conscientiously for the welfare of the village.

The last towering, basket-like mask and swirling skirt disappeared into the midnight under the trees. We women holding hands, we three poor souls who had not borne men but had only produced living pots that cracked in the fire, untwined our fingers and looked into each other's faces briefly.

"Never mind, white woman, you carry a child in your belly, and we are still young," one of them said to me in words that were no louder than the slither of two falling leaves that strike in mid-air.

The other simply put her hand on my shoulder, turned me in the direction of my hut and pushed gently. Maa Koo followed me, helped me undress and get into bed and left without giving me a half-dozen words. She, too, had loved Hey Boy; perhaps more than I.

And after all, what was there for us to say to each other? I had found the bush school of the girls crude but good. It fitted their needs—needs which I sometimes think my own race is only beginning to recognize and pretend to meet with fearful misgivings. I believe the same must be true of the initiation schools for the boys. Good up to some point short of loss of human life.

Were the boys subjected to greater rigors than the girls? I didn't see how that could be! Were they more delicate, possessed of less stamina? Possibly. And Africa admits this, for women are the strapping beasts of burden. I could only guess at what had happened to Jimmy's and my little waif there in the depth of the jungle. Had he failed physically? Or had he shown himself a coward? Or a liar? I almost wished it might have been either cowardice or lying—if white gossip concerning the initiation school were really true—then everlasting peace had come to Hey Boy with the swift, merciful blow of a knobkerrie behind one ear.

I pressed my hands over my heart to dull the pain and whispered through stiff lips, "We will change that. Dear God, we will change that. And we will take the cruelty out of the training school for the girls."

Then, irrationally, lying there in the darkness all by myself, I laughed as I thought of the old women instructresses. I could almost hear them sneer at me out of the depths of their grim personal experiences: "Men are cruel. Life itself is cruel. The girls must know this before they are thrust into wifehood. Is it a kindness to weaken the body and soften the will of a beast of burden?"

The pain in my heart throbbed like a drumbeat and I pressed hard and downward over it and answered the shadowy old women through clenched teeth: "I will change that! God helping me, I will preserve what is good, but I will take the cruelty out of the girls' school. I will take the murder out of the boys' school!"

The very vigor of my reply relieved me somewhat, and I dozed off, but to sleep only fitfully. The pain was always there in my mind and heart and gradually it spread to engulf my entire body. I suppose I fussed or whimpered, for I looked up in a half-waking daze and Maa Koo was standing beside me. She put a hand under the covers and ran it over my stomach, pressing lightly here and there.

"Your little frog is eager to leap out into this dark world," she said calmly.

My baby coming? "No! no, Maa Koo! You're wrong, he isn't

due—for more than a month yet," I protested. "Maybe I ate something for supper—"

"You ate nothing. The ripening men danced out of the jungle before you tasted food. Remember? And you stood for hours on your feet with the other two desolate ones," she answered me.

I stared up at her, struggling to keep from clenching my teeth and pressing my hands hard against my body again. Not over my heart this time, but lower down. She crooked an imperious finger at me, "Come."

But the pain was a long time in dying away and I lay without speaking or moving, only holding my breath. One sweep of my old nurse's arm swept the bed covers off me from neck to toe.

I have never before now told anyone what happened that night—not even mother or brother Norman—but I see no reason why it should not be put down here. Almost without knowing what I did, certainly without giving thought to what my white sisters back at the central mission station would think of my action, I arose and followed my old nurse down the street and into the native birthing hut. I remember that I stumbled along awkwardly between the surges of pain that engulfed me. Once I put out my hand and grasped a branch of the beloved Jo Ellen's rose geranium tree, crushing leaves and a succulent stem against my palm. We were immediately enveloped in a pungent warm fragrance that made me think whimsically of Aunt Elma's farm kitchen on baking day.

I heard Maa Koo mutter, "It is a good sign. The spirits are friendly." But it was pleasanter to hang there to the rose geranium tree and think of sweet-faced, crisply starched Aunt Elma and her saucer-sized cookies than it was to pay attention to my old black nurse or to dwell on what lay immediately ahead.

Two old women were already busy at the fire hole in the center of the floor in the birthing hut. Tuou was settling two clay pots on the rocks so they would not tip over when the fire burned down. The other old woman, a sister-wife of Tuou's, was breaking sticks over her knee into suitable lengths for thrusting into the fire when needed. A stick snapped sharply in her strong hands, and with the smaller length she pointed to a pile of freshly cut fern leaves lying in one corner.

Maa Koo reached up and unfastened the neck band of my nightgown, slid it over my shoulders and down my arms, and let it fall in a circling heap at my feet. I looked down and had a wild desire to laugh. In spite of all the washings my nightgown had endured, I could still trace the outline of the original red and green checks and *P-U-R-I-* before the trade name of the stock feed slid under a fold of the coarse stuff.

But Maa Koo saw nothing funny—or remark-worthy for that matter!—in either nightgown or the happenings of the night. She led me to the pile of ferns, half forced me to my knees, and commanded me to labor as it has been ordained since the beginning of time that woman must labor.

Some time later when the pain was a flood that drowned all rational thought and blotted out memory of emotion, Maa Koo came and squatted on her haunches before me and wound her wiry black arms about my body below my armpits. I leaned my head on her shoulder and sobbed and demanded between gasps for breath why my husband had casually gone visiting somebody somewhere like an irresponsible schoolboy when I needed him so much. My old nurse did not attempt to answer. Instead she hugged me tight or loosely with the onslaught or recession of pain and made little soothing clucking noises like a setting-hen fussing over her eggs.

My baby squalled before he tumbled onto the ferns beneath me, and I would have arisen, but Maa Koo held me down. Out of exhausted, pain-befogged eyes I saw Tuou fall to her knees and elbows and pluck my baby out of the tangle of Maa Koo's and my legs. I had a brief glimpse of him in one of her skinny hands curled up like a kitten in a tabby cat's mouth. Then I closed my eyes, laid my head on Maa Koo's shoulder and my body against hers and waited. As from a distance I heard the child squalling again and I wished it would shut up. I wanted so desperately to rest.

Then it was all over and Tuou's sister-wife brought a pot of hot water and with a handful of rough grass for a washcloth scrubbed every inch of my body from the waist down until pin-points of blood showed here and there.

I don't know how Tuou severed the navel cord, whether she used a hunting knife, a bit of broken shell, or what few teeth remained to her. But the next morning I discovered that according to best native tradition the cord had been tied with three hairs from a cow's tail—but white hairs instead of black since that was the color of skin Mu'ungu had unaccountably given me.

Maa Koo and the women birthing me pulled me to my feet and as Maa Koo slipped my nightgown back over my head, again I saw old Tuou, still like a tabby cat, washing my baby with her tongue. Tuou almost tossed the child into Maa Koo's hands and my nurse, with equal casualness, draped it over one shoulder, holding it by its heels like a chicken ready for market. There, it turned its head from side to side on its rubbery neck and seemingly appalled at life, beat her protruding shoulder blade with its two tiny fists. She pushed me through the door and kept shoving me toward my hut.

We were almost home when a party of hunters who had camped away from the village for the night, returned with their kill, a huge *old man* (gorilla). They called out boastfully to Maa Koo of their prize, and Maa Koo, with the privilege given women of her great age, snorted contemptuously.

"See what we caught during the night," she answered, and held my naked baby up for them to see. "Not an *old man* who is good for nothing but a couple of hours gnawing, but a young man with what of power and wealth before him only Mu'ungu can tell."

The hunters stared curiously. Then when my baby began to squall again, one of them remarked, "It may be he will some time resemble *N'gali* (the gorilla) in strength and fierceness—although he doesn't look or sound much like an *old man* now."

"That will be his black name, N'gali," Maa Koo told me. "The *old man* will be his animal fetish. He must never eat the flesh of gorilla, little mother."

Solemnly I promised her that N'gali would never knowingly eat gorilla.

"Will he have a white name, too?"

"Yes," I answered. "It will be the same as his father's, James Timothy Grove."

We passed into my hut and I went to bed. When I awakened, it was dark again. Maa Koo told me that my baby—Timmy—had nursed three times, and that she had remembered that she was a *mission girl*. I asked her what she meant, and she told me that she had rubbed Timmy from crown to toe with oil and had wrapped him in one of my old petticoats. I laughed at her, kissed and cuddled Timmy, nursed him again, ate half a baked yam and went back to sleep.

CHAPTER
TWENTY-FOUR

Maa Koo took care of the village etiquette of birthing for me. Before he was quite twenty-four hours old she showed N'galisyo (I-Am-a-Little-Old-Man or "gorilla") to every man, woman and child. Naturally he was paraded naked so that every inch of his perfectly formed little body could be examined by critical although friendly eyes. I can still imagine her grasping his buttocks with one hand and pulling his arms and legs out with the other and even shaking him occasionally so that the size and strength of his lungs could be admired. And, of course, evidence of his sex was thrust within six inches of every old man's and woman's nose. It was no baby heifer she and I were trying to palm off on the village, but a real man-bud.

My old nurse also "gifted" as she expressed it, the women who had assisted at my confinement. I am a relatively tall woman, and definitely slender. "Skinny" is the word my family uses. The only possible use I could make of a girdle or foundation garment would be to keep my stomach warm—hardly necessary in Fan Country! But while I was in college, while I was in nurse's training, when I returned to Africa a full-fledged missionary, the kind ladies who clothed me had always included several girdles in my gear. I never had one of them on. But, being an appreciative soul and careful of what was given me, there were usually several girdles in my clothes chest wrapped in tissue paper. From the care I gave them, airing them periodically, washing them occasionally, and carefully packing them away again, my old nurse must have thought them something of value, something of "gifting" quality. Anyway among other things she gave old Tuou and the sister-wife each a girdle. One of the girdles I never saw again. The other—well, the other came to light under circumstances almost as strange and bizarre as the use to which my girdle was put.

I have to smile at what I am told is nowadays a technique being tried out in modern hospitals in these United States, that is, getting new mothers up and on their feet and home before the first week is ended. Maa Koo pulled me out of bed the morning of the third day. I have seen many a native girl bear her child with every bit as great labor and excruciating agony as any white woman—and shoulder her hoe and march off to the gardens the next morning with the rest of the village women. But being white I protested Maa Koo's commands. I believe she would have upset my cot with me in it if I had not finally swung my legs over the side. I grumbled, and so did she: Did I really think I was a little white grub just because she had called me one so often? Would I, if left alone without a wise old woman like herself to guide and control my skittish behavior, spend half my life under dark, warm, protecting covers? Sleeping instead of working as Mu'ungu intended that woman should do through *all* the daylight hours?

She rumbled and spluttered like a boiling pot and I got up and dressed because I knew I had to. And after a few hours I was glad I had, for my legs felt moderately strong and my steps were fairly steady.

In the early afternoon I nursed Timmy and then laid him across my shoulder where he could burp at his lordly male convenience and strolled out into the village. Maa Koo hovered about me like a guinea fowl over her brood when the shadow of a soaring hawk streaks over sand and brush. She was not motivated by any concern for me but sheer personal pride. *She* and I had produced a man-bud!

It was a triumphal progress from beginning to end. I was offered enough palm wine and banana beer to drown a village. The food held out before me would have satisfied an appetite the size of tembo's. My legs gained strength as I sauntered along and before

I knew it I was standing by the plot of ground assigned to Jimmy and me for a garden. The seeds we had planted were up. By squatting and parting the weeds I could locate the hills and rows.

"See?" I called the attention of the women clustered about me, "because we planted a piece of fish in each hill as food, our seeds are up quicker and taller than yours."

"It seems to me that the weeds like the food, too, for they are taller and thicker than ours," one woman remarked.

I did not know the answer to that, so I explained that, if on the morrow, they would come to my hut I would show them how a man-bud, or a female brat for that matter, should be bathed and anointed. Then I would take up my hoe and come to the garden with them and pull up and cut down all the weeds and they could see in the weeks to come how lush a garden can grow.

I was actually hoeing in my garden the next afternoon when Jimmy returned. Maa Koo was sitting in the shade extremely busy doing nothing around and about Timmy after the manner of grandmothers and old nurses. Tuou, the mother-wife, came on flying feet to fetch me, and although her face was as bald of all expression as a barren mountain boulder in shadow, I knew that something was wrong. Terribly wrong!

I dropped my hoe where I stood and started up the path. I would have forgotten baby Timmy, but Maa Koo— Dear God! What would I have done, what kind of person would I have become without that little old hag, that wrinkled bundle of selfless, almost divine wisdom helping to shape my character, standing between me and stubborn self-will and crippling ignorance at every stage of my life? Aside from actually nursing him, Maa Koo had complete care of our man-bud for the next three days. I think there were times when I would not even have fed him had she not thrust him into my bosom.

I could see four black boys standing in front of our hut as I neared it. One of them said to me as I paused to look him in the face before pushing aside the matting of my door, "We took your master to the Big Bwana who beckoned to him. We sat on our heels and waited while they palavered. Now we have brought him back to his kraal. We have told this to Chief Mu'muou and he says our duty is ended."

Abruptly the four—*four*, not six!—turned and stalked off. I laid my hand on the door-matting and entered my hut. Jimmy lay crookedly across his cot, and even in that first blindness after coming in out of the bright sun I could see that his left leg was—even now in my dreams I cry out, God help me!—his leg was as big around as an old-fashioned churn Aunt Elma had herbs planted in on her back porch. And he stank the way the last of an elephant's flesh stinks before a small village, fortunate enough to have killed one of those monsters, devours it all.

If I may digress, I want to say here that of all the fairy tales and fanciful gadgets mankind has created for his own amusement, clocks and calendars are the most ridiculous and completely untrustworthy. Time is emotional, and maturity is of the intellect and spirit. Character and social responsibility are their offspring. And God in his heaven watches their growth as any gardener tends his seedlings. And time clipped off in neat little snippets by the ticks of a clock is an absurdity created by man to assuage his puny egotism when he must face the fact that he is nothing but a fluid drop in eternity, and all that has and will fill the life before and the life to come after him. *Time!* It was man—not God!—who wrote down for other men to read an account of the creation in terms of days. Perhaps that is because language is weak and vague and at best one of mankind's more imperfect creations and as such it serves his needs imperfectly.

But language, faulty as it is, is the only tool to serve between you and me, so I must write: For three days and nights I nursed my husband and shortly past midnight of the fourth day he died. But *three days* is a ridiculous measurement of the eons of agony I lived through. One can say to another: "I suffer. My soul was swept bare and I was appalled at the poverty of my spirit." And what is the concept in the mind of the listener to these stark words? Vague, fleeting, chimerical, and swept out of mind by laughter at the next of life's absurdities as easily as a cobweb is brushed from a corner by a careless finger.

I did not have the story of that trip from Jimmy. He was delirious when I found him tumbled across his bed, and he never regained rationality unless it was for a few fleeting seconds just before his death. The four who came back talked to others and the villagers dropped words more or less casually before me like the scrapings from a cooking pot splattered before a dog. And like a famished dog, I seized upon each morsel and devoured it.

Of the six who set out with Jimmy to visit the Big Bwana who had graciously nodded in our direction, one had immediately become enamored of the ways of civilization. He stayed on with the Big Bwana to work on his plantation—to do woman's work, if you please! Another had given his life for Jimmy.

When the five and my husband came to that portion of burned-over veld which they must cross, they found only two evidences of game. The first was a sleeping rhinoceros cow over which Jimmy almost stumbled because, much blackened from lying in the soot, she looked like a boulder or charred log. After the fashion of rhinoceroses, as soon as she awakened she charged in the direction of the noise which her exceedingly keen ears located for her. Jimmy, his gun in his hand and on the lookout for meat, was a little in advance of his boys, burdened as they were with his safari equipment.

I have heard tales—what man or woman in Africa has not?—of the thunder of a charging rhinoceros' hooves, and of the size of these paleozoic relics of the animal kingdom. Of how imagination magnifies that size for the man in the path of this flesh and blood juggernaut of the veld. And who has not been advised to stand stock-still when charged? The theory being that because the animal's eyesight is as poor as its hearing is keen, any unmoving object will be mistaken for a tree stump or boulder and left alone. I believe there is even a fairy tale told black children to the effect that the rhinoceros horn is not a true horn at all but an immense corn acquired by the stupid beast in ages past before its tiny brain

318 ·

learned the uselessness and folly of blindly and madly butting every boulder beside a path.

Jimmy, in the best safari campfire tale tradition, had stood stock-still "until the shadow of the monster cloaked his knees." So far as I know, aside from an occasional zebra or small antelope and his one elephant, during his few years in Africa, my husband had never hunted anything larger or more dangerous than a few rabbits and quail on his father's farm. His gun was not of particularly heavy calibre, and if it had been, he knew nothing about a rhino's vital spots—and even the best white hunters differ on this last point. What Jimmy must have thought standing there with that monster thundering down upon him, one can only guess. I know he was not paralyzed with fear. Timmy's father was not a coward; he had guts.

But when he saw that the stupid beast was not fooled by his lack of movement and was not going to turn aside, he flexed his knees to leap backward. His heel struck a rock—"Such a little stone to be so malicious! It was no larger than a half-grown coconut"—I was told. But it was large enough. They said Jimmy would have turned a backward somersault had not the rhinoceros swung the horned battering ram of its great head in a sweeping sidewise arc and laid my husband's leg open from hip to knee. Then, again, contrary to veld lore, it had not thundered out of sight, but had wheeled and charged again. Jimmy struggled to rise and saw one of his boys, head-load tossed wherever it might fall, dash between him and the infuriated beast. They say he actually slapped its nose with a back-handed blow as he passed! Guts are not the prerogative solely of men bound up in white skins! They left that boy behind, a bloody pulp on the blackened veld.

Since the boy had given his life for Jimmy, in the name of Jimmy's son—who in the eyes of my parishioners had now inherited me as a chattel possession—I went to the boy's family and paid the customary blood price before I left Fan Country. I did not haggle. I gave what they asked—the gun which had fallen from Jimmy's hands when the rhinoceros caught him. The stock was cracked, and the barrel was roughly S-shaped because the beast had trampled on it. But in so doing, I broke one of the strictest laws of white Africa, for no "bush" native is permitted to own a firearm of any kind, in any state of disrepair; and only black soldiery may have guns in their possession.

The safari made no attempt to bury the dead man. The native boys would see no reason for doing so. And Jimmy must have reasoned that hungry men should conserve their strength and time —and that loss of blood and a filthy laceration can only worsen under a tropic sun and continued strenuous exertion. I know he must have made an attempt to cleanse and bind up his wound, but there was no sign of bandage when he reached home, and his first-aid kit was missing.

I would never have known about his second encounter with game on that desolate, blackened veld had he not suddenly leaped to his feet while Maa Koo and I were trying to minister to the fetid horror his leg had become, and started babbling, shouting, screeching in his delirium about a zebra's tail.

"Our noses told us there was meat on the veld long before our eyes saw the striped carcass. We hurried to it, our bellies growling and our knives in our hands—*and then we saw that the tail had been cut off.*"

The eyes of the boy speaking fell before mine. Apparently he was stricken dumb from some strange quirk of tribal embarrassment, for I could not get another word out of him. Nor would anyone else enlighten me as to why a zebra's tail should so trouble Jimmy now. It was Maa Koo who learned the rest of that episode and told it to me.

Simply, it is this: Ordinarily a hunter will share his kill with any stranger who comes along. But in this part of Africa anyway, when a tribesman's family or village is in the grip of dire hunger, he will advertise that fact to whoever chances along by cutting off the tail of the animal he has killed—if the beast is of such size, or his own physical condition is so weakened that he must go for help, leaving it behind temporarily. No animal so marked is ever touched by another man. I have been told since that a tribesman falling exhausted from starvation beside such a kill would merely turn his face away so that his eyes would not be tortured by the sight of food he might not share, and die—if that were the will of the spirits.

I had not known this custom. How could Jimmy possibly have known it. And how could he, every last inch of him a civilized being, have understood the adamant hold primitive laws have on the lives of primitive men? Jimmy had not sheathed his knife. Instead he had laid it to the flank of the de-tailed zebra, ripped open the skin, and would have cut out a chunk of meat had his boys not laid violent, detaining hands upon him. He would not listen to reason—primitive reason, that is; so using their G-straps for rope, they had bound him arms and legs to two spears and had carried him away from the meat which, in spite of the clamor within their bellies, they could in no honor taste. Then, when the forbidden zebra was far behind them and they were ready to set him on his feet once more, his limbs would not bear his weight "and already the little legless ones [maggots] burrowed into his torn flesh."

I did everything I could to save my husband's life—and there was not a possession in the village I could not have had for the asking if it would have helped. There was no personal service which any man, woman or child would have held back. But when I cut Jimmy's clothes off his body—and chunks of proud flesh came away with the tattered trouser leg—I knew that widowhood lay ahead for me. Under my very eyes as I cleansed his body I saw the red streaks of blood poisoning creep outward and upward under his skin. I gave him all by way of opiates that I dared, and old mother-wife Tuou brought a gourd full of something she had brewed and fed it to him drop by drop. In spite of my scientific training, the old woman was far more skillful than I at handling an injured body without giving undue pain.

I did everything I could! And so did Maa Koo. And so did Tuou. But at the end of the third day there was no duty for our six hands other than to keep his face clean of sweat, his lips wet, and the flies and gnats and ants away from the mass of carrion which his left leg had become. Finally I got up and walked out of the door. I knew where I was going, my steps were purposeful; but out there in the open, early twilight, I stopped short and looked around. It seemed to me that the entire village had gathered before my hut. A thousand pair of eyes stared at me, big, round, full of silent question. If my parishioners, my neighbors and friends there in that recently cannibal village had been white men and women, they would have dropped their eyes and heads and many of them would have shuffled away in embarrassed sympathy. One difference between primitive man and civilized beings is that the so-called savage is not ashamed of honest emotion and he sees no reason for hiding that fact from you when his heart swells and breaks with your own. No futile words were spoken, just many indrawn breaths. I don't know how many hands were stretched out to me, palms upward saying mutely that they would gladly bear any portion of my burden that could be picked up and borne by others. They did not understand it, but they knew that the relation between me and my husband was something a great deal more than that between black men and their two-legged female *cattle*.

I walked past them, through an edge of the crowd that seemed to sway apart rather than step aside for me. Slowly, slowly the outstretched arms swung in an arc so that the promising palms pointed always at me. I walked into the church and noted almost without surprise that small fires glowed in the two fire holes in the floor. I stepped into the sanctuary and went down on my heels like a good native Christian before the knee-high altar. I spread my hands out over the fish old N'ragde had carved, and laid my head on them. There I prayed, not formally with set phrases, wearying God's ears with facts He already knew so well, and pointing out to Him His divine duty. I bowed before Him, completely humbled and helpless and begged of Him to spare my husband as I had often begged my earthly father in childhood for some small privilege.

I prayed aloud intermittently and now and then I was half-conscious of a soft soughing sound like a gentle but strengthening night breeze in the thatch. Then someone coughed, ever so gently, but it recalled me from the gateway of heaven to this earth and I raised my head. The church was full of people, all on their knees, all with their palms and fingers pressed rigidly together and held stiffly and neatly erect, their thumbnails resting on the tips of their broad noses. Unconsciously I clasped my hands together and pressed my thumbnails on my own nose. Chief Mu'muou was peeping at me out of one half-opened eye. I thought I saw him grin.

I once had asked an old Quaker, "What do you mean when you speak of 'a mystical experience'?"

He had taken a sip of blackberry cordial, washed it over his tongue, and swallowed it appreciatively before replying. Then he said, "I can't describe it to thee because it is never the same. When it comes, thee will know. Thee simply feels the presence of God, and there is no mistaking that."

God was with us in His clay-and-dung floored, wattle and mud-walled, thatch-roofed church that night. All I can say is, simply, there was no mistaking His presence. My husband lay dying only a few yards away, but I felt like grinning back at Chief Mu'muou.

"Father, show me Thy will," I prayed. "And give me the strength and the courage—" But I knew He had already given me the strength and the courage.

"Ahhhh Muhhhh!" the folk in front of me whispered.

Then I understood the soughing sound I had heard. The beloved Jo Ellen had been one lone woman in the depth of the jungle and yet a generation after her death the children of her converts strengthened my prayer with their "Amens."

I arose to my feet, and the people before me arose to theirs, noiselessly, decorously, and stood waiting. I hesitated for a moment, and then I folded my hands: "And now may the grace of God and the fellowship—" I stumbled, but I got through the benediction. Then I stepped down from the pulpit and passed through the two halves into which my congregation had divided itself, noticing for the first time that the men were on one side and the women on the other—in the best missionary tradition. I turned my head from side to side smiling at them as I passed through the living lane, and those nearest me put out their hands to brush my sleeves with their finger tips. As the old Quaker had said I would, I knew in all certainty: God walked with me.

Back in my hut, Jimmy's eyes caught mine as soon as I stepped inside the door, and followed me to the chair beside his bed where I sat down. I picked up his hand and his fingers fluttered as though he would have liked to return my clasp. With my other hand I curled them around my palm and held them there.

"I have been in our church," I said to him.

He smiled again, and this time the creases in the corners of his mouth did not fade away. He just lay there looking at me, smiling gently while I told him about the church we had finished while he was gone, and the things these people had remembered of the legendary Jo Ellen's teaching. Once I stopped and we both listened. Outside, faintly, and seemingly far away, a pulsating noise that might have been a drum swelled through the night. Within the next ten minutes three other possible drums joined it. Only they were not drums, there was no music in the beats, no resonance, only regular thudding noises softened by distance. The four beating sounds kept up through the night with only irregular short breaks now and then in some one of them. And I continued telling Jimmy about all that had happened in his absence, not that that was important but I could see that the sound of my voice gave him pleasure, and presently I forgot about the thudding noises.

Maa Koo brought Timmy to me and I fed him. When he had finished nursing I held him up for his father to look at. I stripped off his shirt so Jimmy could see the good chest he had, and his shoulders and the straight bones of his arms. I took off his diaper and showed Jimmy his round hips and thighs. I stood him up on his father's chest, holding most of his weight in my hands so that if he should kick it would be no more to his father than a flip from a gnat's wing. I uncurled Timmy's tiny fingers and laid them on Jimmy's cheek and drew them across his mouth and nose. And when Maa Koo came to take Timmy away, there was as deep a smile on Jimmy's face as he had ever worn in health. His hand stirred toward mine and I picked it up again. This time his fingers curled about my palm of themselves. Tight! So tight it was a sweet discomfort.

From then on we talked a little, I with my lips and he with his eyes, and we were silent for longer periods after the way it is with a man and his wife. Then I noticed that when I moved my head his eyes no longer followed the motion. I bent over and kissed him and there was no breath from his nostrils on my cheek. Sometime later, I don't know how much later, with my free hand I pressed the lids down over his eyes, otherwise I don't think I moved until Maa Koo brought Timmy to me to be nursed again.

She stopped at the foot of the bed, my man-bud astride one age-withered hip. I glanced at her briefly and wished she would go away. But Maa Koo, Christian mission girl though she was, was permeated with the wisdom of the jungle; she never forgot that it is the living and not the dead that must be served.

Still standing at the foot of the bed she said to me, "Little Grub, sometimes I have thought that surely your heart is black, like ours; and other times I have known with certainty that it is not. Why do you not now screech and tear out chunks of your hair like a black woman? It is a good thing to do. Outside confusion helps one to stifle and forget the inside misery. That must be done somehow before the door of another man's kraal closes behind you."

Timmy whimpered and my old nurse laid him in my lap. Then she took hold of my wrist thinking to slip it from Jimmy's grasp, but his fingers were now iron and ice about my palm. He held me as tightly in death as he ever had in life.

"I shall never walk into another man's kraal as his wife," I told my old nurse.

"Widows or pregnant women—I don't know which are the bigger fools," she muttered, but there was no condemnation and not much conviction in her voice.

Timmy fed, I went outside. Chief Mu'muou was waiting there for me.

"That One," he began, "told our fathers how she should be disposed of in death. Three days ago we marked four fallen trees in the jungle. Already the woodsmen are shaping the *bohrrrudhs."*

I wondered what he meant, and seeing the question in my eyes, he motioned for me to follow him. A moment later the thudding, unmusical, drum-like beat which had continued throughout the night was explained. We came upon a group of men, working in relays, two by two, shaping a board out of a tree trunk by the simple means of gouging away the wood on opposite sides until nothing remained but a comparatively straight, thin sheet of wood. Four trees. One board to a tree. Four boards for Jimmy's coffin. I wondered what they would use for nails, and Mu'muou explained to me that holes would be burned along the edges of the bohrrrudhs by the red-hot points of spears, and that they would be laced together with green vines.

I visited all four groups of woodsmen and thanked them and promised that weight would be added my thanks by substantial gifts to come.

When I returned to my hut Jimmy's body had been prepared for burial as Maa Koo knew white people do—and I suppose as mother-wife Tuou had heard from her mother about *That One.*

I went into my boxes and laid out a rose-colored blanket with which to line the coffin and kept on searching for something which might serve as a pillow for Jimmy's head. My wedding dress had served that purpose for my father. The only thing I had now with fine lace and delicate embroidery on it was a tiny garment meant for my baby's christening robe. It would do nicely. But first I slipped it over Timmy's head, and called to Maa Koo to bring a gourdful of water. Together we went into our church. There, before the altar, I sprinkled a few drops on my son's head and whispered, "I christen thee James Timothy Grove." Then I prayed, "Dear God, please love him and watch over him all of his days, for Jesus' sake—and for his own sake, too. Amen."

A little breeze stirred the thatch overhead and I was glad, for it was like the ghost of all the Amens of the beloved Jo Ellen's people and of all their children. Then I went back to my hut and ripped the yoke out of Timmy's dress and made a pillow out of its skirt for his father's head.

I asked Chief Mu'muou where *That One* had been buried, and he pointed to the rose geranium tree beside my—beside what had been *her* door. "They say that when she died that—" pointing to the geranium—"was a tiny plant rooted in a cooking pot, and that she nursed and cared for it like a child. The old one who guarded the teapot, planted it above *That One* so that what she loved would reach down to her with its rootlets—and so that its fragrance would remind us of the beauty of her life."

"We will bury my husband there," I said, pointing to the other side of the door. "And we will plant a branch from her tree above him, also."

CHAPTER
TWENTY-FIVE

I watched the rose geranium cutting on Jimmy's grave put out new little leaves and I knew that tiny rootlets were feeling their way down through the rich jungle earth toward him. I often stroked its leaves for the pleasure of their fragrance—as the villagers still did to the beloved Jo Ellen's tree.

Jimmy's cutting had put out its first cluster of tiny, purple, pansy-like blossoms when two mission boys came across the Hungry Country bearing a packet of letters for me. When I saw them coming I remembered that I had been terribly remiss in an iron-clad missionary duty. I had sent word to no one, either of Timmy's birth or of his father's death. But they—those in our central mission station, even the authorities in far-off America—already knew. That is the way of the jungle. News travels in Africa faster—far faster!—than in those countries whose movements are clogged and whose senses are dulled by the sheer weight and multiplicity of scientific invention.

In my packet of letters there were the usual expressions of sympathy and formal offers of help, and one from my Governing Board. They meant to be kind, so very kind, those men and women in America, but as I read I was impressed by the fact that their thinking was almost as vacuous as my day-to-day submergence of thought in physical activity had been. The secretary reminded me that there were several years of my missionary term yet to serve. This was complicated by the fact that I had been "home" out of turn following my father's death. He congratulated me on the birth of a son and called my husband's death an extenuating circumstance.

Four closely typewritten, extremely wordy pages told me that I might return to America on furlough, or retirement, if I chose. That I might recross the Hungry Country to our central mission station and continue on there abandoning the work started in Fan Country. Or that I could remain there as I was and "continue with the experiment you and your husband started with such high hopes."

I was bewildered, frightened, at times I felt a hysterical desire to laugh wildly. In those moments I told myself, speaking aloud as though I were two people, one expounding to the other, that I was as much—more—without a sense of direction in my life than I had been in my college days, the days of my nurse's training. Then there had been no choice of profession for me, God had left open only the one door through which I must pass. Now everything was blank before me, as impenetrable as a stone wall with no break in its fastness through which I might even glimpse a beyond. I was histrionic, oratorical, even a bit lyrical perhaps at times in my self-pity. But I did not convince myself, for like most glib speech-making, complete honesty was sacrificed to effect. And being orator as well as audience I was conscious of that dishonesty no matter how far I tried to push it into the background. I knew I was only arguing, and arguing futilely against the loneliness and the enormity of the man-sized task that lay ahead of me.

Then old mother-wife Tuou was standing in front of me and it seemed to me she said, "Come, *This One,* Mu'muou wishes to show you the other hut."

Her words didn't make sense, but I got up and followed her. Inside the chief's kraal I remembered. To one side of the hut which Mu'muou occupied personally stood his treasure house with its wealth in ivory and cooking pots heaped with quills filled with gold dust, and the thin copper fans of yesteryear's ceremonial cannibalism, and all the other evidences that human greed supersedes the color of man's skin. It was from among these "oddenda" that he had picked out the gourd given me, the gourd bearing a message in

Arabic from one D. Livingstone to one of the richest, most powerful, and wickedest men of his day.

On the other side of Mu'muou's hut stood a small structure that I had turned toward that day, but had not been invited to enter then or since. Mu'muou was standing before this hut now, the matting door pulled back. He beckoned to me, but for a moment I did not enter. All I could do was stare at Mu'muou's fat thigh for he was wearing one of the girdles Maa Koo had given to his wife as my birthing gift. Meant for my skinny torso, it fitted him nicely on one leg from knee to buttocks, turned upside down, that is. To the supporters he had fastened ornaments and utensils needful to his hourly comfort: his snuff box, the spoon carved from some animal tusk with which he scraped the wax from his ears, a little hide full of twigs which he chewed into tooth brushes, fetishes from his witch doctor—many things. From the bulges here and there I surmised he had found the snug rubber about his skin a convenient pocket.

Again he beckoned to me, and behind me Tuou sucked in her breath gently but quite audibly. That is a gesture that can mean whatever the occasion demands: pity, sympathy, awe—or simple advice from one woman to another to walk softly and feel her way carefully.

I bent over and walked in, balancing myself for two or three steps on the knuckles of my hands. It took a moment for my eyes to accustom themselves to the gloom so that what I saw came into my consciousness gradually. Even so, with first sight I sucked in my breath as noisily as the politest tribesman. A fleeting grin evidenced Mu'muou's satisfaction with my surprise and the expression of it.

Around the walls of the hut, placed at regular intervals, stood low stools, solid segments of tree trunks, some carved, some only stripped of their bark. On each was a chunk of common river bank clay, colored red, yellow, blue or greenish according to the weathered mineral in the stratum from which each was taken. On top of each chunk of clay, thick or thin, stood a skull, all facing toward the center of the hut. No one knows the value of dramatic effect better

330 ·

than a primitive African. Mu'muou let me look my fill before he spoke.

"We Fan men have always been a great people," he began, and I nodded agreement. It was a lecture in tribal ritual he delivered to me that day, standing there in the center of that dark hut surrounded by its grisly contents. In his way, he was as seriously intent as any renowned college professor. And I listened like a student— as the daughter of my father should have listened.

"The old women who recite our history tell us we were great before the mighty onrush of water washed the wicked men off the face of the earth. And we were great before that, for the first man who trod the jungle alone with only one wife was a Fan man." I nodded understanding and pressed my lips together tightly lest he see the smile in the corners of my mouth. Listening to any account of tribal history one never seems very far distant from Father Adam and Mother Eve.

No African tribesman set upon the telling of a tale can ever be hurried through his discourse. But eventually Mu'muou came to a statement something like this: "We people of the Fan are great because we have located the seat of intelligence. It is not in our big muscles," tapping his biceps. "Nor in the stomach," burying an index finger in his paunch. "Nor in the kidneys." We ran the gamut of the organs which do not house that ability which sets man above the beasts. Finally the moment for the denouement had arrived and Mu'muou paused dramatically.

"Did you know, *This One,* that when Mu'ungu made man, He shaped the body first. Then He asked Himself if the head should resemble the head of a bird, or a goat, or a lion— But finally He realized that He had created all possible shapes and forms when He made the animals. So, because he was tired of creating, He seized a gourd and stuffed the big end with all the intelligence He had left over. There was more of it than He had thought at first, more than He had given any of the animals, but He crammed it all in anyway. Did you know that that is why we are smarter than the beasts about us, *This One?* We got more than our share of creation's intelligence when Mu'ungu rammed the neck of the guord down between man's shoulders. Did you know these things, *This One?*"

He knew I did not, and I replied with a question of my own, "Why do you keep calling me, *This One?* You know my name. And up until now, when you have not used my name, you have just said, 'White Woman.'"

He laid a hand on my arm and leaned forward to peer into my eyes as he answered slowly, "What else can we call you? She-Who-Was-Here-Before-You, because she is now gone and only the fragrance of her memory remains, we call *That One*. But you are here with us now. We can see you, hear you, touch you." His grip tightened on my flesh. "You are *This One* to us and our children."

The full significance of his words did not sink into my mind at that moment. Possibly my first reaction was in line with advice I had so often received from my father: "Respect what is spoken to you in honest gravity. You may not be able to understand it, but the odds are great that the reasoning, though devious, is keen."

"Have you ever thought, *This One*—" there was a whimsical note, but gentle insistence nevertheless in his use of the phrase—"what a waste of a god-given gift it is when all this intelligence is discarded at death? And eventually scampers over the veld in the belly of a jackal? Or soars above the clouds in the maw of a vulture? We People of the Fan cannot save all of it. We waste, too. But we gather up the best and save that." He swung his arm around, pointing at the grinning circle of skulls about us.

"When a man of very great ability in some field of human labor dies, we discard the useless body, but the head with its knowledge we keep carefully. We bring up a block of the best river clay and set it on a stool in this hut. We scoop out a little hollow on top and place the man's head in the center of it. Then when the man's intelligence dissolves, it runs down into the clay; and when there is nothing but a dry skull left, all the superior wisdom of that man is locked up in the clay underneath and held there for our use when we need it.

"See that head?" Mu'muou asked, pointing. "He was my father.

No one uses the clay under it but me. He knew *That One* better than any of the rest of his people. He made her welcome and gave her the things she said she needed. It was superior wisdom on his part, for how else can a black man know whether or not a white man or woman brings good or evil into his village? Many times when you and your master first came to us, I entered this hut, spat on the clay beneath his skull, and puddled the spittle about until some stuck to my fingers. Then I rubbed the clay across my fore-head and waited. And eventually my father's wisdom entered my head and it told me that you would do my people much good."

I stared at the skull, then at Mu'muou, and then back at the skull again. "Animism," I was thinking. "Pure animism! But devious, not simple." When, in the history of this tribe, had some brilliant individual devised this method of forcing sober reflection? And so obtained for these people the wisdom which comes only with careful thought? Was this the sort of thing the old Quaker had meant when he spoke of "waiting upon the Lord."

"That fellow was Tatri," Mu'muou went on, now pointing at a skull resting upon a stool where only traces of clay remained.

"He must have died many years ago," I murmured.

"No," Mu'muou answered me. "The number of seasons he has rested here can be counted on a man's hand and foot fingers without touching any one of them twice. He was a very great hunter, and the spirits of good fortune walked with him and guided his spear. He knew his head would rest here when he died, and he used to twit the young men about being impatient with him for carrying it about on his shoulders so long. His clay is used almost daily."

Mu'muou heaved a great sigh and then pointed to another skull sitting on what appeared to be an untouched block of clay. "When Tatri's wisdom is all used up and we toss his dry skull into the swamp, we must turn to N'doofiti. He was a good hunter, a very good hunter, but he was not a great hunter. Sometimes the friendly spirits deserted him, but—next after Tatri, he was our best hunter."

"Do you have witch doctors here?" I asked. "For if you do all of you may learn the secrets of their magic."

"Who can say whether the power of a witch doctor is for good or for evil?" he questioned in turn. He appeared sunk in thought for a moment and then went on, "Strange, is it not? Many men would like the power of evil for themselves, but they will not trust it to a neighbor. We have no witch doctors here."

Around the hut we went, taking maybe a step a minute while Mu'muou told me what had made the possessor of each skull stand out above his fellows in life. In some ways it was a primitive Hall of Fame. A hall whose inhabitants were disposed of as soon as they had nothing more to offer.

Eventually we came to the last skull, standing on a large block of clay beside the door. If there were any differences in the bone contour of this skull from its fellows, I did not see them. The color now was exactly the same, an ashen gray intensified by the windowless gloom of the hut. Mu'muou was silent for a long moment, looking first at me, then at the skull, and then back at me.

Finally he spoke, and his words were both permission to privilege and a command, "Spit on the clay, *This One*, puddle it with your finger tips, and then wipe the mud on your forehead. For you now have need of this man's wisdom and courage."

I stared at Mu'muou. As I stared he himself did as he had commanded me, and I wasn't aware of his purpose until he had swiped a heavy smear of mud across my forehead from temple to temple, and from hairline to eyebrow. In the sultry air of the hut it began to dry immediately, and like any mud to crack and draw. It began to itch, too, and unconsciously I wrinkled my cheeks and nose to ease the discomfort.

"Do you feel the wisdom penetrating, *This One?*" Mu'muou asked in a pleased tone.

"What am I supposed to receive from this fellow?" I countered by way of reply.

It was a strange tale Mu'muou told me, standing there in the roofed twilight of a tribal ritual hut. It took longer in the telling than any of the others, and I shall never forget one single word of it, not if I were to live to become a female Methuselah. It was the story of a favorite son of Mu'muou's, a boy old in wisdom before his body had yet ripened into manhood.

"He was already called Abu Sayheed, the Father of Wisdom, before the hair on his chin was ready for the tweezers of the barber," Mu'muou stated proudly.

The name, Abu Sayheed, stirred memory, but the chief went on with his tale before the memory came into sharp conscious focus before my mind's eye.

This son had traveled "all over the whole world"—probably several hundred miles—in search of wealth for his father's treasure hut. He had brought back many rarities valued by white men, some of which had eventually fallen into dust.

Then one day Abu Sayheed had stood in his father's kraal and had told Mu'muou of a white man possessed of all the power and privilege and magic of white men. A white man honored among his fellows for those intangible things of the spirit which make a man great. But best of all, inside the white man's skull was an intelligence which understood and respected the laws and customs of black men.

"He was beloved of the friendly spirits, the spirits which drift through white men's jungles as well as black men's jungles, for he trod whatever path down which duty lay without fear and no harm ever befell him. He talked often with Mu'ungu, and this greatest of all the gods advised him so that his wisdom was a mighty strength—the kind of strength that is never measured by the size of a man's muscles. Do you understand me, *This One?*"

I nodded yes, and Mu'muou continued.

"His wisdom increased with the years, and he shared it with anyone who came to him. His advice was like a cooking fire and the smell of roasting meat guiding a tired and empty-handed hunter home through swirling river mists. His skin was—" There was only a second's hesitation in his flow of words, but long enough for a swift look at me. "His skin was white, but black men were his brothers. Inside he was like us. See! Do you not think so, *This One?*" He tapped the skull with the tip of a finger.

"My son told me that there was no dissension in the kraal which this man built in the jungle. The foolish ones suppressed their clacking tongues before him and were guided by his wisdom until they appeared the same as strong, upright men. Those of ability walked like chieftains when they left his presence, their conduct was that of sage old men.

"My son served that man for a period without wage. Finally he died and, as *That One* said white men always do, they put his body in the ground. But when everyone was asleep my son removed the dirt from above the dead man, removed this granary of Mu'ungu's wisdom from his useless body, and brought it to me. It was the last gift my son ever brought me, for less than a season later a buffalo tossed him on its horns and trampled his body deep into the mire.

"But that white man's ripened wisdom has now melted and run into the clay and it is mine and my people's. Was it not a great gift, *This One?* Do you feel its power already stirring within your skulls? A widow with only one man-bud to inherit her needs wisdom."

Mu'muou said other things and I stammered replies. But mostly I gaped at the skull, my mind screaming wordlessly: My father's head! My own father's head!

The one or two people to whom I have told this incident have asked me in horror, "Didn't you demand your father's head—instantly!—so you could give it Christian burial? Didn't you report that—that horrible savage to the white authorities and have him arrested?"

No. No! And that's about all the answer I could make except to shake my head. It isn't easy to explain, but Mu'muou—and the millions of others like him—are neither horrible nor savages simply because their customs are different. As for arrest and punishment, the best colonial administrators know that it takes consummate wisdom to deal with a custom which may revolt you and me, but nevertheless has been a power for great good to aboriginal man. When that from which we—you and I, I mean—shrink is destroyed, very often there are other things—which again, you and I would be the last to want destroyed—which die with it.

No, I didn't do anything, neither then nor afterwards. In fact, I didn't think your thoughts until I was faced with your questioning. After all, my father had had Christian burial, and I think he would have called this strange honor done him by a tribe of the people he loved, enshrinement.

As Mu'muou moved toward the door of the hut, he was speaking again—perhaps he had never stopped. "I had another son who was gifted beyond ordinary men. He loved sweet sounds and he made many instruments with which he captured them. There was one that he played with the tips of his fingers. He carried it into the jungle with him, and the unseen folk there taught him the melodies and rhythms that a few men sometimes hear faintly when walking alone under the big trees. But that son—too—is dead—to me."

Memory was not laggard now. I remembered the strange musician who had come to one of Jimmy's musical evenings, the severed hand, and the scars where the wound had been cauterized, the mark of a thief, convicted and exiled from his people. I remembered the silver thimble and the ringing notes he struck with it from his dangling keyboard. I wondered if it was for the theft of a hallowed memento of the beloved Jo Ellen that he had been maimed and driven out of his own land. I remembered that he and his three wives had disappeared into the night as quietly as they had come out of it. I remembered, too, the long look which had passed between Abu Sayheed and this man, without the flutter of an eyelash or twitch of cheek muscle to show that they recognized each other. I remembered how Abu Sayheed stood before my father and, with no hint of begging in his voice, commanded that the stranger be paid royally for his music. A goat and a handful of hens—the bride price of many a strapping woman.

I had not moved, although Mu'muou had motioned toward the door. Now with one broad palm on my shoulder he bent me double ready for the low opening as easily as though I were the green tip of a branch. The other palm applied to my rear helped me along almost too speedily for dignity.

Outside in the bright sunlight I blinked up at him and in my first half-vision I was suddenly reminded of Genesis: "and God created man in His own image." I suppose it was because a white man had first read these words to me that I, like every other white person I know, took it for granted that God also wore a white skin. How else could our image be the same as His if His muscles and organs and bones were wrapped up in skin of another color? But what had been Mu'muou's thoughts when I read those words to him? Was Mu'ungu—the greatest of the black man's gods, and twin to Jehovah of the Old Testament—a white or a black god? It was unthinkable that He could be anything but black, for He had peopled the world He created with men after His own image.

Mu'muou, standing there in the sun, his elbows akimbo, his thumbs stuck in his G-strap where it was no more than a wisp of rawhide over his broad hips, his oiled body shining like polished mahogany, was a fine figure of a man. Then— Oh, my puckish sense of humor!—I almost laughed for it seemed to me that, in spite of my silly girdle circling his left thigh, he looked more like a man and less like a beetle than many a gentleman of my own race over-clothed in cummerbund and swallowtail.

A flake of mud started to crumble off my forehead. I bent my head over and closed my eyes. It helped to hide my twitching lips. Again the chief put his hand on my shoulder and pushed, this time in the direction of my hut.

"Go now, *This One,* and wait," he said. If it had been my father speaking, he would have added the formal phraseology of the preacher, "—and wait on the Lord." The tones and the spirit were the same.

I went, but before I had taken a hundred steps two young women passed me, their babies astride their hips, their short-handled hoes balanced in their hands. How well I knew the scorn with which a village looks upon a woman who lets weeds grow in her garden. And when had I last worked in mine? I shuddered lightly and wondered what was being whispered about me over cooking fires, in the bathing pool, as wood-gatherers crawled homeward under their staggering burden of sticks? Mechanically I turned and followed the young wives.

But at the edge of the gardens I stopped. My plot was as clean—cleaner!—than any other woman's. And yet there had been ample time for weeds to smother out my vegetables.

At the edge of my yam patch, three figures squatted together. One of them, the mother-wife Tuou, stretched out an arm, pointing. The second, Maa Koo, started to rise. But the third, old N'ragde, the wood carver, placed a hand on her shoulder and pressed her back onto her haunches while he himself got to his feet. Stepping over and among the vines very carefully, he approached a spot where Tuou's keen eyes had spied a small drift of unwanted bright green—weeds pushing up through the soft earth almost while they looked at them. Carefully N'ragde stirred the dirt with his fingers so he could lift the weeds out, roots and all, and so kill them completely.

I was standing beside the two women when he returned and exclaimed in surprise, "N'ragde, are you not ashamed to be seen doing woman's work?"

"Since when has curiosity belonged solely to women?" he asked, and grinned impishly. "Your master spoke long and often and loudly in the councils of men that he could grow more and bigger and better flavored vegetables than any woman. Now there are three things which may make a man speak long and loudly on any matter." N'ragde paused and I turned my palms upward toward him in token that I welcomed the gift of his wisdom.

"Fear may make a fool of a man, and words keep his teeth apart so that they will not chatter and disclose his true state. A man may want something so badly that he tries to father it with wind from his lungs.

"And then so strong a flood of truth may well up within a man that no matter how tight he clenches his teeth or presses his lips together, he cannot dam it back." He turned to look at my garden plot.

"The beans are taller than in the other women's gardens," Maa Koo crowed.

"The stems are thicker and there are more leaves on them. They are sturdier plants," Tuou added thoughtfully.

But N'ragde was not to be convinced so easily. "Young men are warned not to boast of their kill at the beginning of a hunt just because the sun is warm on their backs and the animals' dung on the path still smokes and within themselves they feel kinship with the mightiest warrior," he murmured sententiously.

Perhaps I was guided in what I said. Perhaps it was only impulse. Anyway I turned to the old wood carver suddenly. "N'ragde, I must leave Fan Country for a while," I said. "And while I am gone, will you take care of my garden for me? Keep the vegetables always planted, always cultivated, and harvested when it is time for harvesting? Will you do this for me? And will you plant a piece of fish with each hill of seed? If you will, then by the time I return, your curiosity will be completely satisfied. I know it is woman's work I am asking, but will you do it?"

He squinted up at me sidewise, but he nodded assent as he answered, "I am of an age when I can be independent of the foibles of pride. And besides, I am curious to know what manner of offspring this wedding of dead fish and living seed brings forth."

I turned and went back to my hut and started packing immediately. I knew now, without doubt or questioning what I must do. I must return to the land my people call "home." There I must learn as well as I could and as much as I could to do what the people of my strange homeland call "men's work." Then I must come back to Fan Country to do "woman's work"—one and the same thing.

The shadows under the jungle trees had not yet turned from the shimmering green of daylight to the smoke-blue of dusk when I heard N'ragde softly clapping his hands outside my door.

I went out to him and was surprised to see him shuffling his feet in some embarrassment before speaking. "How long will you be away from us, *This One?*" he asked. "I am curious, yes. But how long must I do woman's work, *This One?*"

I felt like laughing. I felt like leaning over and kissing him on the top of his cotton-ringed bald pate. People have said to me at various times: "Do you *love* these people? Do you *really* love them!"

Yes. *YES!* I love N'ragde. And the painful sweetness of love pierced my heart through and through as I answered him in a way he would best understand.

I filled my lungs with air and bellowed out loudly that I had need of a gift of cooking pots. Kindly, generous neighbors came on hurrying feet to fill my need. I chose sixteen big pots of the great number placed before me. Curious eyes watched as I set the pots in a row before my hut, eager hands helped me fill them with loam. Then I borrowed N'ragde's knife and cut sixteen slips from the beloved Jo Ellen's rose geranium tree. Slowly I trimmed off all unwanted leaves and stuck the slips deep into the loam. Then I turned to the old wood carver.

"This is another garden which you must 'tend and keep,'" I said to him as impressively as I could. "These slips will put out roots and become plants. But if one should die, cut another branch from *That One's* fragrant tree and stick it in a pot and make it grow. They will always remain small plants as long as they are in the pots. But at the beginning of each season— Now listen to me carefully, old father, for this is a measure of the time you must wait for me. At the beginning of each season that I am gone, you must break one pot and plant the tiny tree in the ground somewhere between here and our church. When the last pot is broken, and the last tiny tree is planted, then I will return to you shortly thereafter." Sixteen seasons. Four years. As long as it would take me to complete a course of study in an agricultural college.

N'ragde was very quiet for a long moment. Sixteen pots do not make a long row, but sixteen seasons is a long stretch of time in a man's old age.

Then N'ragde went from pot to pot and one by one laid his ten hand-fingers on them counting. When there were no more hand-fingers, and pots still remaining, he began touching them with his foot-fingers. There were only four toes left over when he had finished counting. He looked at them in consternation. Then he began at the end of the row where he had stopped before and counted backward, using his foot-fingers first. When there were no more foot-fingers, he began numbering pots with his hand-fingers. There were four rigidly extended fingers on his left hand when he again stood before me. He held the four up accusingly.

"You demand a large portion of a man's life just because he is curious, *This One,*" he said sternly.

I hesitated a moment, and then I asked, "Old father, how long have you been curious about what goes on in the spirit lanes under the jungle trees? How big a portion of your life have you given over to wondering about such things as that? And when at last you learn the truth of what happens to the conscious you after death, will you ever have the pleasure of discussing it with your friends in the cool shade of the palaver hut? But at the end of sixteen seasons, you will know whether or not my husband was a man into whose ear Mu'ungu whispered much wisdom. Who would dare not listen to your words in the palaver hut? And if a stranger should scoff, the voices of your friends will be loud to drown his ignorance out of your ears. Such friendly, pleasant, convers—"

He waved his hand for me to be quiet. "I see you have visited the hut of skulls," he remarked as though that were no digression. I passed my hand quickly over my forehead. Most of the clay had long since shattered off, but I had not yet washed away what remained. "May your spirit feed on the wisdom of the ancient ones," he intoned solemnly, and walked away.

My garden will be green when I return to my People of the Fan. And a row of Jo Ellen's fragrant trees will stretch from my hut to the church which will be standing, in good repair, awaiting me.

CHAPTER
TWENTY-SIX

There isn't much left to tell of the story of my life—what I have lived of it, that is. But what I have put down here is the reason why I cannot answer simply when you ask me why I must return to Africa. For the rest of my life—God willing!—will be spent there. My *call* to the mission field has come from the country itself, and those of God's children who populate its jungles and velds and deserts.

There was one other charge I laid upon an individual before I left Fan Country. My Mission Board after extensive correspondence with other boards of other denominations had been unable to locate any record of missionary service here in Fusora. None of them apparently had ever had a worker whose name was Jo Ellen. Her beautiful heirloom teapot was mine to keep if I wished. But when I picked the teapot up to pack it away among my earthly belongings, I knew the Board was wrong. I turned to find Maa Koo and the mother-wife Tuou watching me keenly. The beloved Jo Ellen's teapot belonged to her People of the Fan.

I looked from Maa Koo to Tuou and from Tuou back to Maa Koo because my old nurse had moved between me and the other woman. Maa Koo put up her arms and grasped the teapot so that our four hands were wrapped about it together, hers and mine.

"I will keep the teapot until you return, Little Gru— *This One*," she said firmly.

"The years are already heavy on your shoulders, Old Mother," I said to her uncertainly. "Are you sure—?"

"The Ancient One who guarded the teapot before us, *willed* to live out a double lifetime because of the trust placed in her. Was she a better woman than I?"

The teapot slid from my fingers and Maa Koo shuffled across the hut and set it down in its old place, in Jo Ellen's now empty chest. And, blue with tarnish, it will be waiting for me there when I return.

Chief Mu'muou gave me porters, and I recrossed the Hungry Country, back to our central mission station. Brother Norman was father of a new little daughter; and Blanche, his wife, and I bathed and cuddled and nursed our infants regardless of which one belonged to whom. The young doctor, who had taken Dr. Dick's place in my absence, went over Timmy and most unnecessarily pronounced him perfect. I knew that! Aunt Bun was a little plumper than when I had seen her last; Sister Hallie a little thinner. But both good women as always were working hard and effectively. After a few days I went by shimbeck down our tributary to the Great River, from there to the ocean, and thence to this land which custom compels me to call "home."

First of all, here in America, I went to the museum and called on the official to whom my mother and I had given father's collection of Africana. I showed him the gourd Mu'muou had given me, and the scrap of paper inside. He called in an employee who read Arabic and the fellow began haltingly:

" 'To Mutesa, King of the—' m-m-m-m-m-m, titles here, you know. 'To Our Male Parent Who Lives Beyond the Clouds—' A little difficult to change phraseology over from one language into another. 'Honor to your name—' m-m-m-m."

He looked up smiling a bit foolishly, and then bent over the paper again to read the Lord's Prayer from—"Thy kingdom come, Thy will be done . . ." to "Lead us not into temptation, But deliver us from evil."

"Hmmmmm. This, Mrs. Grove, is number three."

Then this clerk in a great American museum told me, the daughter of an Afrophile, something I had not known. That the wicked old Mutesa in one of his softer—or more guileful moments!—had once promised David Livingstone much if the great missionary-explorer would give him a portion of what the Scotsman considered his most powerful charm or fetish. Livingstone had had a native scribe set down on whatever scraps of paper were at hand a half-dozen copies of the Lord's Prayer.

"Two copies have been found and are in museums, one in Mombasa," the clerk went on. "It was supposed that paper being what it is, and the tropics what they are, all the other copies were lost. This is number three—a priceless find!"

Priceless? I sat staring at the scrap of paper uncomprehendingly. Then through my consciousness came the official's voice explaining that such "finds" are usually given the museum, or at least lent for an indefinite period, but— He coughed in embarrassment. Now I must not expect too much, in fact I really must not expect anything; but— The museum had a small fund—a very small fund—out of which purchases were occasionally made after consultation— From his tone I could only infer that he meant consultation with God. I left the matter of price in his hands and the use of Chief Mu'muou's gift to the museum until a decision was reached. After all, I told myself, the Lord's Prayer is hardly my exclusive property, and evidences of the life and labors of the first of the great modern missionaries to the Dark Continent belong to all those who love that exotic land.

Then I traveled westward, visiting briefly along my route. Jimmy's people came first. There was no diffidence in their greeting. The family met me at the train in force—several automobile-loads of them: sons, daughters, children-in-law, grandchildren, three aunts, I remember, and one bachelor uncle of uncertain years.

Timmy was passed from hand to hand so fast and often that when eventually eager hands pushed and pulled me into the back seat of a car I had no idea where my baby was. I bellowed, as I so often have done to attract attention in an African village—it was the only way I could make myself heard above the din of my in-laws. Then I discovered Timmy was on his grandmother's lap beside me, wrapped up in a huge green sweater she always carried with her "just in case" need for it might arise.

While I was with my husband's people, they told me that the brothers and sisters who had inherited what they called "that bit of land" along with Jimmy, had deeded their portions over to Jimmy's son. Like good people the world over, they were embarrassed by their own generosity, and a thousand fairly incoherent reasons were given me for the act, all boiling down to: Timmy was an orphan and had no father to support him. And they were all church people and believed in missions although they hadn't given much time or thought or support to them until Jimmy had gone to Africa.

Mother Grove quieted them with the simple, blunt truth, "We loved Jimmy, Laura dear. And we love his son."

At my next stop, the secretary of our Mission Board told me what I expected to hear from him: That I had the Board's blessing and prayerful support in the pursuance of "my missionary experiment," but that their funds were so limited they could give me no financial help.

The secretary also gave me a letter from Aunt Bessie. She had just had her house redecorated at great expense, she wrote me, and— and— She hedged around for a couple of paragraphs, about as gracefully as an elephant in a banana patch, before telling me to stop at the local hotel where she would call on me in the afternoon. I could only infer that her material possessions were now much too fine even to be sat upon and looked at. And after all, I did have a baby, and children are so-o-o-o destructive. The hotel she named was far from being the cheapest one in town, I learned, but then Aunt Bessie could not be seen entering a second-rate hotel.

I had nothing to do until Aunt Bessie's visit, so I slept late that morning, and was awakened by a telephone call from the desk. The press wanted to interview me, the clerk said. His words didn't make sense, but I got up and dressed and finally admitted a dozen exceedingly curious and voluble—and charming—young men and women. They wanted to know all about the Lord's Prayer, and

"What was I going to do with the money?" Missionaries never had any need of money, did they?

While they babbled, a messenger boy knocked at my door and gave me a telegram. As I read the block letters on the yellow sheet, I began to tremble and I heard someone say, "Catch her, she's going to faint." But I pulled myself together and didn't topple over, although the next voice sounded far away and dream-like, "For heaven's sake! She doesn't know yet."

A hand shoved a newspaper in front of my eyes, but another hand took it away just as quickly and someone began to read to me. There was much said, in that newspaper story, about David Livingstone, a little about the wicked old Mutesa and the thousand women and other slaves who were slaughtered and buried with him in an immense grave so that at his death the despot would have all the savage luxury he had so brutally appropriated to himself in life. The Lord's Prayer was mentioned—the most powerful fetish the great missionary-explorer had to give this tribal King who was now friend and now foe and no predicting from one minute to the next just which he would be. I was mentioned briefly, and the price voted by the museum board for the purchase of this rare treasure.

And then at least a column was devoted to my Aunt Bessie and Uncle Elmer, their wealth, their social prominence, and their devotion to the church and their liberality to missions. I gasped at that last, and the laughter which greeted me said more plainly than words that these young men and women understood the quality of my rich relations' liberality.

The telephone rang while the reporters were there. Aunt Bessie was on the other end of the line, and in a voice strangely softened for her, she said she had invited a small group of friends to meet me at four o'clock. And, "For goodness' sake, Laura, do you have anything decent to wear?"

I went to Aunt Bessie's reception because the habits of even a short lifetime are not easily broken. And because, also, when missionary habits are broken the lives of others can be affected, sometimes with catastrophic results. It was a formal reception—not a small party—for I was the local celebrity of a fleeting moment. And —in a beautiful if hastily purchased gown which Aunt Bessie assured me I could now afford—I was shown off like a prize heifer at a county fair.

That evening Aunt Elma and Uncle Ben came for me. I couldn't see that either of them had changed a mite. They both approved of my plan to become an agricultural missionary. Apparently neither of them had seen that day's newspapers, for after I was in bed Aunt Elma came in, ostensibly to kiss Timmy and me goodnight, but to whisper in my ear that I needn't worry about money for the next four years of schooling. She was gone before I could tell her of my good fortune. The next morning, while Uncle Ben and I were milking, he asked me how much money I needed. Uncle Ben, who had sent my father through school, was now offering to do the same for me. I told him about Timmy's inheritance, and the museum's purchase of Chief Mu'muou's gift.

And there in the cow barn—as I had done once before outside a jungle fetish hut—I looked up into the face of a good man and was reminded that God created us in His own image. All of us—regardless of race, creed, or social privilege.

Mother shocked me when I first saw her. She wasn't exactly at the gate of the Home to greet me when my taxi pulled up; she was half hidden behind an ornamental shrub, clutching some sort of bathrobe around her. The taxi-man gone, she came out of hiding and held out her arms for Timmy. Her robe fell slightly apart and I caught a glimpse of two skinny legs bare their entire length. She trotted up the walk, babbling a grandmother's sense and nonsense to Timmy, led me into the house, and pointed toward an open door.

"A suit is on the bed for you. You're late! Hurry up and change. We're having a barbecue for you down by the swimming pool, and everything is almost ready. If you hurry you can have a dip before we eat."

She was crazy. Yes, I was certain she was crazy! To humor her I peeked through the door, and then walked in and stared at the bed. On it lay a bathrobe, something that looked like a bandana hand-kerchief, and two slightly cupped postage stamps fastened together by a strip of elastic. I turned, went back to mother, reached around Timmy and pulled her robe wide apart. There stood my mother who in her youth had clothed the heathen with unflagging zeal, who in her age had been sent to this strange land to do the same for a new brand of heathen— I say, there stood my mother diapered in a bandana with two cloth postage stamps fastened together across her chest with a strip of elastic.

Mother swung Timmy over her shoulder and held him there firmly with one hand. Then she waved a deeply rose-hued finger-nail within an inch of my nose and said with strange vigor, "Now, Laura, you listen to me, you—you—you slob! Oh, I love you right enough, but that's what you are. I approve of what you're going to do, I think it's a step in the right direction. But, Laura, there are other steps that missions, and missionaries are taking—or should be taking. We're not any less God-fearing—or God-loving—than we ever were; but we're human beings, too. And we're beginning to want to be treated like human beings. There's no reason at all why we should be regarded as impossibly, unlovably, inanely perfect creatures who must live in a pious social vacuum with what are normal pleasures for other people completely denied us. We— We— Oh, go put your suit on. And close your mouth. You look and sound like a fish gasping for water."

Meekly I put the suit on. This was a new mother, more like old Maa Koo. There was still one gasp left in me, and I began. "But, mama! With your belly bare like—"

"Belly!" she screeched. "Oh, Laura, don't be so prissy. And crude. We say *midriff!*"

When I stepped out of the bedroom, it was she who pulled *my* robe back and her gasp of horror equaled all mine had been. Then with quick fingers she stripped the handkerchief off me and re-stretched and retied its meager breadth about my hips with a satisfied "There now!" It didn't cover any more of me than it had before.

Still meek, I followed her down to the pool where a dozen scantily clad, elderly ladies and almost as many saintly, benign, and practically naked old gentlemen greeted me warmly. And I, who had been born and who had grown up in what a great many people call "a very naked land," had some difficulty at first in keeping my feet from streaking for the nearest clump of bushes.

I was the only person at my party who couldn't swim. If I had wanted to count like old N'ragde, I could have numbered my instructors and instructresses by my hand- and foot-fingers and I would have run out of foot-fingers before I had finished.

So I have come to the end of my tale. This is why I sit here, this bright October day in a man's school learning to do a man's work. It is because I have been called by God to do a specialized type of missionary work among a very needy people in a faraway land. It is not necessary now for God to close every other door which life might blow wide before me and leave only that one open through which I must pass. If there were a thousand professions I might enter, or lives I might live— Well, there is only one choice for me and it has already been made. That decision was reached thousands of miles away in the gloom of a tribal fetish hut when I understood that my father's grave was never desecrated—rather that his memory was enshrined in the hearts of a wonderful people.

I know it is amusing to you, my white brothers and sisters, when I explain that what is man's work here in your land, is woman's work beyond the Hungry Country. Apparently it makes you feel comfortably superior—although I don't know to whom, or why.

I did have a little trouble, as I have told you, getting into this school. The officials seemed hesitant about disclosing to me the so-called facts of life of the larger animals. To me! To me who was born under a trailside bush, who grew up in a naked land, who was reared by a black nurse not one generation removed from savagery. To me who bore my child several weeks' hard journey from any other white woman, who was confined in a primitive birthing hut.

That hurdle past, it was felt my presence might be an embarrassment to young men—

To the left of me the poker game is breaking up now. One young man has all of the matches and he is stuffing them into his trousers pockets. On my right the reader is no longer reading. His pseudo-brothel is rolled into a hard cylinder and he is clenching it in perspiring hands. He has slid forward to the edge of his chair and is waiting, already partially on his feet. I glance back at the instructor quickly.

"And so, gentlemen—and Mrs. Grove—in summation: docking of lambs is necessary. It is a simple, easy, quick operation. Rightly performed, it is practically painless. I think that about covers the subject.

"Good afternoon."

He is smiling at me as though grateful for one student who has paid him rapt attention. I smile and nod and slip out of the door as unobtrusively as I can.